SEX
watching

Looking into the world of sexual behaviour

Dedication

This book is dedicated to my parents who into their
80s and 90s continued to be role models and to my
family and friends who supported me when
I needed it most.

SEX *watching*

Looking into the world of sexual behaviour

Milton Diamond

PRION

This edition first published in the United Kingdom 1992 by
PRION, an imprint of Multimedia Books Limited,
32 – 34 Gordon House Road, London NW5 1LP

Editor   Anne Cope
Editorial Assistant   Anna Kirby
Design   Kelly j Maskall
Photography   Milton DiamonD (see picture credits page 256)
Production   Hugh Allan
Picture research   Charlotte Deane

A catalogue record for this book is available from the British Library.

ISBN 1-85375-024-7

10 9 8 7 6 5 4 3 2 1

Originated by J Film Process Singapore Pte Ltd
Printed in Italy by New Interlitho

Contents

I have been fortunate in having lived and travelled in many parts of the world, in North and Central America, Britain and Europe, Japan, Southeast Asia and Polynesia. My present home is in multicultural Hawaii. I am doubly blessed in that I have a profession — that of a teacher, researcher, and therapist in the area of sexuality — which not only allows but demands involvement with a subject of universal interest: sex. Wherever I go I keep my eyes and ears open to sex. In fact, perhaps more than most, I have been sexwatching for most of my life, and it has been and continues to be a fascinating experience.

Every culture has rules for dealing with everyday needs such as eating, working, and socializing, and sexual exchanges and sexuality pervade these everyday activities. The perhaps unremarkable observation I have made is that, despite apparent differences in sexual expression among different societies, there are many, many commonalities. Other societies may seem exotic, but our own Western model displays some of the most interesting patterns.

However this book is more than a sexual travelogue. It is a resource too, a resource for understanding and dealing with sexual questions and issues basic or common to most of us in our everyday lives. I would like everyone to have a greater understanding of this complex subject and to feel more comfortable with it. My reflections will, I hope, stimulate the reader to think more deeply about his or her own sexual beliefs, attitudes, and behaviour.

Preparing this new edition of Sexwatching *has been a privilege and an obligation. The privilege has been the opportunity to repeat and update, and to add more colour photographs, many from my own archive. The obligation has been to do as well or better than last time. Since 1984 of course AIDS has grown from a sexual disease of relative obscurity to one known in every corner of the world. Since 1984 many new methods of regulating reproduction have been invented and perfected, methods that will hopefully reverse our pelvic-focused march toward world overpopulation. In fact AIDS and overpopulation have led much of the world to a more curious and penetrating view of sex.*

I too have changed since 1984. I have travelled, done, and read more, but most significantly I have aged from my forties to my fifties, seen my four daughters mature and leave home, and experienced the death of my wife. These cannot leave me or a book on sex unaffected.

Yet I continue to believe that sex is too often viewed through keyholes, figuratively if not literally. People look furtively when they would love to stare, peep when they would like to read and view at leisure. Most unfortunately, in Western culture, some of the most wonderous and beautiful events of life, such as childbirth and joyful, loving coitus, remain hidden or go unnoticed. I would like to make them visible.

To those who prefer mystery in sexual matters I firmly offer the wisdom of Henry Thoreau: 'I lose my respect for the man who can make the mystery of sex the subject of a coarse jest, yet when you speak earnestly and seriously on the subject is silent!' or of Dr. C.G. Lang, a former Archbishop of Canterbury, who said 'I would rather have all the risks which come from free discussion of sex than the great risks we run by conspiracy of silence.'

Milton Diamond, Ph.D.
1992

Chapter 1

What is sexwatching?

Anyone interested in sexwatching, that is in taking a multifaceted look at sex, must decide what phenomena qualify as sex and what the scope of the watching is to be. Although the media tend to concentrate their view on AIDS, juicy scandal, and the like, a moment's reflection will show sex to be an immensely broad subject, certainly not limited to what people do in bed. Sex and its many manifestations are all around us, but most of us have been taught not to notice or publicly examine them.

Of course sex includes what happens when two people are together in genital play or coitus, or when they strive for reproduction, but it is explicit and implicit in a much wider range of activities. Sex is part of everyday existence, public and private. One can certainly exist without coitus, but not without sex — to be human is to be sexual.

Sexual vocabulary

One difficulty in looking at or thinking clearly about sex is the lack of a precise and rich common vocabulary with which to express our sexual experiences. Many of our sexual perceptions are not adequately expressed in the words available to us. The word 'sex' itself is convenient shorthand for the physical, emotional, and social facts of being male or female. Of late, some prefer the term 'sexuality', thinking it less blunt, more diffuse, more sanitized. 'Coitus' specifically refers to inserting a penis into a vagina, but for most people the word is clinical and the concept limited and limiting. 'Intercourse', a term less rigidly defined, refers to any type of genital activity, but it too seems narrow, impersonal, and lacking in emotion. Vernacular alternatives — balling, screwing, and fucking — are often used derogatorily, although the situation or tone of voice used can make them more or less acceptable. 'Having sex' is a more socially acceptable expression, but any emotional connotation remains safely hidden in the mind of the speaker. 'Making love' is a euphemism with very broad appeal; associating love with sex seems to reduce discomfort and begins to convey something of the richness of the experience. Nevertheless much sex lacks love and much love exists without sexual intent. 'Lover' is a synonym for 'sexual partner', but not all sexual partners are loved.

The purposes of sex

While a great deal of sexual activity directly or indirectly relates to reproduction, having children is not the purpose of most sexual activity. And the ubiquity of self-stimulation from cradle to tomb is testimony that sexual pleasure does not always require a partner. Prostitution, masturbation, daily male-female teasing and flirting, and even most coitus within marriage, do not have reproduction as their goal. Indeed the probability of children would deter most people from these activities. If reproduction were the only goal of sex, coitus among sterile couples or after the menopause would not occur, sex before marriage would scarcely be a subject for debate, and prostitution and pornography would be non-existent. Nevertheless it is procreation, the possibility of progeny, that gives the sex act much of its potency, resonance, and mystery.

A young girl takes a peek at a statue in Vigaland Park, Oslo, Norway. Curiosity about sexual matters is entirely natural in children and adults. Western societies, with the possible exception of Scandinavia and the Netherlands, are among the most sexually restrictive in the world.

To the biologist, procreation is the fulfillment of an evolutionary imperative. To many men and women who believe in God, in an all-pervading life force, procreation is a sacred obligation. For some individuals, coitus is synonymous with the intention to procreate and not indulged in otherwise. It is because sex serves so many non-reproductive purposes that sexual behaviour is so ubiquitous, so pervasive. It seems to provide a social cement, a medium of exchange which most of us use, sometimes willingly, sometimes not.

A visit to Yen Yuen Shek (Lovers' Rock), Hong Kong. Men and women come here to pray for love, happy marriage, and good sex....and also to wish bad joss *(luck) on their sexual rivals.*

Sex gives pleasure — for most of us genital stimulation and response, close body contact, and even flirting and teasing are inherently pleasurable. Sex provides release from tension — intercourse, masturbation, dating, and other social interplay can defuse sexual and non-sexual tension and frustration. Sex is stimulating — any satisfactory sexual experience can heighten perception, alleviate boredom, awaken new interests. Sex offers companionship and intimacy — most of us are afraid of loneliness, and want to be known fully and deeply by at least one other person. Often bodies come together in the hope that hearts and minds will follow, but sometimes bodily intimacy is the most that can be achieved. When there is a meshing of physical and mental intimacy a substantial relationship has developed. Sex is also a commodity — even when it is not blatantly bought or sold, as it is in prostitution, it can be used as an inducement to buy or sell, as in advertising. Often sex is bartered in exchange for goods or services, even for love. But often the barter is an 'apples for oranges' deal: a fair exchange is hoped for, but often the items traded are not equivalent or clearly understood.

Sex is also a form of recreation, available to all classes and conditions of people — 'swinging' or the swopping of sex partners, pornography, blue movies, and 'dirty' jokes are significant forms of entertainment. It is also a spectator sport — there is great interest in the private lives of royalty, politicians, movie stars, the folks next door....Sex is also a means of communication — physical contact, or the lack of it, conveys strong messages about mood, arousal, and feelings. Sex can also be a weapon — desired behaviour can be coerced by withholding or offering sex as a punishment or reward.

In most of the world today, and certainly in the West until 40 or 50 years ago, sex is seen as a marital duty. Traditionally, within marriage, partners have the right of sexual access to one another, whether sex is a pleasure or not. Despite recent court cases that have upheld the charge of rape within marriage, the tradition of sex as one of the duties of marriage is likely to persist.

The picture then is complex but clear. Sex is an infinitely flexible medium which answers different needs and serves different purposes at different times. If sex did not exist, something like it would have to be invented. With such a powerful medium at our disposal, we surely owe it to ourselves to know as much about it as possible.

The ancient world

There are many different frameworks for thinking about sex, each with its advantages and disadvantages, proponents and opponents. Interest in sex is as old as human life. For our cave-dwelling ancestors its mysteries were naturally tied to nature's cycles of life and death. Like other important matters, sex was ruled or influenced by the stars, and by good and evil gods and spirits.

In the ancient world many competing philosophies and religions regarded sex as having spiritual meaning, as being central to an understanding of human existence. But the integration of sex with religious beliefs and practices was by no means consistent. The cultures in which Judaism developed ranged from the sensual to the ascetic. Some early religions called for celibacy, even castration; others not only allowed but encouraged heterosexual and homosexual acts in their temples; some practised prostitution in the service of the gods in temple precincts.

The religious beliefs and practices of Greece and Rome are of particular significance to present-day Western societies. They, more than Judaism, strongly coloured the development of Christian views of sex and are now part of the collective unconscious of much of the industrialized world.

Figures like this, the famous Willendorf Venus, suggest that there may have been various mother goddess/ fertility cults in paleolithic Europe. At this time, around 30,000 BC, great ice sheets covered the northern part of the continent and scattered tribes lived as hunter-gatherers. The link between coitus and reproduction may not have been understood.

The view that human beings are troubled immortal souls trapped inside mortal bodies evolved in Greece during the sixth century BC as part of the Orphic religion. According to Orphic beliefs, a person's proper task in life was to achieve peace in the present world and prepare for a future one. The best way of doing this was to lead a pure life and perform certain rituals. The exact recipe for a pure life, however, was much argued about. Pythagoras (582–500 BC), remembered best for his mathematical theories, taught that leading a pure life involved repudiating sexual desire, which he called a 'fury of the soul'. Plato (427–347 BC) adopted certain aspects of Pythagorean thinking. Although he rejected the cultic aspects of the Orphic religion, he dwelt much on the dualism of Ideas (soul) and Matter (body), and taught that the soul was superior in character to the body and constantly hindered in its function by the needs and desires of the body.

The Greek concept of love was also dualistic. There was sacred love and profane love, *agape* and *eros*, the one spiritual, the other physical. Plato believed that true happiness could only be found through *agape*, non-physical love. This higher love, Platonic love, could lead to self-mastery and an end to the disease of physical craving. 'Copulation' Plato wrote 'lowers a man to the frenzied passions characteristic of beasts and for this reason sexual desire belongs to the lowest element of the mind.'

Roman and then Christian philosophers followed Plato's lead. Diogenes the Cynic (412–322 BC) taught that all desires and appetites not absolutely necessary to maintaining life were to be renounced. Zeno (342–270 BC), founder of Stoicism, was less extreme. He taught that instincts and emotions were not antagonistic to right living, provided they were kept within bounds. Marriage was acceptable provided its purpose was procreation, but passion in marriage was suspect. Seneca (4 BC–AD 65) urged his Roman contemporaries to love with judgement, not with affection. Plotinus (AD 203–262), founder of Neoplatonism, preached that the key to human virtue lay in detachment from worldly (evil) desires. His more extremist followers considered all pleasure sinful, which ruled out not only sex but also horse-racing, going to the theatre, and eating meat.

11

Accompanying these antisexual philosophies of the pre-Christian and early Christian era was a high degree of misogyny. Someone close at hand had to be blamed for the temptations of the flesh, and who better than woman? Eve is the *prototype* scapegoat. The idea of woman as temptress still resonates through Western sexual thought.

In this medieval tapestry Eve gathers apples in the Garden of Eden, offers one to Adam, and is banished from God's grace. Her fault, if any, was curiosity; her sin was disobedience to God.

Jewish thought

Developments in Judaism were quite different. The Jews believed in one God, not in a pantheon, and in a unity of body and mind. For a satisfactory life, body and mind had to be in concert; the one should not be allowed to dominate the other. While the Greek philosophers were city people, the Jews, with their pastoral traditions, saw sex as a natural and indispensable part of life; sex was a gift from God to be enjoyed as a right by husband, wife, and even concubine.

There was no separation of the sexes at the time of the First Temple (tenth century BC). The Old Testament clearly states that a man cannot live a satisfactory life alone; he needs a companion and helpmeet, an equal partner — a woman. Sex segregation in worship developed not as a result of hostility between the sexes, but for just the opposite reason; they were too friendly.

As the Jews became urbanized they adopted some of the attitudes of the Greeks. It was right to resist the temptation to do evil and constantly strive to do good, but the Jews held to their belief that the rewards of a righteous life come in *this* world, not in the next. Other than in a minority of splinter groups (the Essenes were one such), the Jewish religion never denounced the pleasures and virtues of sex or downgraded women. Like the followers of Aristotle, it preached moderation in all things. As the famous medieval rabbi and physician Maimonides wrote: 'The Torah has intended natural man to eat moderately of what he has, drink what he can in moderate amount, and enjoy legitimate sexual pleasure in moderate measure.' In the thirteenth century the Talmudic scholar Nachmanides wrote: 'The Lord created all things in accordance with his wisdom, and whatever he created cannot be shameful or ugly....When a man is in union with his wife in a spirit of holiness and purity, the Divine Presence is with them.'

Christian traditions

From these conflicting currents of Jewish and Greek thought Christianity emerged, oriented towards salvation in a world to come, and taking a generally ascetic view of sex and other pleasures. Abstinence for the short duration of life on earth was fair trade for eternal celestial bliss. This antisexual attitude was reinforced by the spread of Manichaeism during the late third and fourth centuries. The doctrine of Mani (crucified in Persia in AD 276 for his opposition to Zoroastrianism) was based on the struggle of two eternal and conflicting principles, God and light, matter and darkness. Coitus was an act of darkness; even to contemplate it was evil. However, the Manichaeans accepted that not everyone was disciplined enough to deny the sexual impulse. Before his conversion to Christianity, Saint Augustine (died *c.* 605) was a Manichaean and had lived with a mistress, and his struggle to subdue his sexual urges continued throughout his life. The only rationale for sexual activity, he finally decided, reconciling his Christian and Manichaean ideas, was the Old Testament injunction to 'go forth and multiply'.

As the historian Vern Bullough wrote: 'With Saint Augustine the basic sexual attitudes of the Christian Church were set. Virginity was the preferred state of existence, but for those unable to adapt to this state, marriage was permitted. Within marriage intercourse was tolerated, but only for the purpose of procreation....'

*Title page of Andreas Vesalius' *De Humani Corporis Fabrica, *published in Basle in 1543. Vesalius was one of the first anatomists to study the human female reproductive tract.*

The glib assumption that a common Judaeo-Christian heritage accounts for Western sexual attitudes today is wrong. Although they coexisted geographically, Jewish and Christian thinking developed separately. Although some Jewish communities may have been sexually conservative or ascetic, and some Christian communities liberal or sensual, Judaism retained a generally positive attitude towards sex and Christianity a generally negative one.

With minor turns and digressions, it was the limited Augustinian concept of sex that prevailed from the seventh century onwards and became incorporated into Western civil law. In the medieval mind, the State, as an agent for moral good, had a duty to make unlawful those activities that the Church pronounced as sinful. So the State became responsible for punishing any sexual activity not tied to procreation. In many countries today various forms of non-reproductive sexual behaviour (oral or anal sex, prostitution, homosexual activities) are still illegal.

Throughout history the State has used religion as an excuse to make laws for civil or political purposes. The sixth-century Christian emperor Justinian, for reasons still not fully identified, placed homosexual activities in the same category as adultery. Punishment for homosexual acts ranged from doing penance to castration or death. Following the Church's notion of 'natural law', Justinian labeled homosexuality as 'unnatural'. The words 'acting contrary to nature' are still used in some legal codes today.

The old order challenged

The re-urbanization that followed the great plagues of fifteenth- and sixteenth-century Europe — one of which was syphilis, called 'the great pox' because its ravages were even more devastating than those of smallpox — changed many people's sex and family lives. As the State began to wrest power away from the Church, more and more 'natural philosophers' (we would call them scientists today) questioned the established order. In

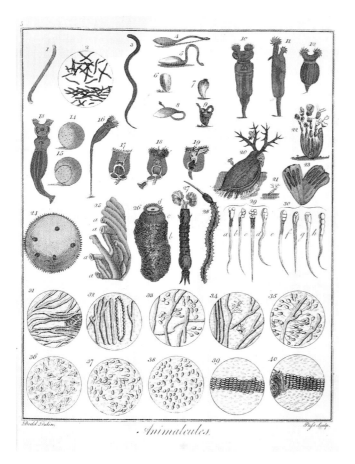

Animalcules

England, in the mid-1500s, William Harvey discovered how the blood circulates; he also investigated the hatching of chicken's eggs. In Italy, at about the same time, Vesalius and Fallopius studied the female reproductive system. In the Netherlands, in the seventeenth century, Leeuwenhoek and de Graaf explored the conjunction of sperm and egg; more work in this field was done by the Dutch anatomist von Baer in the nineteenth century. Slowly the mysteries of reproductive biology were submitted to scientific analysis.

Inevitably the Reformation modified views of sex and marriage. Neither Martin Luther nor John Calvin regarded sex within marriage as sinful. 'God winks at it!' said Luther. It was 'pure, honourable and holy' said Calvin. Even the Puritans, returning to Old Testament fundamentals, praised marital love and marital sex, although they strictly censured sexual expressions outside marriage. In the latter part of the eighteenth century, as France and the American colonies broke free of their monarchic pasts, thinking about human sexuality began to change. Influential philosophers such as Jean-Jacques Rousseau and Denis Diderot advocated a 'return to Nature', not to Greek or Catholic ideas of nature, but to Nature as the play of emotions, feelings, and instincts. The philosophers of the Age of Reason offered two important new attitudes. First, they cast aside the belief that physical impulses were destructive and ought to be controlled. On the contrary, it was good to have 'instincts' and good to express them; it was society's restrictiveness that subverted human joy and perfection. Second, they did not believe that one came closer to God by rejecting natural desires.

Before the invention of the microscope scientists were unable to study tiny life forms. This engraving, based on the microscope observations of Antoni van Leeuwenhoek of Delft and published in London around 1795, shows various 'animalcules', including human and animal sperm (middle row on right).

The beginnings of sexology

Deep-rooted social attitudes do not change overnight. Prior to and throughout the nineteenth century most education and scientific research took place in colleges and universities associated with religious institutions. But slowly and surely investigators began to ask questions specifically related to sex. Much of what they wrote and said we now know to be incorrect, but the significance of their work was that they overturned the idea that it was morally wrong to study sex. They also began to sweep aside the view that reproduction legitimized sex and to show that there was more to human sexuality than interesting differences in anatomy. The social problems of the nineteenth century, which included rampant venereal disease, illegitimacy, and widespread poverty and family breakdown, played a part in encouraging such enquiries. Investigators came from many disciplines and many countries, and for the most part they focused on social and marital problems rather than the acquisition of knowledge for its own sake. Sexology as a science in its own right had not yet emerged.

At the turn of the century, Richard von Krafft-Ebing, a German neurologist and psychiatrist, made an attempt to categorize the sexual pathologies he saw in his patients. Paolo Mantegazza, in Italy, contributed anthropological studies of sex. In France, Jean Charcot wrote of psychiatric and sexual problems and Auguste-Henri Forel published a biological and moral review of sex. Two Englishmen, Richard Burton and later Havelock Ellis, published reports of exotic Oriental sexual practices in real life and in literature. In Spain and the United States, other researchers began to make their mark. But, as the historian Erwin Haeberle has pointed out, the true founders of modern sexology were a group of German Jews: Iwan Bloch, Magnus Hirschfeld, Albert Moll, and Max Marcuse.

Around the time that Sigmund Freud published his *Three Essays on the Theory of Sexuality* (1905), Bloch and the others were well embarked on the road to Sexualwissenschaft ('sexual science') and calling for a broadly based and unified study of sexuality. Bloch himself published what was probably the first large scale review of sex, *The Sexual Life of Our Time* (1912), and in it pleaded: 'To do justice to the whole importance of love in the life of the individual and in that of society...this particular branch of inquiry must be treated...as a part of general science of mankind, which is constituted by a union of all other sciences — of general biology, anthropology and ethnology, philosophy and psychology, the history of literature, and the entire history of civilization.' We can only speculate what prompted such an interest in Bloch, who was a dermatologist/syphilologist. Perhaps he was impressed with the misery caused by venereal disease (AIDS has certainly spurred the efforts of many sex researchers today). Before the advent of antibiotics, venereal diseases filled more long-stay hospital beds than any other group of ills.

Bloch's call was quickly answered. In 1908 Hirschfeld founded the first journal devoted to sexology as a science. In the following year Marcuse also started a journal, this time for a wider audience. Albert Moll, already the author of a major monograph on homosexuality (1891) and another on libido (1897), followed with a comprehensive study called *The Sexual Life of the Child* in 1909.

This small group of men were the begetters of many books and journals, and a great deal of research and therapy. They even made educational films about syphilis and homosexuality, putting the case for more research into venereal disease and for decriminalizing homosexuality.

In 1919 Magnus Hirschfeld founded the world's first Institute for Sexology in Berlin. This was followed in 1921 by the first international sexology congress in Berlin, attended by scientists from Tokyo, Peking, Moscow, Rome, London, Copenhagen, and San Francisco. A second congress was held in 1926.

Sex research in America

Developments in the United States were slower and different in focus. There was no central nucleus of scientific sex investigators as there was in Berlin. There were individuals devoted to reforming attitudes to sex, reproduction, women's rights, sex education, and marriage laws, but encouraging research was not part of their enterprise. In late nineteenth- and early twentieth-century America — even more so than in Europe — nice people did not discuss sex. Certainly respectable professionals did not study the subject.

As the American author Harry Barnes wrote in 1926: 'Sex...is even taboo to intelligent discussion...Even physicians are not lacking who designate all types of sexual matters as nasty...The sexual is looked upon as pre-eminently the field which must not be approached in a scientific manner.'

During the 1920s the climate began to change. The credit for this was mainly due to four events. The first was the founding, in 1913, of the American Social Hygiene Association. Its purpose was to solve the social problems that accompany prostitution, venereal disease, and illegitimacy. One of the first scientific studies of sex in the United States — a survey of the sexual behaviour of 518 college men by M.J. Exner — followed very soon after. The second and third events were the rise of the Suffragettes — their agenda for women's rights included the availability of reliable contraception, safe and legal

Puritanical attitudes to sex, epitomized in this painting by Grant Wood (American Gothic, 1930), persisted in the United States until well after World War I.

abortion, and free love — and the blossoming of behaviourism, a new approach to psychology based on the objective study of behaviour rather than on assumptions about it. Fourth, and most important, was the impetus provided by a group of eminent biologists and psychologists (Walter B. Cannon, Frank R. Lillie, Robert M. Yerkes, and Catharine B. Davis among them) who saw the need to encourage sex research. In 1921 the National Research Council Committee for Research in Problems of Sex was formed. Its first resolution stated: 'The impulses and activities associated with sex behaviour and reproduction are fundamentally important for the welfare of the individual, the family, the community, the race. Nevertheless, the reports of personal experience are lacking and the relative few data of observation have not been collected in serviceable form. Under circumstances where we should have knowledge and intelligence, we are ignorant. To a large degree, our ignorance is due to the enshrouding of sex relations in a fog of mystery, reticence and shame.' In 1938 the Committee started to fund the work of a then unknown entomologist called Alfred C. Kinsey.

But until the 1950s neither sex research nor sex researchers, whatever their country of origin, were taken seriously by the majority of physicians and scientists around the world and certainly not by the public at large. Even 30 years ago the term sexologist had a very suspect ring to it.

Attitudes in Europe and Japan

No British publisher would print Havelock Ellis' monumental seven-volume *Studies in the Psychology of Sex* written in 1896. The book was first published in German in Germany. When copies arrived in London the distributor was prosecuted, and not a single physician or scientist of note came forward in court to defend the book or its publisher. The trial judge, Sir Charles Hall, suspended sentence, but warned: 'It is impossible for anyone with a head on his shoulders to open the book without seeing that it is a pretence and a sham...do not touch this filthy work again [or] it will be my duty to send you to prison for a very long term.' The book finally appeared in English, in 1901, in Philadelphia, but did not go on general sale; it was sold to professionals only. Publication in England had to wait until 1934. By that time it had become a landmark work in Germany, France, Spain, Italy, and even Japan. In Japan in 1922, when biologist Senji Yamamoto and his student Tokutaro Yasuda, tried to publish sexological data collected from some 1,146 volunteers, they too found the law against them. Their report was censured as 'an obscene document' that would 'corrupt public morals'. Yamamoto paid dearly for his scientific daring: he was assassinated by fanatical nationalists who thought his findings defamatory to Japan.

In Europe, the lengthening shadow of Fascism and Nazism began to blot out the emerging science of sexology. Within four months of assuming power in 1933, Hitler sent a Nazi mob to ransack the Institute for Sexology and publicly burn its books and papers. His rantings against Jewish science forced Hirschfeld, Moll, and Marcuse to flee for their lives (by this time Bloch had died). In those territories that fell under their sway the Nazis confiscated or destroyed all sexological material, forbade research, and, in a gruesome return to the Dark Ages, systematically persecuted Jews and gypsies and sent thousands of homosexuals to concentration camps and death. Even in countries outside German control attitudes towards sex research, grudging at best, became less hospitable. The world had more desperate matters to attend to.

Sex research after World War II

After the war, with the forceful and positive leadership of Hirschfeld and his colleagues gone, the focus of sex research moved to the United States. Alfred Kinsey and his collaborators published their classic study *Sexual Behavior in the Human Male* in 1948 and the volume on the female followed in 1953. By this time many academic, clinical, and social disciplines, thanks to encouragement from the National Research Council, possessed experts on sexual matters. In the 1960s and 1970s William Masters and Virginia Johnson

Sexual Behavior in the Human Female was published in 1953. This photograph shows, from left to right, Dr. Clyde E. Martin, Dr. Paul H. Gebhard, Dr. Alfred Charles Kinsey, and Dr. Wardell B. Pomeroy in the heavily guarded room at Indiana University where the case histories for the book were kept. Kinsey claimed that even professional cryptographers could not break the code he used for recording his research data.

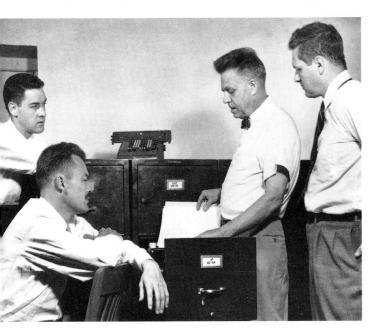

carried the study of sex into the laboratory. They investigated male and female responses to sexual excitement, and also developed methods of treating various sexual dysfunctions.

In Germany and Japan, as well as in Britain, France, Scandinavia, Czechoslovakia, and other technologically advanced countries, the validity and usefulness of sex research gained gradual acceptance. International sexology congresses (the dream of Hirshfeld and Moll) began again in 1974, in Paris. Since then, Montreal, Rome, Mexico City, Jerusalem, Washington, Bombay, Heidelberg, and Amsterdam have all had a World Congress of Sexology. Tokyo and Rio are next on the list.

But even today, in the 1990s, despite the enormous scope for and influence of accurate sexual information, there are fewer than a score of university departments in the world devoted to sexology. Some countries are without a single teacher or researcher qualified in this area. In the CIS (formerly the Soviet Union) and most of Eastern Europe there has been almost no sex research. However, there are signs that *glasnost* and the demise of communism are blowing away some of the cobwebs. In 1990, with the reunification of Berlin, a Third International Berlin Conference of Sexology was held in the Reichstag to commemorate the work of Magnus Hirschfeld, and in the summer of 1992 the International Academy of Sex Research met in Prague. In the same year the Asian Federation for Sexology held its first conference in Shanghai. However, no Islamic government has ever allowed any basic sex research. Even the governments of the United States and the United Kingdom recently rejected calls for national surveys of sexual practices, although in the United Kingdom this impediment was overcome by private financing from the Wellcome Trust; in the United States, researchers are still awaiting an enlightened benefactor. So far, only a few countries — among them the Netherlands, Thailand, and Hong Kong — have done national surveys in order to formulate a response to the spread of HIV disease and AIDS.

Of course the scientific investigation of anything can be turned to propaganda use. Sex surveys are no different. Research findings are eagerly scanned for facts that can be lobbed into battles against the establishment, or against religion, or against the opposite sex. Sex has become a political football. This has not been all bad. When old concepts are challenged, new insights usually follow. It was French philosopher-historian Michel Foucault who, in the early 1980s, put forward the view that society 'constructs' (creates images of) sex in terms of power. Similar ideas have come from G. Rubin, Leonore Tiefer, and other feminist sex researchers who call for a more critical evaluation and interpretation of such 'basics' as the sexual response cycle (see Chapter 5). The *meaning* of sex is prompting as much scientific interest as the *expression* of sex. This is exciting.

As scientists have discovered more and more about sex, there has been more and more that ordinary mortals wish to know. Self-help books and how-to-do-it manuals began to proliferate in the 1950s. Today, on the brink of the twenty-first century, the need seems never to have been greater. There are now several widely respected international scientific journals devoted to sex in general. More importantly, there are also journals devoted to particular aspects of sex (medical, sex for the disabled, history, language). Sex research articles also appear in the periodicals of many learned societies. Human sexuality has become the province of many experts — psychologists, biologists, sociologists, anthropologists, mathematicians, geographers, historians, philosophers, artists, and so on. And with interest in AIDS leading the way, aspects of sex that were once taboo are now

Even NATO (North Atlantic Treaty Organization) has put a toe into the waters of sexology. In 1992 it organized a prestigious conference on the development of sex differences. The Adam and Eve symbolism used in this poster is understood throughout Europe.

being discussed in the popular media.

But things are not yet perfect. I would like to see the separate strands of research increasingly coming together, in the European mode, as the unified science of sexology, and I would like to see research expanded into the fields of ethics and politics, art and religion. I would also like to see society respect the legitimate curiosity of non-experts when it comes to researching and writing credibly about sex. Sex *is* something studied by experts, but it is also contributed to and openly appreciated by the layperson; after all, astronomers are complemented by enthusiastic star-gazers. An interest in sex is entirely natural, not a sign of perversion.

Levels of complexity

Sex is a complex subject, so we should build complexity into the way we think about it. Sex can be seen as a series of increasingly complex relationships, beginning with the individual, then expanding to the couple, the family, and society at large. Understanding the behaviour of the individual makes it easier to understand interaction between sexual partners, which in turn provides a key to understanding how families behave and how societies function.

And at each level of complexity sex can be viewed in different ways: as a set of biologically or socially determined *patterns of behaviour*; as a set of *physiological mechanisms*; as a set of *thoughts and feelings* about sex; as a process of acquiring *sexual identity*; as a matter of *sexual orientation*, developing a preference for partners of the same or opposite sex; and also as a set of events leading to *reproduction*, to conception, birth, and parenthood.

To the layperson, all sexual phenomena may appear interrelated; to the scientist who carefully observes them, they are often independent. Take sex roles and gender roles. In Scotland, gender roles for men include the wearing of a kilt. This would be inappropriate gender behaviour in Japan. But male sex roles in both Japan and Scotland are similar. A *gender role* is society's idea of how boys and girls, or men and women, should behave; a *sex role* is the acting out of one's biological predisposition. Gender has everything to do with the particular society one lives in, and may or may not have much to do with biology. The distinction between gender and sex becomes particularly critical when discussing issues such as transvestism, the women's movement, and the development of sexual identity.

Next, let us be clear what sexual identity is. Early in life most of us know that we are male or female. Accepting their gender roles, boys generally want to follow masculine pursuits and girls feminine ones. Occasionally, despite social pressures to conform to the physical evidence, a boy may be convinced he is a girl, or a girl that she is a boy. Our image of our sexual selves may or may not be in concert with our gender. Sexual identity is the inner conviction that we are male or female, whether or not that conviction reflects our physical appearance or the gender roles society imposes on us.

Sexual identity is often confused by the layperson with sexual orientation. Almost everyone at some time in their life is attracted to another person as a partner for love or sex. That orientation may be heterosexual, towards a partner of the opposite sex, or homosexual, towards a partner of the same sex; or it may be bisexual, towards partners of either sex. But the sexual identity of the person

Sexual orientation may be at odds with religious, political, and other affiliations, as this Dignity demonstration in Honolulu, on behalf of gay and lesbian Roman Catholics, illustrates.

so attracted is not in question; he or she has a clear sexual self-image regardless of his or her orientation.

In the West there are many genetic males who believe themselves female and yet, obedient to the dictates of society, they continue to live and dress as males. Their gender is male while their identity is female. Their orientation, on the other hand, may be towards males or females. Sexual orientation can be independent of gender or identity.

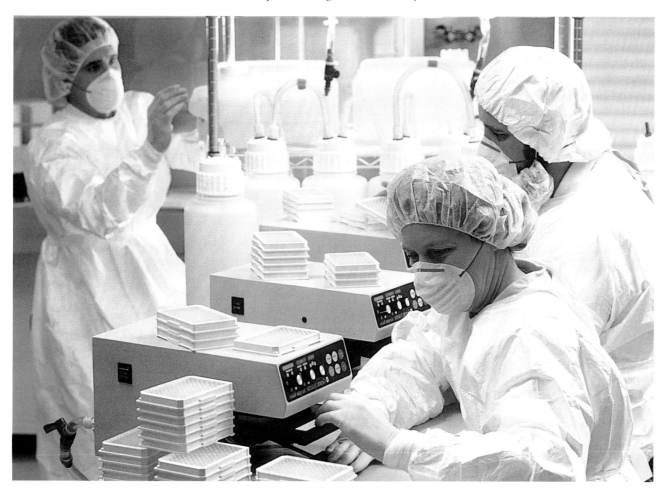

Getting the facts right

Organizing sexual thinking — whether on the basis of levels of complexity or along more traditional academic lines — is one thing, but finding the facts behind the thinking and using those facts honestly is another. How is sexual information gathered, analysed, and used? Sexology, the scientific study of sex, is perhaps more fraught with unintentional and occasionally intentional biases in information gathering and interpretation than the older sciences. Like politics, religion, and history, it can be used to bolster prejudice, create fads, and manipulate behaviour.

Gloved, gowned, and masked workers in an HIV test laboratory. Since the early 1980s AIDS has been the spur to an enormous amount of sex research.

Some time ago I formulated three rules about 'facts' uncovered in the process of sex research. The first is that *facts are always accompanied by attitudes or emotions*. Data collected by a religious fundamentalist group may differ quite radically from data collected by a non-religious or less doctrinaire organization. A writer for a men's magazine may select one set of facts for an article on vasectomy and his counterpart on a women's magazine a completely different set of facts. Polls taken by partisan groups are always suspect. The same set of facts, in different hands, can be used to 'prove' different points. Facts can also be suppressed if they are considered morally or politically unacceptable.

My second rule is this: *researchers talk about populations and trends, but their data are gathered from individuals*. Not only are the researchers themselves individuals, but individuals also tend to look for themselves in others. The inevitable incompleteness of the researcher's own sexual experiences seriously colours his or her acceptance and interpretation of the data collected. As Alfred Kinsey, possibly the most thorough sexual sleuth of all time, once observed: 'The possibility of an individual engaging in sexual activity at a rate remarkably different from one's own is one of the most difficult things for even professionally trained persons to understand.' Someone who has one or two orgasms a year with a single partner has a very different view of sex from someone who has a dozen orgasms a week with as many different partners.

My third rule is, I believe, the most important: *one must always distinguish between what is and what might or should be.* For example, as a widower and as father of four daughters I support women's claims to equal rights and opportunities with men, but as a sexologist I note that progress towards equality is patchy, extremely slow, and may never be attained.

Well conducted national sex surveys in Thailand have been translated into successful population control policy. Now the Thai government is tackling AIDS. This poster campaign associates Thailand's most famous actress and actor with condom use.

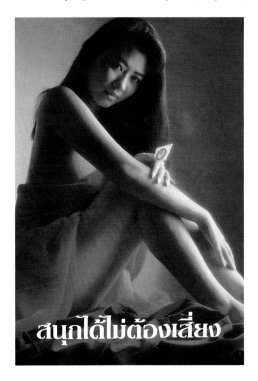 

Personal involvement can very easily lead one to mistake hopes, fears, and ideals for actuality. Since the 1960s, for example, the rate of divorce has been increasing in the West, but it is now apparent, as we enter the 1990s, that the trend is levelling off or even declining. Some observers credit this to economic recession, others to the fear of AIDS, others to a return to older values. But, at present, all such pronouncements are speculation. I believe that societies remain fairly stable in their fundamental sexual values and change them only with great effort. Culture, history, law, and religion possess an inertia that resists change. If someone reports a dramatic break with tradition, I remain sceptical until evidence arrives documenting that the change is widespread and permanent.

The media and many individuals — for the sake of effect — are fond of sensationalizing or prophesying by extrapolating from a few findings, or even one, and the unsuspecting are seduced and caught off guard. Over the last decade we have been encouraged to believe that AIDS is a consequence of anal sex, that pornography is of interest only to a minority and leads to rape, that children are sexually curious only when prompted by an adult, and that homosexuality is more common than ever. All of these sensationalisms are false.

An additional fact is crucial to keep in mind when sexwatching. Scientist refers to it as 'disparity in KAP' (Knowledge, Attitudes, Practices). What a person knows, thinks, and does is not always or necessarily consistent. People frequently know of, discuss, advocate, support, or tolerate practices that they do not or would not allow themselves, and condemn in public what they practice in private. A man may preach fidelity while he is cheating on his wife. Dentists can have toothache, and marriage counsellors, sex therapists, psychologists, and psychiatrists can have sex problems.

Sex surveys

My final *caveat* to the sexwatcher is this: remember that sexual information is only as reliable as the research methods and samples used to obtain it. Data gathered in 1992 from 2,000 teenagers in London, England, may not apply to teenagers in Houston, Texas, or to teenagers surveyed in 1982 or 2002. And simply increasing the size of a sample does not guarantee accuracy. In 1936 *The Literary Digest* asked more than 2 million Americans to predict the winner of that year's presidential election; they gave the nod to Alf Landon, but in the event Franklin D. Roosevelt won.

Sex research bristles with surveys. Those conducted among college students, a relatively 'captive' population, are the most common. Other studies are of patients or clients of one sort or another, who more or less select themselves for investigation. Surveys of both captive and self-selected populations are of limited value; they say a lot about the individuals studied, but very little about anyone else. Best known to the general public are the investigations of Shere Hite, *Playboy*, *Redbook*, *Cosmopolitan*, and others, conducted in the 1970s and 1980s. Although such surveys involve thousands of participants and attract a lot of media attention, they too suffer from sample distortion, representing only those people who choose to offer information about their sex lives (sex research volunteers are generally more liberal-minded than non-volunteers), certainly not about the total readership or group surveyed. Also, the analyses applied to such information are often simplistic. Hite's writings, for example, are a collection of anecdotes and selected abstractions from a minority, not an accurate reflection of the majority. What is the value of information based on a biased sample which is then further distorted by limited interpretation? The Hite surveys nicely illustrate the need for my three rules about evaluating sex research.

Nevertheless valid and reliable surveys of selected issues have been done. Within the last 10 years valuable national studies have come from the Japanese Association for Sex Education, from Thailand, Hong Kong, and elsewhere. Other smaller but equally important studies have been done with smaller groups and dealt with more specific topics. Perhaps the most significant work has been that of the National Opinion Research Center in the United States, providing information on heterosexual and homosexual contacts and various sexual practices. Similar research has been done in the Netherlands by the Dutch National Institute for Sexological Research, and in the United Kingdom a valuable survey was conducted recently by researchers from St. Mary's Hospital Medical School in London.

The Thai and Hong Kong surveys, as well as the American, Dutch and British surveys just mentioned, are particularly sound. Instead of distributing hit-or-miss questionnaires, information was gathered by means of face-to-face interviews, with interviewees representative of the whole population under investigation. Each sample population was matched to the general population for social class, marital status, age, ethnic group, geographical location, and so on. This is the ideal. Unfortunately too many researchers must or choose to settle for less.

Chapter 2

Excitement
and arousal

What is sexually arousing? That is one of the most intriguing questions for any sexwatcher. Think for a moment. What characteristics do you find sexually appealing in others and what things do others find sexy about you? I have often thought that all those things that lead to one person coaxing another into bed, singling out that person from other friends or acquaintances, are more interesting than what they actually do in bed. Bedroom play is a relatively limited part of sexual interaction when compared with the conscious or unconscious desires and strategies involved in arousal, initiation and invitation, persuasion and seduction. Stimuli to arousal are infinitely varied and mysterious.

A man and woman stand on a tropical beach at sunset. A young couple lie warm and relaxed in front of a flickering fire. Media images like these are calculated to appeal to all the senses — sight, sound, taste, smell, touch, and temperature (rarely is sexual arousal or fantasy associated with the cold). Fatigue and preoccupation, the two most common impediments to sexual arousal, are rarely portrayed in such tableaux. But many of us know from personal or vicarious experience that sexual arousal can happen in the most unlikely places, at the least expected times, and even with complete strangers.

Casual encounters

Between 10 and 15 percent of the women interviewed by Kinsey reported never having felt sexually aroused, not even casually. Indeed most surveys and anecdotal evidence suggest that casual arousal is more a male than a female experience, and most clinical studies point the same way. Also, when it comes to coitus, it is usually the man who wants more and the woman who feels pressured to comply. Nevertheless, many women are sexually curious and willing to test their erotic impulses. In one *Playboy* study done in the 1980s a third of the 15,000 female respondents said they had initiated sexual encounters with strangers. Only 4 per cent had been turned down. Most of the male respondents who made overtures to strange women were rebuffed!

R. D. Clark and E. Hatfield tested male and female reactions to sexual invitations from strangers by asking male and female college students ('experimental lures') to approach other college students of the opposite sex with one of three requests: 'Can we go out tonight?', 'Will you come over to my apartment?', or 'Will you go to bed with me?' The majority of the men thus propositioned were willing to have sexual relations with their female lure, but not one of the women.

Data like these are usually interpreted as meaning that men are more interested in physical gratification and women more interested in love and relationships. But even this assumption has been questioned. University of Kansas researchers J. Sprague and D. Quadagno expanded the age range of their sample and found that motives for sexual activity vary with age; until the fourth decade, men seem more interested in the physical side and women in the emotional side, but from age 40 it's the other way around.

No matter how hi-tech and intergalactic our species becomes, the physical features that attract a man to a woman and a woman to a man will remain much the same. Firm breasts and thighs, rippling muscles and a bulging crotch...these are signals that have brought male and female together since our species first walked upright.

Sexual attraction does not rely only on physical beauty and on a sympathetic social situation. People who are disabled or deformed, people whose deliberate style is to be unkempt or unwashed, people of all conditions and classes arouse sexual feelings. A female physician on duty in an emergency room once described to me how a bloody and dishevelled accident victim brought in for treatment aroused her to such an extent that she had to excuse herself from the room.

Physical features

'Love at first sight' is not so much love as sexual attraction. Sometimes the stimulus is obvious — the exposure of a firm breast or long smooth thigh, a hairy chest, rippling muscles, a bulging crotch. But sociobiologists, those scientists who study the links between social behaviour and biological phenomena, believe that secondary sex characteristics — body shape, hair, voice, and so on — are also attraction and arousal signals. Among our pre-speech paleolithic forebears these signals ensured that male and female came together for mating and reproduction. Our responses to these signals, so the theory goes, are innate. At a subconscious level we link secondary sex characteristics with fitness for reproduction and parenting. Subconsciously a man looks for health and child-bearing ability in a woman; she, in her turn, looks for his ability to protect and sustain a family.

By extension, gestures that draw attention to the relevant features of both sexes — a woman swinging her hips as she walks or a man flexing his muscles — enhance our responses. So do activities that call attention to the genitals or mimic copulation. The gyrations of Madonna or Michael Jackson on stage elicit frenzied responses from audiences.

Yet sexual attraction is not as simple as that. Our secondary sex characteristics may be far from ideal, nor are they always on display. Often it is something trivial and accidental — the toss of a woman's hair or her smile, the sound of a man's voice or the way he laughs — that triggers our interest and a strong desire to pursue the encounter.

Arousal at first sight is easy to understand if the people concerned look like Julia Roberts and Richard Gere, seen here in the film Pretty Woman. *But looks are not everything.*

Contenders for the Mr. Universe title flex their delts, pecs, quads, etc. For most women, however, overdeveloped muscles have limited appeal. Power, intelligence, and a healthy bank balance are a safer bet.

Good looks in general

To men, looks are an important factor in sexual arousal. This has been confirmed by a great deal of well conducted research as well as anecdotal evidence. In one *Playboy* study, male respondents ranked breasts, buttocks, and eyes — in that order — as most important. The female respondents who paid particular attention to looks ranked eyes first, buttocks second, and lips and genitals in joint third place.

Of course no single feature works in isolation. Usually it is the total impression that counts, even if one or two especially fascinating features are emphasized. Generally women admit to being less stimulated by looks than by intelligence, common interests, sexual energy, money, and power. Men appreciate such assets, but rank them less highly.

Women's choices seem to be linked to the fact that they are less likely to indulge in sex play and intercourse without psychological involvement and at least a hint of marriage, or a long-term relationship, down the line. They also base some of their decisions on what they imagine to be the socioeconomic status of the man concerned. Men are more inclined to make choices based on physical attraction alone.

In a large study done by Karla Joy and Allen Young in 1977, North American male and female homosexuals were asked which physical or non-physical features they found attractive or unattractive in a sex partner. The most commonly preferred attributes specified by men were cleanliness and 'looks in general'. The most appreciated were, in order of importance, slim build, shapely physique, and relative youth. The women put these same items top too — cleanliness and 'looks in general' first, followed by relative youth and slim build — but in general their responses were more varied than the men's. But for both sexes general attributes were more important than specific features.

All of us package our sexual signals and revealing all is much less interesting than leaving something to the imagination. Here leather, metal, and denim draw attention to buttocks and pelvis, even though the torso is bare. And just how little will that lacy triangle conceal?

Responding to sexual signals

Even among experts there is little agreement as to how sexual arousal or attraction happens. The sociobiological view that it is an inborn, primitive mechanism related to fitness for parenting is a powerful argument, but not universally accepted

Some theorists claim that adult sexual arousal is carried over from events rooted in infancy and learned during upbringing. The characteristics of one's parents, or one's interactions with them as a child, supposedly leave unconscious erotic programs that are then drawn on in adulthood; sometimes they match aspects of the dynamics that attracted one's parents to each other. Other theorists believe that the stimuli we respond to match fragments of previous sexual situations, real or imagined. For example, if the hero or heroine or your dreams has long hair or wears thigh-high boots, or a stranger's voice reminds you of a past lover, these may trigger off sexual arousal.

Sometimes it is a certain *type* of interaction, usually one that boosts your ego, or makes you less anxious, that arouses sexual feelings. A knight in shining armour, or more likely an ordinary man who rescues a woman from a difficult situation, may trigger erotic thoughts. Nurses and doctors, because they are caring and relieve pain and anxiety, are often the subject of sexual fantasizing. Movies mimic reality when they show people sharing a common adventure or experience, especially if it is exciting or emotionally trying, being erotically drawn to each other (the *Indiana Jones* phenomenon).

Another popular theory, credited to American psychologist Stanley Schachter, holds that since we tend to give specific emotional labels to any kind of physiological arousal — we call a dry throat and a trembling voice 'fear', 'anxiety', defensiveness', 'anger', and so on —

The sexual feelings of the Edwardian male (and female) were aroused by the hourglass figure, with its overtones of discipline and helplessness. A waist like this was achieved with ferocious corsetry and surgical removal of the lower ribs.

under certain circumstances we tend to label physiological events as sexual attraction or interpret them as strengthening sexual feelings and perceptions we already have. Numerous experiments support this theory.

Anxiety, aggression, and sexual arousal

In one study in which male subjects were led to believe they would be given mild or severe electric shocks, the positive ratings they gave to randomly assigned partners of the opposite sex significantly increased. In another study, subjects obliged to make prolonged eye contact with a stranger — usually a situation that provokes anxiety — displayed greatly enhanced attraction to that person. In everyday life we constantly, though not always consciously, feel stimulated and threatened by eye contact.

One intriguing study by Donald Dutton and Arthur Aron at the University of British Columbia tested this 'heightened emotion = arousal' theory under supposedly natural conditions. It was arranged that ordinary passers-by, all of them men, should singly encounter a man or woman (members of the research team) either on a suspension bridge swaying 230 feet above rapids, or on a solid bridge 10 feet above a tributary of the same river. The unsuspecting subjects of the experiment were stopped and asked to take a simple psychological test. This was a diversion from the real point of the experiment, which was to discover if the fear associated with the swaying bridge and the low level of anxiety associated with the solid one would directly influence subjects' later attempts to contact the interviewer. The interviewers routinely offered a telephone number to each participant, ostensibly so they could find out the results of the psychological test.

Half of the participants interviewed on the swaying bridge telephoned the female interviewer, compared with only 15 per cent interviewed on the solid bridge. Very few bothered to contact the male interviewer, whether they had been interviewed on the swaying or the solid bridge. Certainly, with men more often casually aroused than women, it is hardly surprising that the woman interviewer was more frequently propositioned, but why did the relative danger of the swaying bridge have such an effect? This finding, and other related investigations, seems to support the idea that there is a definite link between anxiety and sexual attraction.

As a sidelight on this intriguing topic, consider the habits of the Gusii tribe of present-day Kenya. Among the Gusii sexual arousal is said to occur only in combination with hostility and antagonism. Sexual training for girls involves being taught from childhood to encourage male advances while simultaneously frustrating them. Boys, in turn, are instructed to overcome female denial and demand or force coitus. The anthropologist William Davenport comments: 'Normal intercourse has to take the form of ritualized rape if it is to provide mutual gratification.'

Rape, flagellation, and sadomasochism as sexual outlets in Western society reveal that sex with violence is not an aberration of primitive cultures. Are these apparent links between arousal and aggression inconsistent with theories of interpersonal relations that predict greater attraction and

In this 'naughty' Victorian engraving a whiskered onlooker enjoys the double excitement of voyeurism and vicarious flagellation.

arousal in situations of ease and comfort? Just as stress may enhance as well as diminish resistance to disease, increase as well as undermine our ability to withstand insult and challenge, so too it may affect sexual response. We are undoubtedly dealing with separate phenomena linked in ways we have yet to understand.

Measuring arousal

The most obvious way to gauge a person's level of arousal is to ask them how they feel. More methodically, one can watch or even measure a particular aspect of behaviour. In men, erection can be monitored with a flexible ring-shaped gauge fitted around the penis. The gauge registers expansion of the penis from flaccid to erect. In women, tampon-like devices can be inserted into the vagina to record vaginal blood pressure, and pulse and blood volume; both measures correlate with vasocongestion and lubrication, considered to be the female counterpart to erection. In both sexes, temperature-sensitive devices applied to the genitals, breasts, groin, or elsewhere can be used to measure the temperature changes associated with arousal. Unfortunately, a palpitating heart and heavy breathing are not reliable indicators.

Physical and mental excitement

Among sexologists it is well known that many women are not aware whether they have orgasm or not. Less known is the fact that a small number of men are not aware, without looking, whether they have an erection or not. For the vast majority of men, however, there is a good correlation between exposure to erotic stimuli, conscious feelings of sexual excitement, and degree of physiological response. This is also true of many women, though by no means all. It seems that for quite a large proportion of women the links between stimuli, feelings, and physical response are not at all automatic. It is not uncommon for women to demonstrate a marked degree of vaginal vasocongestion and lubrication and yet report no feelings of sexual arousal. Laboratory data, combined with anecdotal and clinical reports, suggest that some women need stronger stimulation before they become consciously aware of what their bodies are telling them.

The element of aggression that permeates a great deal of sexual fantasy is obvious in this poster for an 'adult' movie.

An interesting fact emerged from a group of studies by D. L. Steinman and colleagues in 1981. Heterosexual men and women were shown films of various sexual activities. In both sexes the strongest physiological reactions occurred in response to scenes of group sex. The second and third strongest responses from the men were to films of lesbian activity and films of a couple engaged in heterosexual sex; this order was reversed by the women viewers. Neither group showed a marked response to male homosexual activity, but both men and women were more aroused by watching women masturbating than by watching men masturbating.

Why did the group sex scenes cause most excitement among individuals of both sexes? Possibly for the majority of men degree of arousal is related to the number of women available (in this case on film), while for the majority of women arousal corresponds to the number of relationships witnessed that involve women. The men tended to fantasize more or less indiscriminately over all the women in the films, while the women tended to concentrate their fantasies. The low response to male homosexuality may have a lot to do with the overt taboos against such behaviour that still exist in Western society; both men and women may internalize these taboos to such an extent that they find homosexual male sex unappealing. Extrapolating from Steinman's experiments, it is probably true to say that sexual stimuli and our physiological responses to them are interpreted as sexually arousing provided they are not in conflict with self-image and provided they do not provoke feelings of guilt. If we feel guilt and conflict, there may be no arousal or if we are aroused we do not interpret arousal as sexual.

Clinical and physiological psychologist Julia Heiman, who has done a great deal of research on the subject of arousal, studied both men and women listening to erotic audio tapes and carefully monitored their physiological responses. Selecting those with the strongest physiological responses, she found that every man recognized his feelings of sexual arousal. This was in striking contrast to the women, 42 per cent of whom said they felt no physical response, 54 per cent that they felt no vaginal sensations at all, and 63 per cent that they were unaware of any lubrication. She comments: 'My research finds, indeed, that women like erotica as much as men do, that they are turned on by sexual descriptions, that their fantasies are as vivid and self arousing.' But, she adds, women may be 'slower to *admit* arousal'.

In fact, women may have higher thresholds to *awareness* of arousal. Other studies have arrived at this conclusion, although without agreeing on the cause. Danish sexologists Gorm Wagner and Roy Levin have suggested that women process sexual information differently from men. Dutch investigators Joost Dekker and Walter Everaerd believe that individuals, male or female, unconsciously or consciously, choose whether to interpret erotic stimuli at an emotional level that demands a sexual response or at a more neutral, verbal, level that does not. Do more women do more of the latter? And is this difference between the sexes innate, learned, or a bit of both?

Some investigators claim that since men can feel and see their penises becoming erect, they learn to associate erection with subjective excitement. In women vaginal changes are less obvious and therefore more difficult to link with subjective impressions. Other researchers suggest an opposite view: it is the subjective or learned context of eroticism, they say, that leads to physiological arousal. Attempts to measure physiological and cognitive (mental) arousal simultaneously have indeed shown that physiological arousal seems to precede cognitive arousal, particularly in women. But is may be that certain physiological response thresholds have to be reached before cognitive thresholds are attained. During evolution the body must have had the means to respond to sexual stimuli long before the brain evolved to evaluate them.

Another theory holds that girls, more than boys, are taught to deny their feelings. They grow up more used to repressing socially unacceptable sensations when exposed to erotic stimuli.

Variety and novelty
Novelty and variety are potent arousers. Even between regular partners new clothes, new hairstyles, new places, and new interests can renew sexual ardour. A new partner, in fact or fantasy, is extremely exciting — sex with someone new is one of the most common fantasies reported by both sexes.

This phenomenon has been demonstrated in many species — fowl, rodents, primates. And while in almost all species, including humans, it is more common among males than females, it has been demonstrated in both sexes. Prostitution, and recreational and extramarital sex, are all evidence of novelty-seeking behaviour. There is an old Oriental saying that goes: 'For a man, the most arousing stimulus is another man's wife.' As James Geer and other researchers have shown, both physiological and psychological sexual responsiveness to erotic stimuli decreases with repeated presentation. Loss of interest in a long-time partner is a common complaint.

How and why novelty increases arousal is an intriguing question. Curiosity about the unknown is certainly a factor. There is also something attractive about the forbidden. As Freud said: 'Some obstacle is necessary to swell the tide of libido to its height; and at all periods of history, whenever natural barriers in the way of satisfaction have not sufficed, mankind has erected conventional ones to enjoy love.'

It was the dual force of attraction and repulsion present in sexual feelings that prompted Freud to coin the term 'libido'. Though frequently equated with sex drive, libido is a wider and more complicated concept. It refers to the motivating force that leads one to seek out and enjoy sexual experience, even when this is in conflict with the interests of the ego. According to Freud, our dreams provide us with a forum in which to act out the dictates of the libido without let or hindrance.

However, although both novelty and anticipation often breed desire, they also breed anxiety which can hinder performance. Clinically, conditions such as impotence or premature ejaculation in men or vaginismus and anorgasmia in women often accompany a high level of anxiety. The plot thickens.

Triggers and thresholds

Some researchers claim that triggers to sexual arousal are inborn and then become generalized to a certain extent. More people are heterosexual than homosexual probably because most men are predisposed to be aroused by female features such as breasts and vulva, and most women by such male features as broad shoulders and penis. Within these generalized preferences each society sets

A box of novelty condoms or 'French ticklers', supposedly providing extra physical and fantasy sensation for the woman.

the degree of eroticism associated with these features. But standards for women are much more varied than for men. Some societies prize large breasts, some small, some drooping, some prefer long legs, or a vulva well covered with hair; in others large hips may be the erotic ideal, or a clean-shaven pubic area. In men broad shoulders, firm muscles, and a tapered shape are almost universally appreciated, although there is less consensus in attitudes to body or facial hair, baldness, heaviness, and so on. Societies certainly influence where, when, and with whom an erotic response is appropriate. The attributes of a sumo wrestler may not be attractive in a bank clerk; desirable features in a close relative provoke a different response when echoed in a stranger's face or physique. Our innate ability to be excited and aroused is highly modified by codes of social behaviour.

In sexual matters, familiarity does not necessarily breed contempt, or even indifference. The erotic appeal of breasts is not lessened, for example, in a society or in situations where bare breasts or scanty clothing are the rule. In situations sympathetic to sexual encounters, breasts continue to exercise their fascination. This seems to confirm that certain parts of the body are built-in sexual stimuli. But it is *different* male or female hips or buttocks that seem to maintain the interest.

In general, men are more easily aroused sexually than women — they have lower thresholds of arousal. Teenagers and young adults also have lower arousal thresholds than young children or elderly people. That is not to say that women, pre-teenagers, and the over 60s do not become sexually aroused, just that it takes more to arouse them. Thresholds to arousal are also affected by time. For example, a woman deprived of male company for a long time might find herself highly aroused by the first man she sees. Intervals without sex can lead to heightened receptivity.

Sweet talk, odours, and pheromones

It has been said that while men are turned on by what they see, women are turned on more by what they hear. An interesting conversation, spiced with sweet talk and innuendo, can be highly erotic. Most women are particularly susceptible to the sound of a lover's voice offering sexual suggestion. Seductive talk was identified as a stimulus by almost half the women polled by *Cosmopolitan* in 1980; 8 out of 10 said they found music a very effective stimulus. This was also true of the vast majority of women studied by Kinsey in the 1940s and 1950s. In sharp contrast, fewer than 1 in 10 of Kinsey's male respondents said they were aroused by music. But if use of telephone sex lines is any indication, talk is a hot item for male arousal.

Among animals, sexual stimuli are usually quite specific and very powerful. The female gypsy moth's ability to attract a male from over a mile away is well known. But what human odours communicate, and how they commnunicate it, is still open to debate.

Some researchers still argue that female primates secrete special pheromones called copulins which signal that they are ready to mate. It is doubtful whether human females release copulins or whether human males could detect them if they did. Vaginal odours vary during the menstrual cycle, but they are least intense at ovulation when the likelihood of conception is greatest. Certainly many individuals in modern Western society find genital and body scents erotically arousing, particularly during sex. The Roman poet Catullus wrote of vaginal secretion: 'When you smell it you will ask the gods to make you all nose.'

Here again, the variation among individuals is wide. Many people find body odours offensive. Yet nature must have had a purpose in locating scent glands most numerously and prominently near the genitals, and under the arms and breasts, and giving them wicks of hair to diffuse their secretions.

Men generally have larger sweat glands than women, which correlates positively with intensity of body odour, although 'intense' is not always perceived as 'pleasant'. Women, more often than men, even without training, can discriminate between the odours of males and females. But to date there is no really strong evidence that natural body smells are instinctively arousing for humans. Nor, as yet, is there any evidence of sex-specific odour preferences analogous to those noted in animals. In fact physicians R.L. Goldberg and T.N. Wise have recently reported that individuals born without a sense of smell have sexual histories indistinguishable from those of their fully functioning peers.

Such findings have not deterred perfume companies from marketing cosmetics as if they were proven sexual attractants. Perfumes usually contain extracts of the scent glands of

Rubber and plastic wear are now high fashion rather than 'deviant'. It was French psychologist Alfred Binet who coined the term 'fetishism' to describe unusually intense sexual attraction to an object (panties, fur, high heels, rubber) or part of the body. Almost all fetishists are male.

ungulates (musk), whale secretions (ambergris), or pig urine (androstenedione), which are known to do wonders for the animals concerned.

Some researchers have speculated that the use of perfumes evolved not to attract sexual attention but to mask natural odours that were too erotic for social comfort. Cosmetic manufacturers have been very successful at encouraging us to mask our natural odours or substitute synthetic odours for them, but the overall erotic effect of perfumes and deodorants is not known.

Many people find body or genital odours offensive because they are associated with a lack of cleanliness. Filth is almost universally found repellent. Generally a clean, newly washed smell is considered attractive. It is interesting that the Japanese use the word *kirei* to mean either clean or pretty. Artificial perfumes add to clean smell but are not necessary or always appreciated. Certainly no one perfume has universal appeal.

There is of course a distinction between sexual signals that serve to attract and those that serve to arouse. One can be attracted to a pleasant odour but not sexually aroused by it. For the gypsy moth, attraction and arousal are synonymous as far as we know, but among humans and other mammals the situation is more complex. The stimuli that provoke sexual behaviour can be classified into three functional types: those that *broadcast* sexual interest and serve to attract or repel from a distance; those that *identify* a particular individual as a suitable or available partner; and those that *synchronize* sexual behaviour so that the ready and available individual is paired with the one aroused. Perfume may broadcast sexual interest and style of dress may identify suitability and availability, yet neither necessarily arouses an intended partner. Breasts or broad shoulders are permanent signals that can both attract and arouse.

It has been suggested that, way back along the human evolutionary tree, synchronization of behaviour during the breeding season was not so much a male-female thing, as an all male and all female thing. There is some evidence, for instance, that women who live in close proximity, in dormitories or barracks, gradually synchronize their menstrual cycles.

Sex hormones

Several times in this chapter I have said that men seem to be more easily and more often aroused than women. Learning is certainly a component in this, but there can be no doubt of the influence of androgens, a group of hormones produced by both sexes but in much larger amounts by males. Testosterone is the most important of the androgens. In men it is formed mainly in the testes, but also in the adrenal glands; in women it is formed in small amounts in the ovaries and adrenal glands. In both sexes, testosterone enhances sexual interest and activity.

Castration (the removal of male or female gonads), a practice known since antiquity, not only leads to sterility and deterioration of the reproductive and sexual organs, but also to behavioural changes. If castration is done before puberty, normal physical and behavioural development is inhibited. Done after puberty, castration leads to lower levels of aggression, sexual interest, and sexual performance. From studies carried out in the United States and Scandinavia, where castration was once a punishment or treatment for sexual offences or performed for medical reasons, we know that castration almost

There are many scent glands between and under the breasts. Although body odours may not attract or arouse sexual interest, they are certainly part of the bond between lovers. A lover's smell can linger for hours, a potent reminder of warmth and closeness.

always leads to a decrease in sexual interest and potency, although the rapidity and extent of the loss is quite variable; noticeable changes may take years. Nevertheless replacement androgens can restore this lost responsiveness and ability, in humans as well as animals.

The behavioural role that oestrogens play in females is less apparent when the organs that produce them, the ovaries, are removed. For one thing, in humans, removal of the ovaries is usually followed by a limited but compensatory output of oestrogen and androgens from the adrenal glands. The adrenals are the main source of androgens in women. But reduced availability of oestrogens and progesterone, produced in largest quantity by the ovaries, causes the sexual tissues to decrease in tone and robustness. The vaginal tissues may become very thin, making coitus painful. All fat deposits, which are oestrogen-dependent, decrease. Breasts, hips, and buttocks lose their roundness and firmness. There is often a concomitant lowering of sexual interest, but this seems to be a secondary rather than a primary effect. Replacement oestrogens can reverse these processes and also restore sexual interest.

What happens if the ovaries are left intact and the adrenals removed, as is sometimes necessary in the treatment of certain types of cancer? Adrenalectomy removes a woman's main source of testosterone and markedly lowers her sexual interest and responsiveness. Breast, uterine, or even vulval surgery depress sexual interest to a much lesser degree, even though women typically have a heavy psychic investment in these organs. Most women have no idea where their adrenals glands are or what they do.

Androgens taken by normal men, or oestrogens by normal women, do not have any consistent behavioural effects. Healthy males who take androgens over a long period, male body-builders for example, do not demonstrate heightened arousal or increased sexual activity. Ironically, they will probably find that their fertility decreases. This is because the body has feedback systems that sense high testosterone levels and act to lower or switch off

In India all followers of the Hijra sect are castrated and penectomized and live as women. Here a guru of the sect carries an image of their deity, and one of his disciples displays his pubic region sans genitals. It is not unknown for new recruits to cut off their own genitals.

testosterone and sperm production. A woman taking oral contraceptives is taking advantage of a similar feedback system. The extra oestrogen she takes inhibits ovulation. In some women, high doses of oestrogen increase water retention and the laying down of fat on the breasts, hips, and buttocks.

When men or women take hormones most appropriate to the opposite sex, the effects are pronounced. Basically, men who take female hormones show a decrease in sexual interest and response, and women who take androgens, with some exceptions, report an increase. Over time, men who take oestrogens and progesterone develop the secondary sexual characteristics of women, larger breasts and rounded hips. Muscles soften, and hair and beard growth decreases. Potency and sex drive wane. And it takes very modest doses of female hormone preparations to initiate such changes. Even microscopic amounts of oestrogen inadvertently ingested by male workers in pharmaceutical companies have brought about such changes. This is one of the reasons why acceptable hormonal contraceptives for men have been so difficult to formulate. Preparations that effectively prevent sperm production need to be free of demasculinizing side effects.

A classic study of the effects of androgens on women was done in the 1940s by Udall J. Salmon and Samuel H. Geist. They were first alerted to the effects of testosterone on women in 1937. To paraphrase their report: 'Our attention was first drawn to this phenomenon...by a woman who had had her ovaries removed and was being treated with androgens. During the course of the treatment the patient volunteered that she was experiencing a resurgence of sexual desire after a period of quiescence of some 10 years.' Their paper went on to report on 101 women treated with testosterone for various gynaecological disorders. Of 29 originally described as generally unresponsive sexually since puberty, 20 were considered to have developed normal erotic responsiveness, four improved their general responsiveness but remained unable to experience orgasm, and of the other five, three reported greater clitoral sensitivity but no other increase in responsiveness. Among the other 72 women treated with androgens, 64 reported an increase in sexual arousal and responsiveness. In this context an 'increase in sexual arousal and responsiveness' was defined as 'increased susceptibility to psychosexual stimulation', 'increased sensitivity of the external genitalia' and 'greater intensity of sexual gratification'. I should add that 20 of Salmon and Geist's subjects reported excessive arousability, although this subsided within several weeks of discontinuing androgen treatment.

Why, if they are so potent, have androgens not become standard aphrodisiacs? Because, as we have said before, in normal young men they seem to be of limited value and in women there may be a price to pay. There can be undesirable side effects. If dosages are too high, women who take androgens become masculinized, just as men who take oestrogens become feminized. Prolonged use leads to acne, muscle development, clitoral enlargement, growth of body hair, and a deeper voice. However, new research suggests that very low dosages of androgens may help women who have lost their normal androgens (through surgery or the menopause) to regain their sexual interest without becoming virilized. Men who lose their normal androgen levels (through injury or loss of their testes) can benefit from testosterone.

We still do not fully understand the mechanisms that translate hormone levels into behaviour. No doubt these mechanisms are psychological as much as biological. Consider this illustrative case. A woman who had been taking 'medicine' (testosterone) for a cancer condition reported what for her was a most unusual occurrence: she was sexually aroused by the bus conductor and other men she saw in the course of her daily activities. This had never happened before her illness. A pious, churchgoing woman, she did not act on her feelings of arousal and indeed found them oppressive. The feelings only went away when the androgen therapy stopped. Sexual arousal had been fostered by the androgen, but erotic behaviour had been inhibited by guilt feelings and the lessons she had learned as a girl.

Inhibited sexual desire

Despite the apparent ease of sexual arousal for most people, there are individuals who exhibit little or no ability to become sexually aroused. Clinicians sometimes refer to this situation as 'anarousmia', inhibited sexual desire (ISD), or hypoactive sexual desire disorder (HSDD). In times past, the colloquial term used was 'frigidity', more often applied to women than to men. In 1987 the American Psychiatric Association estimated that some 20 per cent of the total American population had HSDD. Kinsey found low arousability about twice as often among women as men, and things do not seem to have changed much over the years. J. Bancroft and colleagues, sex therapists and researchers in Britain, reported in 1983 and again in 1987 that between 40 and 60 per cent of their female clients complained of general sexual unresponsiveness. A 1991 study of Texas college students also found large male-female differences in reported frequencies of desire. Most significantly, Texas investigators J. Gayle Beck and her students found that whereas 90 per cent of male respondents desired sex several times a week or more, only about 50 per cent of the women felt similarly. Complaints of disparity in sexual interest or asynchrony of arousal are among the most common problems heard by marriage counsellors and sympathetic friends.

Lifelong lack of sexual desire or responsiveness is rare but not unknown. One of Kinsey's most intriguing findings was that about 1 in 7 women claimed *never* to have been sexually aroused by a person or situation. Not uncommonly, low levels of arousability are associated with restrictive, sex-negative upbringing. But this is not always the case. Understanding the cause of inhibited desire is one of the most confounding of therapeutic challenges. How is one to separate a constitutional basis for HSDD from a historical or contemporary basis?

Masters and Johnson called lack of sexual interest 'low sexual tension', but did not elaborate on the reasons for it. Helen Singer Kaplan, the well-known American marriage and sex counsellor, has spent a good part of her professional life trying to fathom such 'problems of desire'. Regrettably, by the time most people come for therapy such problems are difficult to deal with. As Kaplan emphasizes, lack of interest in sexual activities and sexual dysfunctions are often entwined with other profound marital conflicts. Also, lack of sexual desire must be distinguished from sexual aversion or avoidance.

Those oppressed or depressed by a lack of desire resort to all sorts of nostrums (many of these are discussed in Chapter 4). Or they may seek professional therapy. The commonest therapies in the sexual area are 'talk' therapies; their purpose is to reduce general anxiety, give clients permission to be sexual without feeling guilty about it, give information if it is needed, improve rapport and communication between partners, and generally decrease routine behaviours that lead to habituation and boredom, and increase novelty-seeking behaviours ('Take a vacation/hot tub together. Buy sexy underwear. Send the kids to the grandparents.') Talk may be coupled with verbal and physical exercises to facilitate sexual arousal and decrease sexual inhibitions ('Give each other a shampoo. Slowly stroke or caress your partner as and where he/she desires.') In cases where lack of desire is thought to be constitutional, tranquillizers, anti-anxiety drugs, or hormones may also be prescribed.

Lack of desire as a lifelong characteristic can be the result of low androgen levels — as we have seen, the androgen testosterone fuels libido in both sexes. Various genetic conditions (Klinefelter's syndrome, for instance) are also known to be associated with a low level of sexual interest. Low arousability may also be linked with dysfunctions of the brain; in some men, for example, the culprit appears to be overproduction of the hormone prolactin by the pituitary. Prolactin stimulates milk production. But most people don't have any of these obvious medical problems and, as the Scottish psychologist Ronan O'Carroll has pointed out, no convenient drug or hormone is consistently effective in enhancing sexual desire.

Anarousmia is occasionally an insidious accompaniment to disease, or may follow from feelings of helplessness, despair, and depression, or sometimes from fear or misinformation. Believing, rightly or wrongly, that one's partner has a venereal or other infection or is uninterested in proceedings can quite easily lead to a loss of sexual appetite.

But let us look at the matter from a different perspective for a moment. American psychotherapist David Schnarch has suggested that the concept of sexual desire, as generally understood, is too limiting. Sexual desire is not an *entity* which initiates sexual activity; rather it is a multidimensional *process or state of awareness* that exists before, throughout, and after sexual activity. Interpersonal politics are part of it. Being comfortable with wanting sex, wanting to be wanted sexually, and wanting to reciprocate sexual affection are also part of it. And who sets the standards for sexual desire? We ourselves, our partners, the American Psychiatric Association? What frequency, or intensity, or type of sexual activity should be regarded as the norm?

For most of us, in our own life and in the lives of those we see around us, sexual indifference develops insidiously. Usually it is the partner who retains sexual interest who brings up the subject: 'Are you seeing someone else?', 'Is it something I've done, or something I'm not doing?' It is not always so simple. Feelings over non-sexual matters can build up to inhibiting anger, resentment, or disappointment. As with all relationship problems, improving communication is a vital first step.

Understanding the responses of others

Since such a wide variety of specific and general stimuli elicit sexual responses, it is sometimes difficult to understand the preferences of others. But here again there is a discrepancy between the sexes. To quote Kinsey: 'Even the sexually least responsive of the males can comprehend something of the meaning of the frequent and continuous arousal which some other males experience. To the third or more of the females who have rarely been aroused by psychological stimuli, it may seem fantastic to believe that there are females who come to orgasm as a result of sexual fantasy, without any physical stimulation of their genitalia or any other part of their body.' (Perhaps 2 per cent of women are capable of fantasizing to orgasm, but the phenomenon appears almost non-existent in men.)

Socially, the implications of such discrepancies are great. They go far beyond the fact that sexual partners may have to contend with quite different levels of arousal, excitement, and desire. They reach into the wider world in which teachers, social workers, legislators, and judges, on the basis of their own limited experience, make decisions of huge importance to many thousands of people. It is difficult to accept that other people may be very different from oneself. For example, the strategy of the 'Just say no' may seem sensible to some but ludicrous to others.

Some conclusions

We are all unique, with a certain propensity for sexual arousal. Some of us have low thresholds, some high. Some of us respond to many stimuli, some to fewer. Our inherent biases are partly genetic and endocrine, but they are only biases, not inescapable prescriptions. Our emotion-sensitive nervous system, with all its inborn predispositions, is modified by social and cultural learning, and by the trial and error of experience.

Scientific research into sexual arousal is still in its infancy. We still lack good laboratory studies in which stimuli are carefully controlled and individual responses monitored. But if we can marry laboratory data with more impressionistic and subjective measures, it should be possible to get a firmer grip on what turns us on and how.

In fact it makes good sense that perpetuation of our species should depend on highly individual and varied reasons for arousal. Sex drive, however construed, does not have to be demonstrated by everyone, but it does need to be demonstrated by a sufficient number of people to maintain a rich gene pool. If men and women did not find each other attractive for such a variety of reasons the gene pool of our species would become impoverished and the rearing of viable offspring would be in jeopardy. Perhaps the same evolutionary imperative that has me looking for certain physical features also instructs me to look for certain personality traits. Where the human species is concerned, evolution occurs through learning and acculturation as well as through the random mixing of genes. Accumulated wisdom and the teaching of elders complement and influence our biological heritage.

From another perspective, it would be sad and frustrating if we all responded only to

specific stimuli in specific circumstances — that is the fate of the fetishist. Given the choice, I would rather have a system in which arousal is more variably obtained and more variably satisfied. I would also choose a world in which the total process of sexual enjoyment is more important than orgasm, and in which desire persists through orgasm and beyond. I would also like everyone to possess the means of achieving sexual satisfaction. This would ensure that everyone, not only those with stereotyped beauty, had the maximum possible chance of finding a partner. This is the kind of world that evolution has already created for us.

What is this advertisement selling, socks or sex? The endless permutations of personality and physical type among both sexes mean that everybody has the maximum chance of finding a partner.

When I consider, pro and con,
What things my love is built upon —
A curly mouth; a sinewed wrist;
A questioning brow; a pretty twist
Of words as old and tired as sin;
A pointed ear, a cloven chin;
Long, tapered limbs; and slanted eyes
Not cold, nor kind, nor darkly wise —
When so I ponder, here apart,
What shallow boons suffice my heart,
What dust-bound trivia capture me,
I marvel at my normalcy.

DOROTHY PARKER,   *The Searched Soul*

Chapter 3

The body you love with

At one time or another all of us look in the mirror and evaluate our appearance, comparing what we see with an imagined ideal constructed from watching other people and learning the values of our particular society. Many of us come away from the mirror wishing we were prettier or more handsome, taller or shorter, slimmer or heavier, or that certain parts of our body were a different shape.

Each society has its own ideals which are publicized and praised in popular culture. In contemporary Western society these are represented by movie stars and sports personalities, fashion models, and pin-ups. A review of those images most popular or currently in fashion shows that the ideal is not always constant.

The fact is that very few of us fit the stereotypes. Generally we manage to accept and live with our shortcomings even if we are unhappy about them. Advertisements, magazine articles, and stage and screen idols aggravate our insecurities while sharpening our desire to be considered attractive, sexy, likeable. Even fashion models and actresses, at the top of their profession because they apparently embody the ideal of the moment, suffer from self-doubt. Twiggy, the model of the 1970s, said she couldn't understand what all the fuss over her was about — she was so thin. Moncur, another world-famous model, commented: 'You exist through others' eyes. When they stop looking at you, there's nothing left.'

First meetings

There is no denying that physical attractiveness is a major factor in how one is evaluated as a potential sex partner. A study done by American researcher Elaine Walster among students at a college dance showed that physical attractiveness was the only factor directly related to whether students wanted to see their dancing partners again. Other attributes such as intelligence, personality, sociability, masculinity-femininity, introversion /extroversion, and self-acceptance had no such direct effect. The students concerned were assigned their partners for the evening on a random basis. Later they were asked how much they liked their partners and whether they wanted to pursue the relationship. The more physically attractive the partner, the more affirmative the answer. Interest in personality, intelligence, or social confidence seemed far less significant. All efforts to find additional factors that influenced attraction failed. Evidence from other studies has shown that, logically or not, strangers who are considered physically attractive are imagined to be sexually warm, responsive, sensitive, supportive, sociable, outgoing, and exciting.

Particularly when a relationship is beginning, most people unconsciously base their assessment of their partner on his or her looks. And yet many studies of adolescents and college students show that looks are invariably placed *after* characteristics such as personality, sincerity, and dependability when respondents are asked to list desirable qualities in a potential mate. And intelligence usually comes lower on the list than looks. This is the 'disparity in KAP' phenomenon at work. Why, then, are looks so powerful during first encounters?

The ideal male torso? Maybe yes, maybe no. Many women prefer their men chunkier and hairier. Evolution has seen to it that men and women find each other attractive for a multiplicity of reasons.

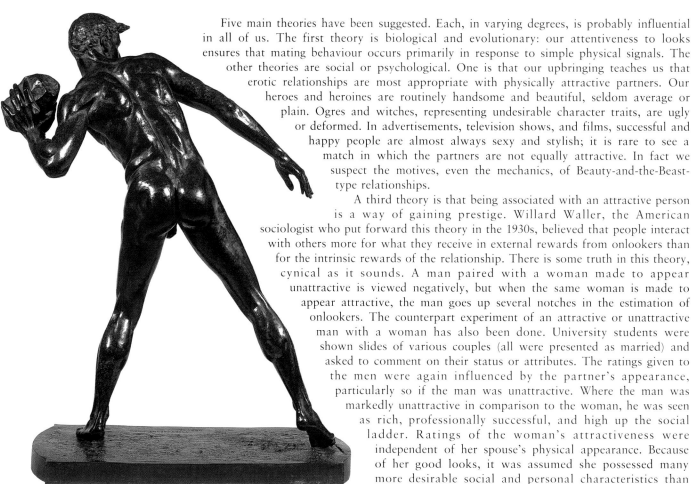

Five main theories have been suggested. Each, in varying degrees, is probably influential in all of us. The first theory is biological and evolutionary: our attentiveness to looks ensures that mating behaviour occurs primarily in response to simple physical signals. The other theories are social or psychological. One is that our upbringing teaches us that erotic relationships are most appropriate with physically attractive partners. Our heroes and heroines are routinely handsome and beautiful, seldom average or plain. Ogres and witches, representing undesirable character traits, are ugly or deformed. In advertisements, television shows, and films, successful and happy people are almost always sexy and stylish; it is rare to see a match in which the partners are not equally attractive. In fact we suspect the motives, even the mechanics, of Beauty-and-the-Beast-type relationships.

A third theory is that being associated with an attractive person is a way of gaining prestige. Willard Waller, the American sociologist who put forward this theory in the 1930s, believed that people interact with others more for what they receive in external rewards from onlookers than for the intrinsic rewards of the relationship. There is some truth in this theory, cynical as it sounds. A man paired with a woman made to appear unattractive is viewed negatively, but when the same woman is made to appear attractive, the man goes up several notches in the estimation of onlookers. The counterpart experiment of an attractive or unattractive man with a woman has also been done. University students were shown slides of various couples (all were presented as married) and asked to comment on their status or attributes. The ratings given to the men were again influenced by the partner's appearance, particularly so if the man was unattractive. Where the man was markedly unattractive in comparison to the woman, he was seen as rich, professionally successful, and high up the social ladder. Ratings of the woman's attractiveness were independent of her spouse's physical appearance. Because of her good looks, it was assumed she possessed many more desirable social and personal characteristics than her unattractive partner.

Does physical beauty reflect inner beauty? The nude, especially the male nude, has been a major theme in Western art since Classical times. This is Victorian sculptor Sir Hamo Thornycroft's contribution to the genre. In Western art the genitals are not given undue emphasis.

The fourth theory is the antithesis of the notion that beauty is only skin deep. In one study, men and women were presented with photographs of attractive and unattractive people and asked to speculate on their personality. Both sexes gave similar responses when rating either sex. Attractive people were expected to possess almost every personality trait considered socially desirable, from modesty to extroversion, from sensitivity to strength and supportiveness. Those rated as average or unattractive were less often given the benefit of these generous assumptions.

Lastly, there is the theory that we respond positively to attractive people because we hope they will give us something of value, sexual satisfaction if nothing else. Perhaps we also believe that in some mystical way the association will confer attractiveness on us.

The desire to be sexually attractive develops in adolescence. Teenagers universally entertain feelings of insecurity matched by a strong desire to belong and to be accepted by their peers. Disappointment with physical growth and development may be a significant obstacle to socializing and establishing sexual relationships. Skin and hair, because they are constantly on display, are often a cause for deep self-criticism.

In Oriental countries, there is no tradition of interest in the ideal human body (or even in the nude, for that matter). But in the West the muscular ideal for men has been pursued from Grecian times, if not earlier, and is now an international competitive sport. Ideals for women, as mentioned earlier, are more variable, cross-culturally, and remain so even in the West, as we shall see. Having beaten a path into most traditionally male sports, women now have body-building contests of their own. In typical female beauty contests there is as much emphasis on a beautiful face as on an ideal body, but in body-building as a male sport the focus has always been on the size, proportion, and muscular definition of the limbs and torso, ignoring the attractiveness or otherwise of the face. Should female body-building lay more emphasis on the development of curves and beautiful proportions? Some aficionados of the sport think so.

I for one am highly doubtful that female body-building marks a move towards a more muscular ideal for women. What it probably represents is a new approach to health and well-being. According to Harvard University researchers P. Whitten and E.J. Whiteside, who studied male and female swimmers of different ages in regular training, regular exercise can improve your sex life whether you're 40, 60, or older. Many of their subjects, who swam at least three times a week for 45 minutes, claimed they had sex lives more typical of 20- and 30-year-olds. Even those of 60+ felt they were 20 years younger when it came to sex. But, careful, sports fans! Those who trained hardest in the Harvard study (more than 18 hours per week) reported a *decline* in sexual interest and fewer sexual experiences. As in all things, moderation is best.

The slimming obsession

In the West, fatness is viewed as morally reprehensible, especially in the under-40s. This is because we have bought into the idea that weight is a matter of self-control; being overweight somehow represents a failure of self-control, a lack of desire for self-improvement. But fatness is a cultural value, not an absolute. In countries where hunger is endemic and occasionally devastating, the female ideal is fleshier; under such circumstances, fatter usually equals healthier.

In the West millions of women and girls accept the heavily promoted view that slimmer equals healthier, and more attractive. In extreme cases slimming is excessive and obsessive. Anorexia nervosa is an illness of excessive dieting in which eating, and even the idea of eating, becomes repugnant. Every year there are deaths from anorexic malnutrition. A related problem is bulimia, heavy food bingeing followed by enforced vomiting and abuse of laxatives. The anorexic individual becomes so skeletal that she (rarely he, since female anorexics outnumber male by almost 30 to 1) is not particularly attractive, but there is little doubt that such extreme tactics are tied up with acceptance of the 'slim is beautiful' message.

Feminist psychotherapist Marlene Bosking Lodahl believes that anorexic females are far from rejecting their femininity. 'These young women' she comments 'have never questioned their assumption that wifehood, motherhood, and intimacy with men are the fundamental components of femininity... their obsessive pursuit of thinness constitutes...an exaggerated striving to achieve it.' With anorexic males the problem seems to be low self-esteem, general despondency and passivity, a fear of women, and an inability to sustain relationships.

When girls and women become concerned with their bodies, their preferred methods of improving on nature are diet and dress rather than sport or exercise. That is why dietary problems are far more common among women than men, especially in professions where slimness is *de rigueur*, among dancers and fashion models, for example. Exercise tends to be a strategy mainly for middle and upper class women. But among women of all social strata dietary issues are a continual distraction and the prognosis is that this preoccupation will increase. Winners of the Miss America Pageant and also the beauties of *Playboy's* centrefold — all reflections of stereotyped ideals — have been getting slimmer over the past 25 years.

Yet, over the same period, the average American female under 30 years of age has become heavier. In America today, about 15 per cent of men and 25-30 per cent of women over 30 are significantly overweight (more than 20 per cent over recommended weight for height and build). Men have also been getting heavier over the last 25 years,

Before and after dramatic slimming. 'Desirable weight' tables are based on data from life assurance companies and merely reflect the weights of insured persons (by no means the majority of the population) surviving longest. They do not necessarily reflect optimal weight for health.

but most of them seem not to worry about it or are unwilling to take preventive measures (men seem more concerned with hair loss). Margaret Mackenzie, an anthropologist who has studied obesity and diet, comments: 'Upwardly mobile women in this era are competing with men, yet most of them are still conditioned to thinking of success personally and professionally in terms of sex and beauty, which are equated with thinness.'

Western and Japanese fashion generally promote the slim ideal, although present Indian and African preferences are typically more weighty. This is displayed in fashion models who, in the West, would be considered heavy. In arranged marriages, one of the selling features of the prospective bride is full-bodiedness. In Africa, where AIDS is call 'slim disease' because of the weight loss that accompanies the later stages, buxomness is a 'folk' criterion of health.

Surgical improvements

If none of the usual solutions works, there is always surgery, for those who can afford it. Facelifts, belly tucks, rump and thigh reduction, breast reconstruction, hair transplants, and nose jobs are all means of achieving a physical reality more in keeping with one's fantasy. In the United States and other Western countries the steady and rapid rise in cosmetic surgery in the last decade looks likely to continue in the 1990s and into the next century. New procedures are partly responsible, the two most popular being liposuction (selective removal of fat deposits from hips, thighs, belly, buttocks, and other areas) and the opposite procedure, in which fat or silicone is implanted to achieve fuller, firmer contours. Recent concerns over prosthetic breast implants and restrictions on the use of implanted or injected silicone are only likely to slow the trend. Implants have been faulted for poor design, manufacture, and research, and there have been cases of disfigurement and worse associated with silicone implants (see Chapter 14).

As elective surgical procedures become more popular, practitioners and clients are opting for the term aesthetic surgery rather than cosmetic surgery. 'Aesthetic' has a more positive aura: everyone approves of aesthetic reasons; cosmetic reasons are somehow suspect. The distinction is not a semantic superficiality if it eases a conscience or bolsters feelings of self-worth. The desire to be attractive, or at least better looking, is not solely narcissistic. Good looks increase feelings of self-worth and self-confidence. A great deal of well conducted research confirms that good looks smooth the way for many everyday relationships, whether they involve strangers, friends, or lovers. Certainly, good looks open doors, but no amount of muscle building, slimming, or surgery will compensate, or at least not for long, for an insecure personality or a lack of social graces.

Biologists readily accept that the force of appearance is very strong. They see it as part

Keeping fit is a weight control strategy predominantly used by middle-class women. But the benefits of a trim tummy and shapely buttocks are more than aesthetic; they are important for gynaecological health and sexual enjoyment.

of a consistent evolutionary trend in which mating behaviour is primarily triggered by simple physical signals. But the phenomenon deeply worries social scientists. Indeed most of us would prefer social interaction to be based on something less fortuitous and more substantial than mere looks. It is rotten luck as well as fundamentally undemocratic to be handicapped by physical characteristics one can do little about. But, as we all know, good looks have their downside. They can actually put people off ('He's good-looking and he knows it', 'She's a conceited bitch'). In looks, as in most thing, it doesn't hurt to be average. If our appearance is not ideal, we tend to develop characteristics, social skills, and personality traits to compensate.

Am I normal?

Confidence about one's body, and a sense of comfort and ease, are prerequisites for making the most of one's heritage to sexual pleasure. Am I normal? Am I an acceptable sexual partner? Such anxieties are common, but since the variety in size and shape is great and the diversity of taste extensive, the answer is almost always 'Yes' to both questions. Becoming familiar with the function and appearance of one's body and genitals, and acquiring an awareness of the myths and unnecessary anxieties related to sex, are important steps towards confidence as well as comfort.

In some individuals emotional and physical confidence is certainly tied to the appearance of their genitals or breasts. Many men wish for a longer penis and many women for larger breasts, believing that bigger is better. But size has little to do with erotic ability, sexual attraction, or satisfaction. Nor is the desire for bigger breasts absolutely comparable with anxiety over penis size. Though most people are familiar with a number of physical stereotypes for clothed and unclothed bodies, few have detailed knowledge of the appearance of a variety of genitals, so no real standards exist. In both sexes, personal fears and fantasies thrive on ignorance. So, at this point, let us look at some basic facts and dispel a few well-worn myths.

Sensual versus reproductive

Biology and medicine divide body structures into systems according to their functions — nervous, respiratory, digestive, excretory, reproductive, and so on. Some organs obviously serve several functions. The breast, for example, is a sexual and a secretory organ. Biology textbooks, and many books on human sexuality, present the genitals, or genitalia, as structures involved in both sexual activity and reproduction, dividing them into male and female, internal and external. This overlooks two important facts. First, most sexual expression takes place without reproduction. And second, modern technology allows reproduction without sexual expression. It therefore seems logical, philosophically and biologically, to distinguish the sensual system (those body parts primarily associated with sex play) from the reproductive system. In fact, the sensual system evokes more complex responses physically and psychologically. Some parts of the body belong to both the sensual and the reproductive system, some to one only.

Sun, sea, sand, skin contact.... The skin contains millions of nerve endings specialized for the reception of touch, pressure, stretch, vibration, and temperature sensations.

Skin and the pleasures of touch

In my opinion, the skin is most important organ of sexual response for both males and females. The genitals and, particularly for women, the breasts are typically considered most important — they are highly sensitive and most people are very specifically aware of their demands for stimulation during sexual arousal, petting, and coitus — but before, during, and after sex play the whole skin is responsive to sexual communication.

The skin is like a huge antenna with a sensitive surface area of about 2 square metres. Touching and being touched, holding and being held, and other stimuli such as blowing, licking, and nibbling are among life's greatest delights. Skin contact is a vital source of human pleasure from birth and throughout life. Touching can create and transmit feelings of love, warmth, security, contentment, and sexual desire, all depending upon context. Anthropologist Ashley Montagu speaks of the development of 'skin hunger', an innate need or desire for body contact. Lack of body contact and relaxed touching is often a problem between sexual partners. Common complaints are: 'She never holds me in public, only when we're in bed', or 'He makes a grab for my pelvis as if that's all I am.'

It is a myth that women require more physical contact than men. Both sexes appreciate being stroked and touched. A lack of physical intimacy can mirror other problems in a sexual relationship, or it may reflect social teaching which discourages touching unless sexual intent is present. Japanese, North American, and Scandinavian societies are relatively non-physical compared with Mediterranean, Slav, Latin, and many Polynesian and African societies where touching, even among new acquaintances, is common. The infant desire to be held, groomed, and stroked is strong and springs from roots deep in our primate ancestry, but it is often frustrated by cultural traditions.

An erogenous zone is any part of the skin that is particularly sensitive to stimuli that are experienced as sexually exciting. The skin of the genitals, breasts, face (particularly the mouth), ears, neck, and thighs are most sensitive in most people, but, depending on the individual, any part of the body may be specially sensitive. The degree of variation in sensitivity is truly enormous and the only real way to know what kind of stimulation your partner enjoys is to experiment or ask. Women tend to have a greater number of erogenous zones than men. According to Kinsey, some women can be brought to orgasm solely by having their eyebrows stroked or from gentle blowing on body hair. No men have been found to respond to such indirect stimulation.

Taboo zones — areas of the body that cannot be freely touched — are not necessarily the same as erogenous zones. Usually they are taboo in anything other than an acknowledged sexual relationship. Full social and sexual development involves learning who, how, when, and where to touch, and how to allow oneself to be touched. Only lovers and parents with small children have free access to all parts of each other's bodies. Even so, personal preferences determine individual taboos. In industrial societies it is generally acceptable to touch babies and toddlers anywhere except the genitals in affectionate contact, but as puberty approaches — as girls develop breasts, for example — the boundaries are redefined and licence to touch is taken away from parents and awarded to boyfriends and girlfriends instead.

One can pick up many clues about relationships by observing the physical access that people give each other. Any physical contact involves a certain invasion of body space and to touch another person without direct or implied permission violates rules of conduct in all societies. Of course taboos can be social or religious, as well as sexual. In present-day Thailand, as in traditional Hawaiian culture, it is improper to touch the top of another person's head, as this is regarded both literally and metaphorically as the highest part of the body. Among some sects of orthodox Jews and Muslims, non-related men and women never touch.

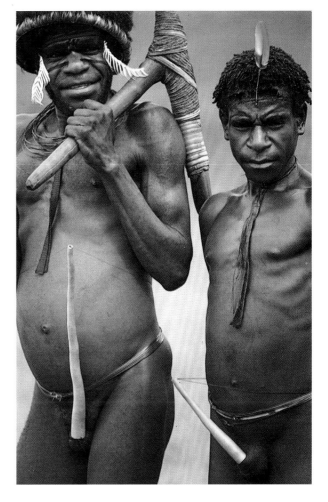

Dani tribesmen in West Irian, Indonesia, wear leather penis covers for protection and display.

The external male genitals

The male organ most capable of erotic sensation is the penis. The biological sexual function of the penis is to penetrate the female and deposit sperm; it is also the urinary outlet. Typically it is soft (flaccid), but in response to erotic stimuli (urinary or other reflexes are also occasionally effective) it becomes erect and engorged with blood. Erection increases its length and girth. Softening (detumescence) is the process of returning to flaccidity. The erection and detumescence of a penis are fascinating to watch. Both can be brought on by various physical or mental stimuli, but neither is routinely under voluntary control.

Penis size

Penises vary greatly in shape and it is a myth that a bigger penis is necessarily better. Just as some men are attracted to large-breasted or long-legged women, some women find a large penis erotic and exciting. In any case, variations in penis size become less marked when the penis is erect. In other words, a penis that is small when flaccid tends to enlarge more during erection than a large one.

The majority of women have no physical or psychological difficulty in accommodating a long penis and may even enjoy the deep pressure it applies to the cervix. On the other hand, many women are disturbed by the generally unrealistic fear that they might not be able to accommodate a large penis and some do find the actual sensation painful rather than pleasurable. Considering that the vagina is most sensitive at its entrance rather than in depth, some women say that girth is more desirable than length. But, as one might expect, most men have an average-size penis to match an average-sized vagina. For most women, how the penis is used (and the man behind it)

'Travelling Lovers' from a set of 24 woodblock prints by 18th-century Japanese artist Suzuki Harunobu. The conversation and the subjective fantasies of the lovers are noted in the background. In Japanese erotic art the penis is always larger than life.

matters more than simple dimensions.

Few men are unaware of the size of their penis and it is safe to say that, at some time or another, most feel somewhat inadequate. This is partly because evaluations are often made while the penis is flaccid. Concern with penis size and shape is not unique to modern or Western man. In Japanese erotic art a thick, large penis is almost always on display; ceramic figures from Central and South America and statues from ancient Rome, Etruria, and Crete are commonly endowed with prominent genitals; traditional and modern African and Hindu art often focuses strongly on the genitals.

While every study of heterosexual males confirms that penis size is highly important and that almost all heterosexual men wish they were better endowed, concern about penis size is not limited to heterosexual relationships or necessarily associated with wanting to impress a woman. A 1979 study of 1,000 gay men, carried out by James Spada in the United States, revealed that about 37 per cent thought that the penis size of a partner was very important and 42 per cent thought it unimportant; the other 21 per cent thought it somewhat important. Almost all, however, expressed apprehension that their own penis was too small; even those with penises of 6 to 8 inches in length when erect wished they were larger. In the gay community individuals excessively concerned with size are common enough to be identified as 'size queens'.

It is probably safe to say that most men identify so strongly with their penis that the rule is 'love me, love my penis', and any slight on size or shape, or avoidance of the penis in sex play, is taken as a personal rebuke. Praising and paying attention to the penis is equally taken as an important personal compliment. Since so much of a man's satisfaction is derived from his penis, he tends to assume that his partner also derives supreme satisfaction from penetration. Certainly most women do enjoy stimulation from the penis, but they are also capable of being more diffusely aroused and satisfied, and by more varied stimuli. This is something men are commonly unaware of.

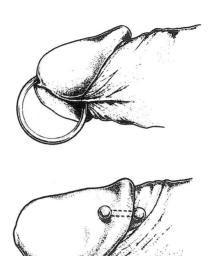 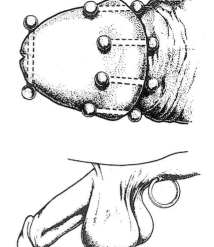

Penis ornaments. Studs and rings through the glans (top left), corona (top right and bottom left), and perineum (bottom right) are said to increase the pleasure of arousal and coitus.

No consistent relationship exists between penis size and the ability to give sexual satisfaction. Unless there is marked disparity between the genitals of the partners and coitus is the only activity undertaken, such concern is unwarranted. But when a man who feels anxiety about his penis reluctantly or hesitantly engages in sexual play, the result is often fulfilment of a self-fulfilling prophesy, lack of satisfaction for himself or his partner. The problem is less anatomical than psychological. Used with pride and concern for the partner, any penis can be satisfying.

Nor is there any consistent relationship between penis size and body size. There are slight racial differences — Orientals on average have smaller penises than Caucasians, and Negroes have larger. To some extent penis size is commensurate with vaginal size of the race concerned, but, as mentioned above, the ability of the vagina to accommodate is great. It is certainly a myth, although believed in Japan, Thailand, Europe, and elsewhere, that the size of a man's nose indicates the size of his penis; in Japan it is believed that a woman's lips and mouth represent her vaginal size.

Lastly, no pill, potion, exercise, masturbatory technique, or external device

A male genital tatoo and cock ring, both used to enhance eroticism. Here the penis is in its flaccid state. When erect, size differences are less obvious. Cock rings are supposed to prolong erection.

45

will affect penis size. Charlatans gladly separate fools from their money for 'medically approved' gadgets or techniques that promise to enlarge a penis. At best, these are ineffective. At worst, they can be harmful; some vacuum-like devices can rupture blood vessels in the penis. A less harmful but no less bizarre practice among the *yakuza*, members of the underworld in modern Japan, is that of inserting a pearl under the skin of the penis. This is supposed to give superior sexual satisfaction to the woman (although it is not known if women share this view) and so enable the *yakuza* to maintain a hold on the prostitutes they pimp for; supposedly the pearl-penis provides more sexual gratification than that of any customer. Penis inserts, ornaments, and adornments have been common in Southeast Asia and elsewhere for years.

True hermaphrodites, possessing both testicular and ovarian tissue, are extremely rare. In Greek and Roman times such individuals were looked on as favoured by the gods.

Some anomalies

Individuals have consulted me not only on the size of their penis, but also wondering if they were misshapen, the penis curving to the right, left, or sharply up or down. Except for a rare few, all were within normal variation and perfectly capable of satisfactory sexual encounters. The exceptions were able to engage in satisfactory relations by changing coital position or using a pillow to alter the angle at which the penis enters the vagina.

About 1 male in 1,000 has a penis that is unusually small due to a chromosomal anomaly, an XXY rather than the typical male XY chromosome set. This is Klinefelter's syndrome. The extra X chromosome means that such individuals usually develop feminine breasts (gynaecomastia) and have a low sperm count; they also tend to be obese and display a low level of sexual interest.

Even more rare are males diagnosed as having a micropenis. Any astute physician will detect this at birth; it is not a condition that develops as a boy grows. A micropenis is too small even to effect insertion. Medical treatment with hormones may be useful and a prosthesis can help. Counselling is always recommended in cases where the child is reared as a boy, since the psychological impact on the affected individual is great. Some paediatricians recommend rearing such individuals from birth as girls, with appropriate surgical reconstruction of the genitals to fashion a vulva.

The debate hinges on whether satisfactory male sexual identity can be achieved without a functioning penis. Those who believe that social forces outweigh chromosomal ones recommend surgical intervention. But since, as it now seems, biological factors are difficult to override, many physicians regard psychological support (with prosthesis) as the most appropriate treatment. The degree of success in establishing either a male or female identity is highly variable and much remains to be understood about this condition.

In one in every few hundred Caucasian males the urinary outlet, the meatus, opens not at the head of the glans but on the underside of the penis (there are no statistics on the occurrence of this condition among other racial groups). This is known as hypospadias and is typically quite embarrassing to a growing boy and his parents despite the fact that the physical evidence is hidden and the problem itself is relatively common. Corrective surgery is usually carried out before the boy reaches school age to minimize psychological distress. Long-term studies show that after surgery physical, sexual, and social development generally proceed along normal lines. A small percentage of males born with hypospadias, however, remain reluctant to engage in sexual activity despite reconstructive surgery. They may require, and often benefit from, psychological counselling.

Epispadias is a condition similar to hypospadias in some ways, but more serious and, fortunately, extremely rare. Here the meatus is on the top surface of the penis and appears to split the penis. In dealing with this problem, psychological counselling is always recommended.

Scrotum and testes

The scrotum, a wrinkled sac of skin that hangs behind and below the root of the penis, is also highly sensitive in sexual arousal. It contains two egg-shaped testicles (testes) to which are appended the epididymides (singular epididymis) in which sperm mature and are temporarily stored. Attached spermatic cords carry the sperm to the penis.

The scrotum is quite flexible and distendable. Sensitive to touch, temperature, and sexual stimulation, it can hang loosely or retract close to the body. Typically, ejaculation is preceded by the testes and scrotum being drawn up tight against the body. This contraction is only slightly susceptible to voluntary control. In fact the scrotum and testes perform a visible alternating contraction and relaxation cycle — a more or less continuous, slow, wave-like movement. In response to threat or painful stimulation, the scrotum pulls towards the body; this is called the cremasteric reflex.

The testes are the male gonads. They manufacture sperm and the hormones, mostly androgens, crucial for male development and functioning. Normally they hang at different heights, the left one usually being lower than the right, but the reverse is not uncommon. This is probably to reduce the pressure of one testicle against the other as the body moves. Even slight pressure can produce sharp and lasting pain.

Cryptorchidism, or hidden testicle, is a common condition affecting between 2 and 5 per cent of males at birth. During gestation the testes develop inside the body near the kidneys. Normally they migrate to the scrotum prior to birth, but sometimes, and for unknown reasons, one or both may fail to descend properly. The scrotum of a male infant is routinely examined to check for this. If descent is delayed beyond several months, hormonal or surgical treatment is usually given in order to induce descent into the scrotum. If the testes remain too long within the abdominal cavity, the body's internal heat can kill the sperm-producing tissues, causing infertility. The scrotal environment is about 3°C cooler than the internal body temperature and more hospitable to sperm production.

Recent findings have complicated decisions in cases of cryptorchidism. It is now known that a significant percentage (estimates vary widely) of undescended testes, even if surgically drawn down, will become cancerous, but as yet there is no way of predicting in which individuals this will occur. So the decision has to be made whether to leave the testes in place for developmental, endocrine, fertility, or psychological reasons, or remove them to prevent potential malignancy. The tendency among physicians is to leave them in place but keep regular surveillance. Either way, the decision is not easy.

Why nature has evolved this relationship between temperature and reproduction in the male is an intriguing matter. It probably has something to do with the fact that our pre-mammalian ancestors had body temperatures lower than our own.

External female genitals

The general region of the external female genitals is referred to as the vulva. Most girls, as well as boys, grow to adulthood quite ignorant of the fact that vulvas vary greatly in appearance. Considering that the medical term for the crotch region is pudendum, Latin for shameful, this is not difficult to understand. Having been taught that it is not nice to attend to one's genitals, many women have never even looked at themselves, let alone others. Many men, experienced or not, are similarly unaware. If you have not yet looked closely at your own body or at that of a partner, do so. It's a fascinating exercise in sexwatching.

Vulva

Typically, the view of a mature woman's vulva mainly reveals the mons pubis or mons veneris, a hair-covered mound formed by a soft fat pad over the front of the pubic bones. On further inspection, with the legs apart, an inner and outer set of lips can be seen. The outer lips (labia majora) are elongated rolls of fatty tissue that run just below the skin from pubis to anus and are covered with hair. The inner set of lips (labia minora) remain hairless throughout life. They cover the vaginal entrance, so that typically the vagina is not seen. These inner lips vary greatly in shape and size from woman to woman. They may have any colour from pale pink to dark purple, and the colour intensity deepens during sexual excitement. Betty Dodson, a woman artist, classifies vulva styles as Baroque, Danish modern, Gothic, Classical, and so forth, the names reflecting the symmetry or asymmetry, size and shape of the labia. Dodson says she was inspired to paint and classify women's genitals in order to liberate women from negative feelings about their appearance 'down

A female genital tatoo. From puberty onwards, the labia are usually hidden by pubic hair.

there'. She considered herself deformed until a new lover convinced her that her vulva was beautiful and of common shape.

The vestibule, which leads directly into the vagina, is a basin-shaped area bounded by the labia minora. Like the latter, it is a highly sensitive and erotic area for most women. Above the vagina, also opening into the vestibule, is the urethral meatus, the urine outlet. Anxiety that urine may get into the vagina or be released during coitus is rarely warranted. Sphincter muscles normally prevent urine release unless it is deliberate. If some urine is passed, it is sterile and of no hygienic significance. A woman may be embarrassed if this happens during coitus, but most men are unaware of it unless it is particularly copious. It just appears to be added lubrication. Urination prior to sex play usually solves this problem.

The vagina opens in the floor of the vestibule. While the opening is more or less round, the vagina itself is not the inflexible tube-shaped receptacle it is often pictured to be, but a flexible glove-like space whose walls part to accept and conform to any shape, fingers or penis, that enters.

Most women know even less about their internal sex organs than their external. Newspaper health columnist Ellen Frankfurt, in her book *Vaginal Politics*, encourages readers to inspect their own genitals internally and externally, and the bestselling women's health book *Our Bodies, Ourselves* gives detailed instructions on how to do a vaginal self-examination, including inspection of the uterine cervix. It is a little awkward, but not difficult. All it requires is a long-handled mirror, a strong light source, and a plastic speculum. Many college sex education classes encourage voluntary self-examination, and more and more obstetricians and gynaecologists, particularly as more women enter the field, have been doing so too.

This illustrates the very different attitudes accepted by and for men and women. Every man has the opportunity to examine his own penis and see that of other men, to become familiar with the form and make comparisons. Women have had no such physical or psychological familiarity with their own sexual organs until quite recently.

Hymen

This is located at the opening to the vagina. In fact it marks the boundary between the external genitals, which develop from the skin, and the internal structures of the sexual-reproductive system. In some women the hymen may be more or less retained as a perforated, soft sheet of thin skin. In some girls this tissue, present during infancy, seems to dissolve with growth, so that only slight remnants survive at puberty. Hymenal remnants are seen as soft tags around the vaginal entrance. First coitus may or may not result in bloody separation of tissue. In some sexually experienced women a goodly portion of the hymen remains, depending upon the relative size of the vaginal opening, the hymen's ability to stretch, and the size and activity of the penis it accommodates. This great variety makes it impossible to say with certainty, on the evidence of the hymen alone, whether a woman is a virgin, whether she has masturbated, or indeed anything else about her sexual activity.

In some cases the hymen is unusually thick or strong. Reasonably forceful entry of a penis will usually overcome the obstruction, although the woman may feel some discomfort. In rare cases, it may be necessary to consult a physician, who can snip open the hymen to allow access.

Various cultures foster the myth that all first instances of hymenal penetration are painful and cause bleeding. Among the Kurdish people proof of chastity and bloody penetration is given by displaying stained sheets from the marriage bed for all the village to see. In both the West and the East where vestiges of such myths remain (in many communities in China and Japan, for example, and in Italy, Greece, Spain and Turkey), cultural demands are still such that a midwife or physician may be called upon to place a suture in the entrance of the vagina so that a penis feels some obstruction and penetration causes some superficial blood. This is no more than a sacrifice to ignorance and tradition.

In some women the pain caused by hymen rupture interferes with the enjoyment of first coitus; in others the pleasure of sex more than compensates for any pain. But there is not always pain, or even discomfort, where coitus is a natural development of sexual play. A classic study of 475 French and Belgian women by Marc Lanval in 1935 revealed that half felt their first coital experience was 'good' and half felt it was 'bad', the only two choices he offered. A more recent study of college students in New Jersey found that about one third of respondents experienced severe pain during their first coitus; a quarter did not experience pain. But, as investigator David Weis pointed out, pain was not the most important aspect of the experience. Three out of four women students said that their feelings of pleasure, satisfaction, excitement, and romance more than compensated for any pain felt. Pain was most often associated with first coitus at a younger age and with a conservative or repressive view of sex. Positive feelings were also related to previous experience with masturbation and with non-coital sexual activities; when coitus occurred, it was a 'culmination of a gradual process of sexual rehearsal'.

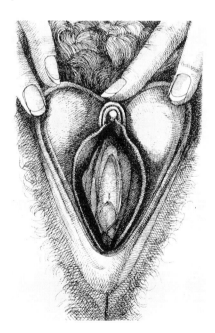
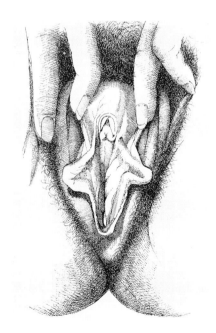
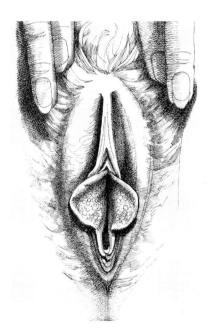

Clitoris

The clitoris (from a Greek word meaning hidden) is a relatively concealed structure. It is covered by a foreskin formed by the forward ends of the labia minora and can usually be exposed by moving these aside. What is then seen is an organ, somewhat analogous to the penis, that varies greatly in size and shape from woman to woman.

The clitoris is unique in that its primary function seems to be to receive erotic stimulation. This can be direct, or indirect from movement of the labia, vagina, or mons region. For many women the sensitivity of the glans clitoris, particularly after arousal, is such that they prefer indirect stimulation. Nevertheless, several studies have found that the majority of women find stimulation of the shaft of the clitoris very enjoyable, both in masturbation and partner contact. Unfortunately, as Hite and others have noted, most

Three different vulva types illustrated by Betty Dodson in her book Liberating Masturbation, *first published in 1974. Vulvic figures and amulets were once common in Europe — the proverbial 'lucky' horseshoe is a degraded vulva symbol.*

women find it difficult to ask their partner to stimulate them in this way and also feel guilty about masturbation, particularly when they are with a partner. Typically, women like clitoral stimulation to be part of a total involvement and not to seem like an obligation. It should be soft and slow at first, gradually building more pressure and speed. A technique frequently preferred is that stimulation should start with whole hand massage and then evolve to the use of only one or two fingers. As with other erotic techniques, individual nuances in preference are great; experimentation and communication, asking and telling what is wanted and found exciting, are the key to satisfaction.

The G spot

Though no longer as topical as it was a decade ago, the G spot is still controversial. Does it or does it not exist? Anatomists and physiologists still disagree, although practitioners of Ayurvedic and Unani medicine in India and Southeast Asia have no such doubts.

The G spot has been described as an area 1–1½ inches across located about two fingerjoints deep to the vaginal entrance. Its sensitivity to stimulation was first noted by the physician Ernst Grafenberg, the inventor of the first practical intrauterine device. In 1950 Grafenberg wrote: 'An erotic zone always could be demonstrated on the anterior wall of the vagina along the course of the urethra...Occasionally the production of fluids [due to its stimulation] is so profuse that a large towel has to be spread under the woman...this convulsive expulsion of fluids occurs always at the acme of the orgasm and simultaneously with it...expelled not from the vulva but out of the urethra in gushes...it has no urinary character...no lubricating significance.'

American researchers Beverley Whipple and John D. Perry dubbed this interesting zone the 'G spot' in Grafenberg's honour. In 1982, with colleague Alice Ladas, they created a popular publishing sensation with their book *The G Spot and Other Recent Discoveries about Human Sexuality*.

The existence of a possible source of female ejaculation remains unproven. Few women seem able to locate their G spot. There have been many studies as to the nature of the spot itself, with inconsistent results. Some say the spot exists, others not. Some say that the fluid expelled is urine, others not. (if you find such uncertainty annoying, remember that studies like this are not the kind that usually receive government or other official funding. Even grants for national KAP studies, far less controversial than the quest for the G spot, have not been forthcoming. When it comes to investigating sexual pleasure, researchers are usually on their own or attract only small grants; consequently, they can only enlist small numbers of subjects, often without extensive laboratory collaboration.)

From the data currently available, it is not possible to say what percentage of women have a G spot, what percentage have a gush of fluid at orgasm, and how frequently and under what conditions. Some researchers claim that a G spot is present and easy to locate in all women, others doubt its universal existence. William Hartman and Marilyn Fithian, two highly respected investigators following in the footsteps of Arnold Kegel (noted for his work on vaginal exercises to control incontinence and strengthen the muscles of the pelvic floor), claim that the most sensitive areas of the vagina are located not at the '12 o'clock' position as reported for the G spot, but at the '4 o'clock' and '8 o'clock' positions.

On balance, on the basis of my own findings, but more importantly on the basis of a review of the literature and conversations with many of the researchers involved, I am convinced that the G spot exists, but that it is not readily responsive or easily detectable in all women, and certainly not readily self-palpable. I also accept, on similar grounds, that some women 'ejaculate' at orgasm, that the fluid emitted may or may not be distinct from urine, and that emission may be followed, as in males, by a refractory period.

The work of Czech researcher Milan Zaviacic and his colleagues is particularly intriguing in this respect. They conducted a study of 27 women and found that although all of them had discernable G spots, only 10 of them expelled fluids on stimulation (this was not necessarily considered erotic) and in some cases only after prolonged stimulation (more than 15 minutes). The fluids expelled were distinct from urine and somewhat akin to male seminal fluid.

But what I find almost as interesting as the quest for biological fact is the avid interest that greeted the findings of researchers such as Whipple and Perry. It is understandable that most sexually active people want to give and receive the erotic pleasure they believe others enjoy. However, it would be a pity if the G spot and female ejaculation became yet another source of anxiety. To envy what happens in another person's bed to the extent of devaluing the pleasures of your own, or to feel inadequate because of what you think other people enjoy, is a waste and a shame.

Breasts

The message that comes across from magazines such as *Playboy* and *Penthouse* is that, for sex appeal, women with small breasts need not apply. As we shall see in the next chapter, most men prefer, as an ideal, fairly generous bust proportions. What do women themselves prefer? As we shall see, a breast size that is pleasing to both men and women cannot be defined.

Breast development is one of the first signs of puberty in both boys and girls. In girls, breast development may be evident a year or so before menarche, the onset of menstruation. Depending upon the culture, girls who develop more slowly than their age mates often feel embarrassed or humiliated. The pubertal growth period occurs at just the age when young people are most anxious to be

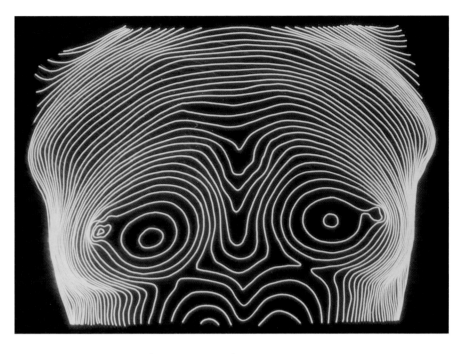

accepted by their peers. In boys, breast development also causes embarrassment and anxiety, but it is the body's way of building up an extra store of fat in preparation for the growth ahead. Breast development can occur in males at times other than puberty, or persist long after its completion, but such conditions, called gynaecomastia, are usually associated with certain drug treatments, medical problems, or alcoholism. These have the effect of increasing oestrogen levels in the body either directly or by altering normal hormone metabolism.

Hypnosis and prayer, pills and potions, exercises and diets — women have tried almost everything to increase breast size. Exercises can build up the back muscles and so increase overall bust measurement, and also tighten the pectoral muscles beneath the breasts, but

Two contour maps showing a young woman's breasts before (above) and after (below) surgical implantation of silicone prostheses. In this case, surgery was done for purely cosmetic reasons.

they cannot significantly increase breast size. Since the breast is mostly filled with fat, it is only by gaining weight that size will materially increase. But distribution of the extra fat cannot be controlled; it could equally well be deposited around the hips, thighs, or waist. The other main constituent of breasts, apart from fat, is glandular tissue, the special tissue that secretes milk. Pregnancy is therefore a stimulus to increased breast size. Hormone preparations may be helpful in those rare cases where small breasts are due to hormone deficiency; a deficiency of this kind typically shows itself in other ways and is therefore relatively easy to spot and treat. Like most other aspects of growth and body development, breast size and shape is genetically determined. All of us have at least some physical characteristics

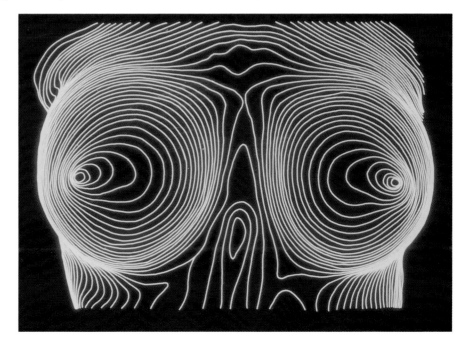

which we recognize in our parents or grandparents.

Large breasts are not desirable *per se*. They can be a source of social or physical discomfortand the kind of attention they provoke is sometimes less than flattering. Very large breasts may be too heavy for postural muscles, resulting initially in pain in the neck and shoulders, and then in poor posture, which predisposes to low back problems as well. In the United States, breast reduction is the third most common elective surgical procedure after rhinoplasty (nose jobs) and breast augmentation.

There is no ideal breast size or shape that simultaneously pleases men and women any more than there is an ideal and universally satisfying penis size or shape. Few women want breasts so large that they are out of proportion with the rest of their body or steal attention from their total appearance and personality. Each woman's shape has its own appeal and many men find small breasts attractive, erotic, and stimulating. As one small breast fan put it: 'Anything over mouth size is wasted.' For some men it is not the shape but rather the natural hang and swing of the breasts or the projection of the nipples behind a soft blouse that is erotic. For others it is the artificial accentuation offered by an uplift bra.

Most men assume that most women appreciate having their breasts and nipples stroked and kissed, and are surprised to find that there are women who take little or no pleasure from such stimulation. Men themselves seem to be fairly equally divided as to whether they find occasional stimulation of their breasts and nipples pleasurable and arousing; some men do, but an almost equal number find it distracting and unappealing. Some women can be brought to orgasm by breast and nipple stimulation alone, but this is almost unknown among men. For both sexes it is usually the nipple and its surrounding areola that are more sensitive than the breast itself. Blowing, sucking, and licking produce sensations that each have their own appeal.

Anxieties about the appearance of breasts and nipples are not uncommon. Areolae, the pigmented areas around the nipples, vary greatly in size and not uncommonly sprout hairs. These hairs can be plucked out, like any other, if they are a cause for concern. Some women worry that one breast is a different shape or size from the other or that one nipple or both may not protrude. These are common occurrences and not abnormal. Like most other individual features, they are usually of little or no concern to a loving partner. They do not in any way interfere with nursing or sexual pleasure. In any case, during sexual arousal inverted nipples become erect and respond in the same way as protruding nipples.

Less common is the presence of supernumerary nipples or breasts. These are extra breasts or nipples that develop in the armpit or along the so-called milk-line from armpit to normal nipple. They can easily be removed if they cause embarrassment. The adored heroine of the popular Japanese love story, *Gobancho yugiri ro* (Fifth District Shop) by Minakami Stomu, now made into several plays and movies, has supernumerary breasts.

Lastly, no woman need be apprehensive that her breasts are not adequate for nursing. It is a myth that women with small breasts produce insufficient milk.

Circumcision: male and female

Despite their great disparity in size, both the penis and the clitoris have a root, a shaft, and an expanded head called the glans; the rim of the glans is called the corona (crown). Covering the glans in the uncircumcised male is a loose hood of skin called the foreskin, or prepuce. In the female the prepuce is called the clitoral hood. The prepuce, glans, and skin on the underside of the penis and clitoris is attached by a thin strand of skin called the frenulum. The glans, prepuce, corona, and frenulum are the most sensitive areas of both the penis and the clitoris, and their stimulation during sex play gives pleasure to most people.

Male circumcision is the removal of the foreskin covering the glans. For most males, child or adult, circumcision is not medically necessary. Nevertheless it is often recommended for reasons of hygiene, particularly in the United States, where circumcision is routinely done in hospital soon after the birth of male babies. In Britain and Europe the practice is less frequent and much more dependent on the preferences of individual physicians. Those in favour of circumcision are generally urologists or paediatricians who have seen the problems that can develop with a retained foreskin. The most common is smegma, a cheesy accumulation of dead skin, dirt, bacteria, and fluids under the prepuce; if not regularly cleaned away, smegma can become a source of irritation and infection, not least for sexual partners. Secondly, a prepuce that is too tight (a condition known as phimosis) hinders normal erection of the penis, making coitus painful or impossible. Without circumcision, penile infection and phimosis are not uncommon.

There is no definite evidence that circumcision affects penis sensitivity one way or the other. Studies of men who have been circumcised as adults or as infants have not revealed anything consistent. Some men report that after foreskin removal in adulthood exposure of the glans did provide a different sensitivity for some months, but this decreased with time; a few complain that after arousal the glans of the circumcised penis is too sensitive for direct stimulation.

Circumcision of an Australian aborigine boy, part of initiation into manhood.

One argument against circumcision is that the foreskin is nature's way of protecting the glans from undesirable and extraneous stimuli. And without a foreskin, the argument continues, the glans will be extra sensitive and so decrease the individual's capacity for prolonged coitus. Actually, circumcised or not, there is no evidence of any greater or lesser capacity for prolonging coitus or reaching ejaculation more or less quickly. Nor is there any evidence that circumcision facilitates or hinders masturbation.

An additional argument against circumcision is that it can cause unnecessary trauma and perhaps subconscious psychological damage. Some people also point to the risk of faulty surgery, which may result in a disfigured or dysfunctional penis. There is no evidence whatsoever for the first argument, and cases of faulty surgery are extremely rare.

Interestingly, one major study revealed that a large percentage of women did not know whether their husbands were circumcised or not. Among those women who had experience of both states and could recognise the difference, no marked preference was found either way. Some women voiced a liking for the cleaner or neater appearance of the circumcised penis, but others found erotic appeal in the glans emerging from the intact foreskin.

In the female, two different but related procedures are worth mentioning. One is comparable to male circumcision and, depending on the culture in which it is practised, involves removing various amounts of prepuce, clitoris, or even parts of the labia. This is the custom in some Arab and African cultures where males are also routinely circumcised. In some societies it is believed that circumcision will lessen a woman's sexual appetite, deterring her from masturbating or straying from her husband; in other cultures it is a sign of religious or group affiliation. Female circumcision has become an issue in Western sexual politics, where it is interpreted as representing the view that a woman's body and desires should be subject to controls imposed by the dominant male culture. The practice is uncommon in the West on either cultural or hygienic grounds, but in Middle Eastern and

African countries it is widespread. The fact that it is often done by laypersons without the proper skills or instruments adds fuel to the controversy.

As with many other issues, the matter is not simple. There are reports of enhanced sexual response following at least one type of female circumcision. One clinical researcher, Leo Wollman, an obstetrician-gynaecologist and psychiatrist, reported: 'My opinion, based on clinical experience, is that the sensuality of the clitoris is greater when there is no tissue covering the clitoral head...Of 100 consecutive patients referred by psychoanalysts and clinical psychologists to the author for treatment of frigidity, 68 benefited by surgical female circumcision; of the remaining 32, 28 showed no need for this procedure; 4 refused to be treated by this technique. The technique of surgical circumcision in the female involves a small dorsal slit of the membrane covering the clitoral body....The ideal result from a female circumcision, where it is indicated, is an increase in quality of the orgasm, as well as an increased rapidity in achieving this sensual result in love-making.'

The second procedure, technically called clitoridopexy, was initially promoted by various feminists and professional sex therapists in the 1950s following the work of Robert L. Dickinson, a pioneer sex researcher. Dickinson reported that freeing the clitoris, enhancing its mobility by separating any adhesions tying it to its hood, would increase sensitivity and the probability of female orgasm. Another American researcher, Thomas P. Lowry, editor of two books, *The Classic Clitoris* and *The Clitoris*, has been quoted as saying that this procedure may be 'tremendously helpful' when clitoral adhesions exist. Masters and Johnson have claimed that clitoridopexy has doubtful value, but Kinsey supported the practice.

As with male circumcision, there has been no controlled study which has proved that either female circumcision or clitoridopexy affects erotic sensation for better or worse. The preponderance of opinion in the West now is that female circumcision is an unwarranted mutilation and a cultural anachronism even in those societies where it is still widely practised. It is outlawed in Norway, Sweden, and Denmark, but most legislators do not concern themselves with the issue, leaving the matter to personal discretion. While Britain's Royal College of Obstetricians has called the practice 'barbaric, futile and illogical', there are private physicians in London who perform clitoral surgery for immigrant women. Surgical reconstruction after circumcision is possible, but more difficult than the original operation. There is even stretching. Just as lips and ears can be stretched for cosmetic reasions, so too can the labia or foreskin.

The debate is complicated, because it is not argued on similar grounds on both sides. It is an argument that attracts irrational gusto. For example, where female circumcision is part of religious tradition, it is seen as the fulfillment of a covenant with God; the opposite view is that it may cause unnecessary pain, is of questionable hygenic value, and affirms the subordinate status of women.

In some cultures male circumcision is required by religious custom and may even be made deliberately traumatic, as part of a pubertal rite to mark transition to adulthood. In the pubertal rite of some Australian aborigines the glans penis is split to resemble that of a kangaroo. Other societies, like the ancient Hawaiians, practise subincision (slitting the underside of the penis) and the Ponapeans of the Caroline Islands remove a testicle as well. Youngsters are proud to admit having undergone such traumas. Like risking death to slay a lion or a whale, they are ways of testing and asserting manhood and membership of a particular group. Such practices are so entwined with traditional and personal beliefs that rational argument for or against is difficult, and when pressure for change comes from outside the culture in question, it has a presumptive aspect that is seldom welcome. In 1980, at the World Conference that marked the United Nations Decade for Women, the issue of female circumcision and clitoridectomy was discussed. Delegations from various African countries either left the conference or advised their sisters to mind their own business in regard to these practices.

There is enough clinical data, personal feeling, and social pressure to keep the debate on circumcision, male or female, in currency for some time to come.

Buttocks

I mentioned the erotic attraction of buttocks in Chapter 2. They may be more than an arbitrary stimulus. Contraction of the buttocks reflects, more than any other factor, the development of the tensions involved in erotic arousal. The buttock muscles are among the strongest in the body and they come into play during intercourse and masturbation; a small percentage of women masturbate simply by tensing and relaxing their gluteal muscles.

Fondling the rump is considered pleasurable by both men and women. But involvement of the anus and rectum in sex play is highly individualistic, culture-related, and linked to sexual preference. More than half the heterosexual respondents to Kinsey's surveys in the United States indicated that, while it was not commonly part of their sexual repertoire, they had had experience of anal stimulation or anal intercourse. Despite the increased risk of HIV infection and AIDS, the practice seems only to have decreased slightly in frequency in the last decade. The few recent studies available indicate that some 10 per cent of heterosexual couples regularly enjoy anal intercourse.

Among homosexual males, recent surveys show that between 50 and 75 per cent regularly engage in anal intercourse and manual stimulation of the anus. A 1986 survey of gay men in London found that 53 per cent engaged in anal sex, surveys in Mexico and Costa Rica in 1989 came up with a figure of 75 percent, and a 1990 Australian study with 95 per cent. Actually, anal intercourse is a worldwide sexual technique for heterosexuals as well as homosexuals because it is a method of contraception. In some cultures, anal techniques are part of male initiation rites.

The anus and rectum are the terminal parts of the digestive tract. The anus is highly pigmented and surrounded by ring-like sphincter muscles that are normally tightly closed. The anal region, vagina, and penis share the same nerve roots. This partly explains why males and females can find anal stimulation erotic. Like the vagina, the anal region is most sensitive close to its opening. Deeper inside, pressure and stretching are easily felt but are more painful than pleasurable.

Anal intercourse is sometimes thought of in terms of dominance and submission. Some individuals refuse to allow penetration while perfectly willing to play the role of penetrator; others feel psychologically uncomfortable with a role they think of as dominant. More often, anal intercourse is regarded as an extension of natural sexual curiosity, of the desire to know a partner's body as fully as possible, and to find as many ways of giving and receiving pleasure as possible.

While some people are repelled by the idea of anal intercourse, others find it appealing. As Masters, Johnson, and Kolodny have stated: 'Anal intercourse is often thought to be

The buttocks, more than any other muscles in the body, reflect the development of sexual tension. Contraction of the gluteals and other pelvic muscles leads to general engorgement of the genitals, particularly the penis and clitoris.

primarily an act of male homosexuals. However, numerically speaking, far more heterosexual couples engage in this activity than homosexuals, and many homosexual men have not had experience with this type of sexual behavior.' The practice occurs because it is acknowledged as another option in the cause of mutual sexual pleasure.

A note of caution is appropriate here. Anal intercourse has been found to be the sexual practice most likely to transmit HIV, the virus that causes AIDS. So, unless you are certain that your partner is HIV free, it is a risky practice, although less risky to give than to receive. If in any doubt, forego the pleasure, or at least always use a condom. Since the rectal sphincter is tight and lubrication in this area is minimal, penetration should be slow and gentle, with the penetrating partner applying plenty of lubrication so as not to damage the rectum or cause pain (haemorrhoids are definitely a contraindication to anal intercourse). The most highly recommended lubricants are those that are water-soluble and contain a spermicide/bactericide such as nonoxynol-9. As a simple matter of hygiene, fingers or penis that have been inserted into the rectum should be washed before oral or vaginal play.

Pubic hair

Hair growth in the pubic region is one of the first signs of puberty. Distribution may be sparse and localized or widespread and luxuriant, and the growth pattern differs in men and women. While in both sexes pubic hair grows in the shape of a shield (escutcheon), in men the upper border tapers up towards the navel and in women the line is relatively horizontal. Even the sight of pubic hair is exciting to most men and to some women. Stroking it or gently pulling it can be quite erotic. Several centuries ago false pubic hair-pieces, merkins, were fashionable. At the other extreme, some cultures and certain groups within cultures prefer a shaved pubic area, as in Egypt and the Sudan.

The removal of body hair from the pubic region, armpits, legs, and other parts of the body has become a feminist issue. Many women feel that shaving, electrolysis, depilation, and waxing are done only to please men; they find the whole process inconvenient, sordid, sometimes painful, and degrading; why should they feel embarrassed about their own bodies? Other women feel they do it for themselves, for their own aesthetic reasons.

The debate on this issue, as with circumcision, is tied to cultural and social expectations. In most of Western Europe it is usually women of the middle and upper classes who remove body hair; working-class women and those living in rural areas tend not to bother. In Spain and Latin America, a woman's moustache or body hair may be considered sexy but not necessarily in good taste. In Japan pubic hair is considered so erotic that it is one of the hallmarks of pornography. In contrast, in some Arab countries, pubic hair is considered unclean and unacceptable; women are expected to shave their pubic, genital, and underarm areas.

The mouth

Lips and tongue together are an extremely sensual organ, ranking highly with men and women alike. *The Perfumed Garden*, the classical Persian love manual, states: 'A humid kiss is better than hurried coitus.' The mouth is sensitive to tenderness and passion and a kiss can suggest or accompany genital penetration.

Most erotic play in Western societies includes oral activity. For some people the mouth rivals the genitals in erotic significance and some women can come to orgasm through kissing alone. But kissing as we know it, like many other sexual practices, is not universal. Among some cultures it is unknown or rare. Some Eskimo and Truk Islander groups rub noses and partake of each other's smells rather than kiss. Such was the practice in traditional Hawaii. In fact the Hawaiian term for 'stranger', now reserved for Caucasians, is *ha'ole*, which means 'without breath', since the newcomers didn't 'kiss' properly. Other techniques involve sucking the lips and tongue of the partner, as among the Kwakiutl Indians, and among the Trobriand and Truk Islanders.

Erotic mouth-to-mouth kissing includes movements of the tongue and lips to simulate the action of penis and vagina in intercourse. Tongue, lips, and teeth can be used with amazing versatility to stimulate, press, tickle, caress, lick, suck, pull, blow, nibble, or nip any part of the body. Kissing the breasts and genitals is a common part of sexual play, although the idea and the act of using the mouth to directly stimulate the penis or the clitoris and vagina are still distasteful to many people. Like the skin, the mouth has enormous sensual potential. If one partner feels the other is too quick in moving to coitus and orgasm, oral activities

A 19th-century Japanese woodblock print. In Japan, kissing ia a particularly intimate form of contact and pubic hair is considered highly erotic. Albums of prints like this enjoyed limited circulation, and were specifically intended to spice up love-making.

have a broad potential well worth exploring both as an *hors d'oeuvre* and as a dessert!

In sum, how we are 'turned on' depends on our biology, our experiences, and the culture we live in, and the relative strength of these influences will be different in each person. Also our age, health, education, occupation, and marital status will have a bearing on how we approach and react to new situations. The body we bring into the sexual arena has its own eroticism, which can be appreciated as it is or modified to please ourselves or a partner. Knowing our body has to be the starting point. To quote from the women's classic health book *Our Bodies, Ourselves*: '...ignorance, uncertainty — even, at worst, shame — about our physical selves create in us an alienation from ourselves that keeps us from being the whole people that we could be....'

Chapter 4

Aphrodisiacs & anaphrodisiacs

Aphrodisiacs are named after Aphrodite, the Greek goddess of love who was formed from sea foam when the god Chronos killed and castrated his father and threw his genitals into the sea. They are substances purported to excite love or sexual desire. Anaphrodisiacs do the opposite. Folklore, medicine, and modern therapy have all attempted to solve the problems of unrequited love, unmatched or unsynchronized desire, too much or too little passion. The search for aphrodisiacs and anaphrodisiacs — charms, spells, rituals, potions, philtres, diets — is age-old and universal. As this anonymous sixteenth-century English ditty says:

Good sir yf you lack the strengthe in your back
and would have a Remediado
Take Eryngo [sea holly] *rootes & Marybone* [marrow bone] *tartes*
Redde Wine & riche Potato.

An Oyster pie & Lobsters thighe
Hard Eggs well drest in Marow
This will ease your backes disease
and make you good Cocksparrowe.

An Apricock or an Artichock
Anchovies oyle and Pepper
These to use do not refuse
Twill make your backe the better.

Of course the ideal aphrodisiac would have to be all things to all people. It would have to be 'partner specific'; it is the love or desire of a particular person, not of the world at large or of a complete stranger, that is desired. It would also have to be 'time specific'; a woman may want to prolong her partner's erection but not delay his orgasm indefinitely.

In certain circumstances, almost anything — from recreational and illegal drugs to charms, incense, candles, pornography, and memories of past loves — can enhance the subjective experience of sex. However, in this chapter I will be concentrating on substances, natural or fabricated, that are effective in the majority of individuals involved, whether they are aware of taking them or not. An aphrodisiac, if it is genuine, should work without the placebo effect. That said, medicines throughout history relied at least in part on the mind set of the person taking them.

However, no potion, powder, or drug exists that can selectively and safely manipulate both sexual desire and performance in both men and women. No charm or magic has such power either. In this age of chemical miracles and designer drugs we are perhaps coming closer to this desired goal.

'The Lady and the Unicorn', a 16th-century French tapestry. The mythical unicorn symbolized chastity, purity, virginity, and all the moral virtues, not, as is commonly thought, male potency. So, by the law of like assisting like, powdered unicorn horn would have been an anaphrodisiac.

Like helping like

Many folk preparations from around the world come under the heading of 'sympathetic' medicine and follow the 'doctrine of signatures'. Their claimed efficacy comes from their similarity to the body organ or process in question. The horn of a rhinoceros or deer represents a firm, erect penis. Olives represent testes and oysters vaginal labia. Peppers create a sensation of heat and cooked okra represent vaginal lubrication.

Belief in such sympathetic potential is a feature of various folk and traditional herbal therapies and magical procedures. The 'success' of such treatments is usually quite coincidental, or the result of the extra care and sensitivity that accompany the situation in which they are given or taken. If they do not work, it can always be said that they were not prepared or used properly. In fifth-century Rome, Caelius Aurelianus warned: 'To distil the true essence of Satyricon [sexual desire] is no light task; many fail to render the liquor efficacious through ignorance of the root's idiosyncrasy. For it is to be noted that of the twin testicles of this plant [probably the tuber *Orchis mascula*] the one is ever flaccid, soft and wrinkled and shall therefore be discarded, since its virtue is of a nature called Saturnine by Celsus, which has the contrary effect of repressing and extinguishing desire.'

The Roman historian Martial thought that 'bulbs' (probably onions) were effective for whatever ailed one sexually. The success of the remedy depended simply on taking enough: 'He who is unable to show himself a man in the Cyprian joustings [natives of Cyprus were once held to be extremely licentious in their behaviour] let him eat of bulbs and he will be doughty enough. In the same way, should your anus languish, do not cease eating of bulbs, and charming Venus will once more smile on your frays.' In modern parlance, if one teaspoon doesn't help, try two!

When partners conspire to use a 'love potion', the result is often a self-fulfilling prophecy. Whatever the effect of the potion, love-making may be enhanced by the relief from responsibility that the introduction of such an outside element affords: 'I was under the influence....' On the other hand, someone who sticks pins in a doll is likely to behave aggressively to the person represented by the effigy; in consequence, he or she may well abandon any effort to be sexually pleasing.

At one time potatoes and tomatoes were looked on as 'love foods'; eating them conferred sexual and reproductive potency. Chocolate too had this reputation. As long as they were exotic and difficult to come by, they kept their mystique, but once in common use their love-enhancing powers became discredited. The rarity of truffles today allows them to keep their reputation (undeserved) as aphrodisiacs.

Ginseng

Korean ginseng root (*Panax ginseng*), not to be confused with Siberian ginseng, has a vast reputation as an aphrodisiac. From India and Russia to Korea, Japan, and China, it is believed to enhance general health, relieve tiredness, and improve sexual prowess. The more the root resembles the human form, the more efficacious it is. A visiting Shanghai physician recently gifted me with two large humanoid roots. Unfortunately, from him and two other Chinese physicians, I could get no concensus as to how to prepare the plant for proper aphrodisiac effect. There is no scientific evidence that sexual performance or desire is enhanced by ginseng.

Spanish fly, mandrake, and yohimbine

These three substances are often cited in the Western world as aphrodisiacs. Spanish fly is the common name for a powder made from ground *Cantharis*, *Mylabris*, or *Lytta* beetles. The powder is a powerful irritant which causes inflammation of the skin as well as the mucous membranes of the digestive and urinary tract. The substance may have earned its reputation from farmers seeing cattle eating the beetles and noting that they then behaved as if they were in heat. In men, Spanish fly can cause erection, but there is a price to pay. The erection is usually painful, not pleasurable, a reflex reaction due to pelvic irritation. Women given Spanish fly may begin to moan, but this is a moan of pain, not arousal. In both men and women, ulceration may be

Thorn-stuck effigies of a man and a woman found fixed to a door at Castle Rising, Norfolk, England. In almost all societies, witchcraft has been used as a means of conjuring love and physical desire.

Humanoid ginseng roots on sale in a colourful box. Ginseng is the great cure-all of Chinese medicine. In Korea ginseng is given for a variety of female complaints, from irregular menstruation to painful contractions during labour.

induced in the digestive and urinary tract. Therefore Spanish fly is not only ineffective as a love potion but also highly dangerous.

The mandrake of aphrodisiac fame belongs to a group of plants of similar reputation and general appearance (*Podophyllum peltatum* in America, *Bryonia dioica* and *Tamus communis* in Britain, and *Datura stramonium* and *Mandragora officinarum* in Europe and the Middle East). Somewhat like ginseng root in the Orient, mandrake is reputed to be effective because of its resemblance to the human form or, more specifically, to a penis. It was recommended as an aphrodisiac in Ancient Egypt and Greece, and the Roman historian Pliny mentions it as an anaesthetic. There is also mention of it in *Genesis*: 'When Leah went out to meet Jacob she said to him "Thou must come in unto me, for surely I have hired thee with my son's mandrakes".' In fact the active principles in mandrake root are atropine and scopolamine, both of which are sleep-inducing. Jacob and Leah may have slept together, but perhaps that was all they did. In large doses, mandrake causes mental confusion and hampers respiration. So, like Spanish fly, it is to be avoided.

Yohimbine is prepared from bark of the yohimbe tree (*Pausinystalia yohimbe*), an African species mainly restricted to the Cameroons. Its principle effect, well researched, is to improve blood circulation. Several drug companies use it as an ingredient (mixed with testosterone and other substances such as strychnine) in preparations designed to induce erection. However, recent studies in men with erection or libido difficulties have been contradictory; some studies found that yohimbine was effective, others not, and the reasons for this are not understood. So the usefulness of yohimbine remains in doubt.

Organs from animals

Testes or testicular extracts are quite commonly used as male aphrodisiacs and rejuvenators. Sheep's testes sold as 'mountain oysters' or beef testes sold as 'prairie oysters' may be enjoyed as gourmet delicacies but are without special powers. Injectables from these and other animal tissues are considered unethical in the United States but are permitted in Europe and elsewhere. Some of these injectables contain placental or animal foetus extracts ('a foetus is young so it must be rejuvenating'). None have any real effect.

Every culture has its special aphrodisiacs. To this day many rhinos, elephants, deer, sheep, and other animals lose their lives so that their penises, testes, horns, tusks, or other organs can be used to improve the sex lives of those who believe in their value. The wilder and rarer the animal and the more difficult it is to catch, the greater the potency of its organs and appendages. In Asia, the contents of the gall bladder of a poisonous species of

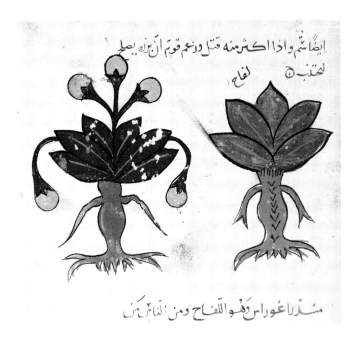

من البارس وهو التفاح ومن الناس كن

A 13th-century Arab manuscript illustration of a mandrake plant. Once included in the materia medica of physicians throughout Europe and Asia, mandrakes were reputed to be without aphrodisiac power unless 'pulled groaning from the ground by a black dog at midnight'.

snake are particularly prized (erroneously). Technologically advanced societies put their faith in other kinds of aphrodisiacs; coca cola and aspirin, for example, were considered a good bet about 40 years ago, and more lately marijuana or cannabis.

Alcohol and marijuana

Perhaps the most widely used sexual stimulant is alcohol. Indeed its use is so ancient that there is serious debate as to which came first, the grinding of grain to make bread or the fermenting of grain to make beer. In moderation alcohol does seem to lessen inhibitions and interpersonal tension. Since these often hamper sexual interest, ardour may indeed be increased by reducing them. Alcohol also reduces discrimination, so fewer restraints exist. But there is no evidence that alcohol by itself stimulates sexual activity. As Shakespeare observed and physiologists have confirmed, alcohol 'provokes the desire, but it takes away the performance'. Neither does marijuana directly stimulate sexual behaviour or induce amorous desire in an unwilling person, although, like alcohol, it certainly reduces anxiety and inhibitions.

Many substances, including alcohol and marijuana, appear to be effective because the persons using them expect a specific result and act in such a way that their expectation becomes reality. This is the famous placebo effect at work. Also the situations in which such drugs are used often reflect a tacit understanding that sexual activity will follow.

Controlled studies of the effect of alcohol and marijuana, extensively reviewed by Raymond Rosen and R.C. Schiavi, have shown mixed results. Large amounts of alcohol depress emotional expression, including sexual desire. In men impotence due to alcohol is common. To be sure, the amount of alcohol which constitutes a large dose varies from person to person, but as a rule of thumb two shots of whisky, wine, or beer per hour are enough to induce a feeling of expansiveness, warmth, and comfort. This would be enough to reduce inhibition about initiating or accepting sexual advances and, simultaneously, about vocally and forcefully rejecting them. At twice this level of alcohol in the blood — at around 100mg of alcohol per 100ml of blood, a concentration of 0.1 per cent — decision-making and discriminatory abilities diminish markedly. Sexual advances, or the rejection of such advances, may be quite forceful. Erection is still possible, but orgasm in both sexes is generally delayed. At higher blood alcohol levels, erection may be difficult to achieve or maintain; orgasm is also unlikely, if not impossible, whether one is a man or a woman.

The British pharmacologist Peter Taberner found that, after comparable doses of alcohol, women seemed to be more inebriated than men, and became more talkative and excited. But in regard to the sex effects of alcohol he gave more credit to psychological factors than to the amount of alcohol consumed: '...of all the forms of alcohol, champagne is probably the most likely to be successful as an aphrodisiac.'

Prolonged marijuana use (i.e. daily for more than two months) severely reduces both sexual activity and sperm production in men because it depresses the production of androgens. But in women it seems to correlate with a higher probability of coital orgasm. However, both men and women commonly report that 'grass' seems to make sex more pleasurable and last longer. Since marijuana is known to influence perception of time, it is difficult to test whether such reports reflect reality or altered perception.

Not everyone is a judicious user of either alcohol or marijuana. Chronic and large uses of either do not improve one's sex life, in fact quite the opposite. Both depress the central nervous system and both are associated with low testosterone levels.

Wild oats and life extenders

Popular self-help literature has recently touted preparations with trade names like Exsativa and Wild Oats. These are powders made from oats (*Avena sativa*), vitamin C, and nettle extract (*Urtica urens*). They are non-toxic and have acquired a reputation — through television talk shows as well as presentation at scientific gatherings — for restoring sexual interest and erectile ability in men. In women, they seem to be ineffective. Unfortunately, the only research on such preparations has been done by an institution with a financial stake in their success. Independent scientific studies are needed.

Not so long ago *The Wall Street Journal* gave front-page coverage to 'An Anti-Aging Aphrodisiac' with the generic name of deprenyl. Originally used to treat Parkinson's disease, Canadian researchers found that deprenyl extended the lifespan of rats. According to personal testimonials in *The Wall Street Journal*, the drug enhanced erection and libido. Here too independent scientific studies are needed.

Cocaine, increasingly although illegally used as a recreational drug, has some reputation as an aphrodisiac (Sigmund Freud was one of the first to note its effect on sexual activity). When it is inhaled like snuff or taken intravenously, the resulting 'high' often gives a feeling of power, and with it feelings of potency and desirability. Erection is often prolonged and orgasm delayed, Extended cocaine use can lead to priapism, prolonged and painful erections in men, and prolonged vaginal dryness in women. In both sexes copulation time may be extended, but orgasm may never be reached. Long-term use is almost always anaphrodisiac in its effect, marked by a decline in both sexual interest and ability. 'Crack', a potent new form of cocaine, is particularly brutal in this regard. There are female and male crack prostitutes who sell their services for the drug. The drug provides the pleasure, not the sex.

Other drugs reputed to enhance sexual experiences are amyl nitrite and isobutyl nitrite. These induce physiological changes — increased heart rate and blood flow — which may or may not be interpreted as signs of sexual excitement. These drugs, called 'poppers' because they used to be sold in thin-necked glass phials which had to be snapped open to allow their volatile contents to be inhaled, have become popular particularly among gays. According to some users, their effect is intense. Because, among other things, they relax the anal sphincter, they are usually inhaled at the start of sex play or at impending orgasm. They are not necessarily innocuous, however. An increase in blood flow can be catastrophic if one happens to suffer from heart, cerebrovascular, or retinal problems.

People crave pleasure sensations. Those provided by heroin and cocaine, derivatives of the opium poppies seen growing here, are more likely to take the place of sexual pleasure than enhance it.

Ubiquitously available drugs such as amphetamines, antidepressants, tranquillizers, stimulants, and anti-psychotic preparations account for more than 60 per cent of all prescriptions in the United States. Since these drugs are given to people who are not functioning normally, their sexual effects are hard to define, but generally speaking when depression or anxiety are relieved, libido and potency tend to increase. In many people amphetamines and stimulants seem to energize sexual response. Relaxants, although they tend to reduce potency and orgasm, also reduce inhibition. The general picture with prescription drugs is that at the dosages usually prescribed little sexual effect is detectable, although effects vary from person to person. The effects of taking illicitly obtained prescription drugs, or of using street drugs, are even more variable, since neither dosage nor content is properly controlled.

Anaphrodisiacs

Are there any substances that reliably *decrease* arousal or ardour? Zealous parents and guardians have been known to seek anaphrodisiacs to control the sexual behaviour of those in their care, as have legal authorities in the treatment of sex offenders. And people not easily aroused themselves have looked for methods of cooling the enthusiasm of others. Common among soldiers, sailors, and prisoners is the myth that their food is routinely doctored with various ingredients to dampen sexual interest. But, as with aphrodisiacs, the list of substances reported to do the trick is long, while the list of efficacious ones is short.

Saltpetre (potassium nitrate) is probably the most often mentioned of all anaphrodisiacs. There is no evidence, however, that it has the power to inhibit sexual interest or performance. It can increase urine flow and in large doses can be fatal — an unnecessarily drastic solution! Its reputation may be due to the fact that it was once used medicinally to reduce fevers, with the faulty reasoning that it would similarly lower the 'heat' of sexual ardour. Its main use, prior to modern refrigeration, was in the curing and storage of meat, so the idea may have arisen, among those forced to subsist on cured meat, that their food was drugged.

While certainly not taken as such, heroin, opium, and other opiates are effective anaphrodisiacs. Along with their sedative and anaesthetic effects, these drugs diminish libido, potency, and orgasm. Sexual interest is replaced by passivity and a craving for the drug itself. As with crack prostitutes mentioned above, male or female opiate users may sell sexual favours, but it is for drug money, not for sexual pleasure. With detoxification from heroin, the rebound of sexual interest and potency is usually quite rapid.

Barbiturates are indeed 'downers' when it comes to sex. Initially, like alcohol, they take away inhibition, but with increased use they also take away sexual interest and potency. In women who abuse barbiturates, menstruation and ovulation become irregular.

Pharmaceutical companies have been successful in developing several antisexual drugs. One is cyproterone acetate (CA), which acts by competing with testosterone so that the hormone cannot do its work. Effective in men, the drug reduces libido, erectile potential, and capacity for orgasm. Although it is still considered experimental in the United States, in several European countries CA is given to male sex offenders.

And lastly, perhaps, nicotine deserves a mention. It is a powerful vasoconstrictor, decreasing the diameter of blood vessels, making the heart work harder, and impairing blood flow to the skin and body extremities. In some men it has been reported to impair blood flow to the penis and therefore hamper erection. Is this why cigarettes are smoked after sex rather than before? Studies on women have yet to be done. Nicotine is only one of the nasty constituents of cigarette smoke; some of the others cause lung cancer, damage nerve sheaths, and increase blood viscosity and decrease its oxygen-carrying capacity, none of which are conducive to a healthy sex life.

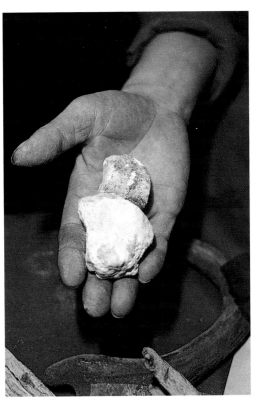

'Dinosaur bone' and petrified oyster shell, when properly prepared, are supposed to reduce ardour. As one fossil said to the other....

Modern chemistry

After thousands of years of trial and error we are now in a position to conduct extremely sophisticated research into sex-active substances. Unfortunately, legitimate pharmaceutical companies are not doing much in this field. They prefer to work on more 'reputable' projects, where the ethics of human testing procedures are less questionable. Drugs developed for non-sexual purposes are routinely scanned for sex-active effects, however. But the human subjects they are tested on are usually 'sick' in some way, or their placebo effect may not have been tested on a control group, so the results of such tests must be regarded with caution. Also, the number of people involved in such trials is usually small, dosages and duration of use vary greatly, and measures of effect are not consistent from one report to another.

Many drugs prescribed for serious medical conditions can act as anaphrodisiacs, affecting desire, performance, or both. Such drugs usually influence the central or peripheral nervous system and include painkillers (narcotic analgesics), minor tranquillizers or anti-anxiety drugs (benzodiazepines, beta blockers), antidepressants (MAOIs, tricyclics), diuretics (thiazides), and drugs which affect processes in the brain (phenothiazines, lithium, Levodopa). Anti-hypertensive drugs (ACE inhibitors, beta blockers, Methyldopa, reserpine) can be life-saving, but they can also inhibit erection or lead to anorgasmia.

Levodopa can dramatically improve motor function in individuals otherwise incapable, and with this improved function comes a restoration of sexual interest and performance. But in normal individuals, Levodopa and similar drugs do not produce improvement. Similarly, in individuals with certain endocrine problems, hormone therapy can help, but in normal individuals extra hormones have little or no effect.

And yet potions, philtres, tonics, pills, and natural and designer drugs directly or indirectly intended to enhance sexual performance are, if anything, more numerous today than ever. With modern advertising the packaging and presentation have changed, but the message is the same: this product will restore flagging vitality, make you feel years younger, give you a new zest for life. As old nostrums lose their appeal, new ones with names like Gerioptril, Prokopin G, and Gerovital take their place. Often they contain procaine, a local anaesthetic, or alcohol. Others are made from ginseng, garlic, gingko, and guarana extracts.

Health food stores tout SOD (superoxide dismutase), Coenzyme Q, and RNA supplements. None of these have proven aphrodisiac effects, and other claimed effects are still controversial.

Nor have LSD or any other of the alphabet clan of drugs (MDA, DOM, 5-HT, PCPA, MAI, and so on), or even the new designer drug 'ecstasy' any proven aphrodisiac power. They have all been tried, hopefully. Barbiturates, hypnotics, and sedatives have been used to induce relaxation, and tranquillizers and antipsychotics to reduce anxiety and antisocial behaviour. Feeling physically and mentally relaxed and receptive may make one feel sexier, but this is not a reliable or consistent response. In one person a drug may stimulate the imagination and lead to heightened sexual activity, but in another it may lead to greater introspection. Drugs are not always predictable in their action, and their side effects can be more than distressing. So although drugs taken for specific medical conditions may have a beneficial effect on overall health, their effects on sexual activity seem to be mostly neutral or undesirable.

'Make love like a tiger; rut like a stag.' Tiger and deer penises on sale in Hong Kong.

The ethics of using sex-active substances

As a couple may wish to experience different gastronomic pleasures by becoming gourmets or vegetarians, or by adding or cutting out salt or wine, I see a similar case to be made for people mutually wanting to experience different sexual pleasures. Surely when two people conspire to spice up, figuratively and literally, or tone down their amorous or erotic adventures, it is presumptuous to approve or disapprove. As an informed sexwatcher, I would like them to be aware of possible negative side effects but, issues of legality aside, there is no moral problem involved. The wish to tinker with nature, especially if what is 'natural' is unsatisfying, seems to me wholly legitimate. Whether it is more or less sex that is wanted, the desire for a remedy that is a few swallows away is very understandable. Nor is the motive for change always selfish. A sympathetic lover may recognize reluctance and inhibition in a partner and genuinely want him or her to enjoy erotic experiences more fully.

Very broad ethical issues are involved in using drugs or any other means to rectify disparity in sexual interest or performance. Should such disparities be regarded as a purely personal matter, in which case aphrodisiacs become recreational choices, options in sex play? Or are they medical problems requiring pharmaceutical treatment, psychiatric disturbances requiring therapy, or symptoms of an insecure, sex-obsessed society that needs to revise its values? And in cases of rape and other sexual offences, should we use drugs, relearning therapies, physical punishment, or imprisonment, or all four simultaneously?

Moral and legal issues aside, aphrodisiacs are a fascinating field of study, with a literature that is arcane and fabulous. Here is a good example of the genre, from Norman Douglas' *Paneros* (1932), which carries a message with which I wholeheartedly agree: 'To lovers we therefore say: devour partridge, and oyster and asparagus for their pleasurable taste, rather than in the hope of performing prodigies with the beloved....And put not your trust in Arabian skink, in Roman goose-fat or Roman goose-tongues, in the arplan [musk deer] of China that "maketh a man renew his youth and astonish his household", in spicy culinary dishes, eringoe [sea holly] root, or the brains of love-loving sparrows...in pine nuts, the blood of bats mingled with asses' milk, root of valerian, dried salamander, cyclamen, menstrual fluid of man or beast, tulip bulbs, fat of camel's hump...the pounded tooth of a corpse, wings of bees...garlic, the genitals of hedgehogs, Siberian iris, rhinoceros horn...the blood of slaughtered criminals...or stag's horn crushed to powder: aphrodisiacs all, and all impostures.'

Chapter 5

Body language

Most of us, as part of our sexual delight, enjoy observing the sexual pleasure and responses of a partner. His or her facial expressions — smiles, frowns, grimaces — sounds, body movements, and skin texture are in themselves erotic. In many ways they are also the most private of all responses, usually seen only by a cherished and privileged partner. In most Western societies it is considered a gross invasion of privacy, indeed illegal, to wilfully observe others in sexual activities without their permission, or oblige others to watch such activities.

Sexual activities are considered so private that Kinsey and his colleagues in the 1940s and 1950s were criticized and ridiculed for expecting the public, or at least the American public, to believe that people could be encouraged to talk candidly about sex and answer questions honestly. Less than a generation later William Masters and Virginia Johnson shocked the public again by announcing that, with the permission of those involved, they had not only interviewed scores of men and women but had observed them in sexual encounters. More than that, they had filmed many of the intimate details and measured them with scientific instruments. By such means they had detected things that millions of lovers over thousands of years had failed to notice. Surprising? Not really when one considers that most sex takes place in the dark and in circumstances where the participants are less than concerned with scientific accuracy.

Intimate signals

The questions men and women ask each other often reveal that intimate signals are not always recognized or understood. Such questions may not be asked easily or in so many words. 'Do you want to make love?' may be a kiss or a touch which is sensitive to similar or different feelings in return. Asking 'Are you ready to go to bed?' may really mean 'Let's have sex.' 'Are you ready?' is a question between partners who care about pacing their movements so that both reach a satisfying climax. 'Did you come?' and 'Couldn't you tell?' also reflect a common reality: orgasm is often unrecognized by those closest and most willing to observe. And if that peak sensation goes unrecognized, how many other less intense moments of sexual intimacy remain unappreciated?

Words are not always the most loving or effective way to signal desire or a particular sexual response, and even non-verbal signals are not always consciously given. Being sensitive to tiny clues — dress, facial expression, body movements, tone of voice — that another person is unaware of giving adds a richness to any encounter.

Signals such as a thumping heart and heavy breathing are unambiguous in a sexual context — they signify physical and emotional excitement — but the smaller tell-tale signs of sexual arousal are less easily perceived or correctly interpreted, even by people of considerable sexual experience. One of the problems is that behaviour does not always match thoughts and feelings. A man can have an erection that is neither pleasurable nor desired. In very rare cases this may be due to disease, but usually it is a reflex action — a full bladder or nervous anxiety can cause an erection. Desire for coitus, however strong, is not always accompanied by an erection. This is a common experience and the causes are many; anxiety, fatigue, and preoccupation head the list. Similarly a woman can exhibit contradictory signs. The vagina can wet copiously independently of sexual arousal, or remain dry even when coitus is much desired. Orgasm may be desperately willed but remain elusive.

On earth as in heaven…. The monkey god in this Thai print is getting frisky. The gods in the Buddhist pantheon are far from austere. Sexual and erotic behaviour among the immortals is not seen as a lack of perfection.

The sexual response cycle

One of the major discoveries of Masters and Johnson was that sexual activity to orgasm is accompanied by a very distinctive set of physiological changes. This train of events is called the sexual response cycle. There are five stages in the cycle: rest, excitement or arousal, plateau, orgasm, and resolution.

This discussion of sexual response attempts to deal with the subject as part of a total picture of mind and body. The descriptions I am about to give are not models to be lived up to. Variation is great and these generalities are intended to give the reader a better understanding of how male and female bodies work during sex play and coitus. This may sound mechanistic, but my aim is to provide firm ground on which to base an appreciation and indeed a questioning of sex in a wider context. I should also point out that the responses involved are the same whether in the context of homosexual or heterosexual activity, whether in intercourse, oral sex, or masturbation. The following discussion emphasizes those body changes which can be measured scientifically. As yet, however, we have no way of gauging what goes on in the mind, or even agreement as to what it is within the mind that we should monitor or measure. Mental responses are undoubtedly as important as physical ones.

Most of the time we are sexually at rest, in neutral as it were, busy doing non-sexual things. Consciously or unconsciously these things may be related to sexual pursuits, but they are not accompanied by any of the physiological events that signify sexual arousal. Thoughts or fantasies about a real or imagined lover can intrude on everyday activities but leave one sexually at rest. A man at rest has a flaccid penis; a woman at rest has a relatively dry and relaxed vagina.

Gentle, exploratory touching often accompanies arousal. 'Weak at the knees' or 'butterflies in the stomach' sensations correlate with increased blood flow to the pelvis.

Arousal phase

As sexual interest increases, in response to some psychological or physical stimulus, the arousal phase begins. In fact some sexologists claim that between rest and arousal there is a 'desire' stage; the well known therapist Helen Singer Kaplan considers this stage more important than arousal *per se*.

In both men and women arousal is marked by an increase in blood flow to the pelvis (vasocongestion) and an increase in muscular tension (myotonia). In women this combination produces vaginal sweating (I use this term because physiologically the process is akin to sweating and serves functions other than lubrication) and in the men erection of the penis. Almost all men are aware of their own erections, but many women are unaware of their vaginal sweating. If one must look for equivalent processes in male and female, then it is vaginal sweating, not erection of the clitoris, that is the counterpart of erection of the penis. The clitoris becomes engorged with blood and may also enlarge, but in most women it does not become erect. These are not processes that are usually under voluntary control. Wishing does not necessarily bring them about or cause them to go away.

Sometimes the cause of sexual arousal seems obvious — reading an erotic novel, seeing or being with an attractive or sexually provocative person, viewing a sexually explicit video. But often the upsurge of desire cannot be pinned down to any obvious stimulus. It is as likely to happen during periods of boredom and inactivity as during passionate involvement with another person. But whatever the psychological or physical stimulus, desire and excitement persist only as long as the stimulus persists. Many a sexual episode falters at this initial stage. A very complex interaction between two people is involved. Difficulties at this stage ('Never interested', 'Can't get it up', 'Never wet enough') consume large amounts of personal introspection and therapy time. But if excitement continues to mount, the plateau phase of sexual response is reached.

As arousal proceeds, interest focuses on the breasts and genitals, areas that are highly sensitive and responsive.

Plateau phase

During this phase the penis becomes more rigid and deepens in colour, the scrotal muscles tighten, drawing the testicles closer to the body, and the testicles themselves increase to two or even three times their usual size. Sometimes a few drops of fluid (called 'love drops' by some) appear at the meatus or opening of the penis. This fluid is produced by the bulbourethral glands at the base of the penis and it cleanses and lubricates the urethra (the duct inside the penis) in readiness for ejaculation.

In women, excitement first causes the labia to swell. The inner lips double or triple in thickness, become reddish-purple, and sometimes draw apart. The vagina, in addition to sweating more copiously, flushes deep pink or red. Its inner two-thirds balloons while its outer third narrows and tightens (Masters and Johnson coined the term 'orgasmic platform' to describe this region of narrowing and tightening). The clitoris also becomes extra sensitive and, in a seemingly protective reflex, withdraws under its hood. In almost all women and about 1 in 2 men nipple erection occurs during the plateau phase. The pigmented areas around each nipple, the areolae, become larger as the breasts themselves become engorged with blood; this is especially marked in women who have never given birth. As sexual tension increases from excitement to plateau stage, the

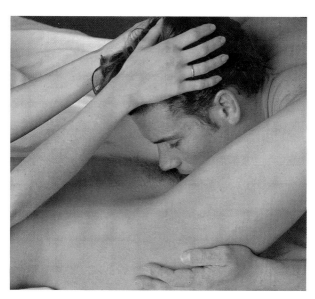

Cunnilingus, oral stimulation of the vulva, clitoris, and entrance to the vagina, is a form of foreplay that many couples enjoy.

nipples appear to retract — this is because the breasts swell slightly around them. Also, about 7 in 10 women and 1 in 4 men develop a transient rash-like flush across the chest, breasts, back, and neck. This event was one of the striking discoveries of Masters and Johnson. Although easily seen under good lighting conditions, it is not difficult to understand why generations of lovers should have failed to notice it.

Many other physiological events — a general increase in muscle tension, a pounding heart, and faster, deeper breathing — also accompany the advancing plateau phase. Tension becomes particularly noticeable in the thighs and buttocks, around the mouth, and in the strap muscles on either side of the neck. These signs of apparent stress, disconcerting sometimes to an inexperienced partner, mark a build up of sexual tension and a reaching for release. Taken together, they usually signify 'yes' in answer to the question 'Are you ready?'

To return the compliment and add a different pleasure to the experience, she may fellate him, taking his penis into her mouth. Again, this is a play that both can enjoy.

Orgasm

If sexual activity continues, a point of no return is reached and orgasm (also referred to as climaxing or 'coming') follows. Orgasm is, in simple terms, the rapid reaching of peak sexual tension closely followed by its rapid release. Orgasm may be subjectively experienced as many different things (as a 'symphony', as an 'explosion', as a 'tidal wave'), but the physical events that constitute it are much more down to earth.

Orgasm in a man is typically accompanied by ejaculation, the spasm-like release of sperm and semen. Ejaculation is not the same as orgasm. Usually they occur together, but either can be experienced without the other necessarily occurring. Just before ejaculation a man usually passes the point of no return: he knows he will climax and can no longer prevent it. He tends to thrust vigorously and deeply, and tightens the muscles in his thighs and buttocks; other muscles may also contract spasmodically. His breathing becomes laboured and irregular. With orgasm and ejaculation he will probably reflexly withdraw his pelvis and halt his thrusting movements. Ejaculation may or may not be accompanied by sounds, but it usually involves a brief loss of awareness, *la petite mort* (little death) as the French call it (just enough time for an unscrupulous prostitute or her accomplice to pilfer a wallet!).

Orgasm in women is more variable both in frequency and in its physical manifestations. Most men regularly experience orgasm during coitus and tend to worry if they do not. But for women things are not so reliable. Only about half the women interviewed in various studies report regularly experiencing orgasm during coitus; between 10 and 25 per cent of adult women have orgasm rarely or never, and between 75 and 90 percent experience it irregularly. Many women also pass a point of inevitability, when they sense they will go to orgasm. During orgasm, the orgasmic platform of the vagina contracts, the contractions being few or many, weak or strong, and tailing off in frequency and intensity. In both men and women, orgasm also involves contractions of the anal sphincter, the ring of muscle around the anus.

A normal uterus — one that is not bent forwards (anteflexed) or backwards (retroflexed) — has a complicated response to sexual stimulation. Some women find stimulation of the cervix, the neck of the uterus, by a finger or penis arousing and pleasurable; others find it uncomfortable, even painful. During arousal the cervix pulls up into pelvis, tenting away from the vagina. As a result, the floor of the vagina (the posterior wall) changes shape, forming a shallow basin which can retain a small pool of semen. The cervix becomes fully pulled up during the plateau phase and remains there during orgasm, but the mechanism for

*Orgasm is the sudden release
of tensions built up through
the arousal and plateau phase,
a moment of complete abandon.
The amount of noise and
commotion that goes with it
varies, but noisier does not
necessarily mean better. Couples
should experiment with different
positions to see how they prefer
to bring it about, simultaneously
or sequentially...or not at all.*

this elevation is not known. During orgasm the body of the uterus contracts rhythmically and these movements may persist during resolution. Some women are not aware of these contractions, some feel them as cramps, and others find them highly erotic and pleasurable. Interestingly, uterine orgasm is more often reported during intense masturbation than during coitus, but is not felt to be as satisfying.

The signs of orgasm in women are richly varied. Some women have a response similar to that of the typical male described above — vigorous movements of the pelvis, muscular tension in the thighs and buttocks, laboured breathing. Others may show a more explosive response, with a great deal of involuntary movement and noise. They may laugh or cry uncontrollably, or look and sound as if they are in pain (a very small number of men do this too). This can be frightening, even embarrassing, when it is first encountered, but it is quite normal.

Recent controversy has focused on the question of whether female ejaculation occurs. Some women have reported a heavy loss of fluid from the vagina or urethra at orgasm. Female ejaculation is linked to the existence of a sensitive G spot, described on page 50.

For perhaps a majority of women the plateau phase is prolonged and orgasm is not explosive or obvious, not so much a distinct climax as a crossing over into a more relaxed state. For those men and women who show it, the skin flush is most developed at orgasm. In some women climax occurs with little noticeable movement or noise. But in neither sex is a great expenditure of energy — scratching, writhing, loud cries — any measure or guarantee of satisfaction. An orgasm with little noise may be just as satisfying as one with a lot. Again, the best way to be sure that a partner feels satisfied is to ask.

While both sexes usually feel very positive about the experience of orgasm, the answer to the question 'Did you come?' is not always physically obvious, even to the most attentive and loving partner. That is why it is helpful to establish a convention whereby each tells the other, verbally or otherwise, whether climax has occurred and whether to continue. A gentle kiss on the ear or eyelid is one way.

Orgasm, like other phases of the sexual response cycle, is a highly individual expression. Almost all men (between 90 and 98 per cent depending on the survey) masturbate at some time from early adolescence onward and therefore recognize the sensation of orgasm, or at least the fluid that accompanies ejaculation. Fewer women masturbate (between 30 and 60 per cent), and few do it as regularly as men. They, and also those women who have quite dramatic orgasms, may find it difficult to accept that some women do not easily reach climax or even know when they have.

The resolution phase can be a time of great tenderness and closeness. The urge to sleep is a purely physiological reaction to the release of tension. Rather than being seen as an emotional 'switching off', as a rejection of intimacy once the peak moment is over, it should perhaps be seen as a mark of trust.

Resolution phase

In general, the time immediately following orgasm is experienced differently by men and women. Men tend to become passive and refractory (unresponsive to further sexual stimuli), and the penis becomes limp as blood flows away from the pelvis and muscle tension decreases. This is the resolution phase of the cycle, a more or less rapid return to physical and emotional rest, expressed most directly in the urge to sleep. Some women also return quickly to rest and sleep, but few go through the refractory period that is typically part of the male experience. Most women remain sexually responsive during the resolution phase. Some are still sexually excited, invite more stimulation, and climax again before returning to a state of rest. It is this phenomenon, a second orgasm reached without returning to a pre-plateau level of arousal, that is somewhat sensationally labelled 'multiple orgasm'. It is a feature of the sexual response cycle of between 10 and 15 per cent of women investigated, but of fewer than 1 per cent of men. The reason for this disparity is not understood, but it most certainly involves something built into the central nervous system. Both men and women have reason to desire males to be able to maintain sexual interest and erection, so social forces favour multiple male orgasm, but biology seems to have decreed otherwise.

Occasionally resolution may be delayed due to prolonged tension in the genital and pelvic area and uncomfortable or painful retention of engorged blood. This is known as 'blue balls' or 'love nuts' in men and 'lower back pain' or 'pelvic congestion' in women. Re-engaging in sexual activity (coitus or masturbation) may achieve the desired release, but the problem does resolve itself in time.

Differences in response

If the duration, intensity, and psychological significance of each phase of the sexual response cycle were the same for both sexes, and for people of different temperaments, there would probably be very little sexual frustration. But they are not the same. Not being able to engage a partner in willing erotic arousal — not being able to stimulate or experience desire — is as frustrating as a plateau phase that is too short or too long, or an orgasm that never materializes. Some people prefer to prolong the arousal phase, others the plateau. Some find the afterglow of the resolution phase more satisfying than the tension of plateau or the brevity of orgasm.

Even for those who regularly experience it, orgasm occasionally fails to occur. More men than women express frustration about not climaxing, but then, for many women, physical and emotional satisfaction does not seem to be as closely linked with orgasm. Coitus can be deeply satisfying even if orgasm does not occur; the pleasure comes from the warmth, the trust and the sharing, from the knowledge of being sexually desirable and adept at pleasing another. If one never experiences orgasm, so what? It is unhelpful to focus on orgasm to the exclusion of all else. Nevertheless the absence of it can undermine a relationship and become a source of serious worry and low self-esteem.

Orgasm has, rightly or wrongly, great significance for most people. If orgasm rarely or never occurs, for whatever reason, sexual activities are frequently accompanied by feelings of sin, guilt, or anger, particularly when the individual concerned has had a strict religious upbringing. For some, the failure to experience orgasm is not the result of inhibition but of physiological ignorance; not knowing their potential for orgasm, they cannot aim for the sensation. For others, orgasm is within reach but they forbid themselves to reach it; they see it as an unacceptable loss of control. There are also those who desperately want to climax and get quite close but somehow never reach the final release; in such situations a trained therapist can usually help.

Because climax is not a totally reliable response and because its desirability is greatly stressed, orgasm is often faked. With women less likely to climax than men, more faking is done by women, often with the most loving and altruistic of motives, but occasionally to terminate an encounter that has lost interest. It is sometimes said that the reason so many women fake orgasm is because so many men fake foreplay, the implication being that men ought to take more time and pay more attention to 'preparing' their partners for orgasm. Perhaps women should supply their partners with more information about what they need to become fully aroused.

Faking orgasm raises various emotional and ethical questions. Both partners' egos are involved. Lack of orgasm can be interpreted as sexual incompetence, fatigue, lack of interest, or lack of responsiveness. Faking salvages the feelings of one or both partners, but it also sweeps important issues under the mattress. If you think about it, one of the partners is not given the chance of adapting to the other, of helping him or her to reach orgasm. If partners cannot be honest in this most intimate of moments, how firmly grounded is the rest of the relationship? According to some therapists, faking may further block the orgasm response of the faker, making orgasm less likely on future occasions.

On the other hand, total honesty in sex is rare and not always the kindest course. Disparity in the sexual response cycles of men and women means that compromise, mixing honesty and candour with tact and practicality, is often necessary. Faking once in a while is a compromise. Perhaps it should be thought of as good manners rather than as a betrayal of self or partner.

Synchronizing responses

In a casual encounter, when partners find the pace and enthusiasm of their sexual responses mismatched, neither may feel a sense of failure ('It's just one of those things' or 'It never works out the first time'). But for a young married couple who find the same mismatches occurring night after night, the stresses may spread, with bitterness, blame, and frustration ultimately shadowing their love and commitment. In the West we like to think we live in sexually sophisticated times. Nevertheless sexual topics are still surrounded with a great deal of uncertainty, prejudice, and mythology, and this has not changed much over the past decade even with the more open discussion of sex engendered by AIDS.

One stumbling block to couples trying to solve their sexual problems is that while there may be sympathy between partners, there may not be empathy, the ability to stand in the other person's shoes.

A dramatic change in sexual response is usually temporary. Commonly, it is closely tied to other demanding or unexpected experiences — a new job, a problem with a relative, financial trouble, a change in the fundamental relationship between the people involved. There may be a downward slide, with accompanying depression, or an acceleration of

An Indian woodcarving depicting an extremely athletic version of kakila, *the '69' position, involving simultaneous cunnilingus and fellatio. The* Kama Sutra *comments: 'So immensely pleasurable is* kakila *[the Crow] that for its sake many courtesans have deserted respectable virtuous citizens and taken up with slaves, barbers,* mahouts *[elephant drivers], and other low types.' According to Juvenal and Martial the Romans called men who indulged in cunnilingus 'crows'.*

interest with manic overtones. There may be an undiagnosed medical problem, or a fear that is being repressed.

One or both partners can take steps to make sure the culprit is not medical. If the reason is psychological, it can often be solved by communication, however difficult this may be initially. For some people the advice of a counsellor, as a concerned but not emotionally involved mediator, may point to new avenues of mutual exploration. The deeper the bond between partners, the easier it is to restore or create satisfactory sexual dialogue, although if therapy fails the disappointment will be deeper.

The significance of orgasm

There is no universally accepted pace for sexual activity, any more than there is a standard frequency. Simultaneous orgasm is only one route to shared and equal pleasure, but it is an ambition that preys on some people's minds if it does not occur. In fact the chances are quite high that simultaneous orgasm will *not* occur. For example, most women require deep, forceful penetration and sustained clitoral stimulation to reach orgasm, but when men reach orgasm they usually stop thrusting and withdraw pelvic pressure. After orgasm many women are still mentally and physically ready for more sex play, but their male partners may not wish to be touched, at least for a while, and may want to go to sleep.

At the turn of the century dominant medical opinion was that female orgasm was unhealthy and improper and that women were physically and psychologically incapable of enjoying coitus. As long as sex remained something that men *did to* women, the concept of premature ejaculation was unknown. Indeed, from the woman's point of view, the sooner ejaculation occurred the better, since coitus was something to be endured rather than enjoyed. But as the sexual status of women changed, it began to be accepted that women could and did enjoy coitus. Even so, they were not credited with having an independent capacity for orgasm. This was something that a man *did for* a woman; her pleasure was within his gift.

Western society has now arrived at the concept that sex is something men and women *do together* and that both are responsible for their own and each other's pleasure. Today a man must restrain his own orgasm until he can be sure of satisfying his partner as well. But it is just as logical to ask a women to speed up as to ask a man to slow down. The perceived importance of simultaneous orgasm is the direct result of social pressures towards equality of the sexes. This new mutual responsibility is not universally accepted or welcome. It has created higher expectations, a felt obligation to be sexually adept, a demoralizing perception of 'failure' on the part of one or both partners if sex is not a delightful experience. The issues here are those of symbolism and egotism. For some partners there is a shared sense of pride and pleasure, for those less lucky a feeling of inadequacy or disappointment ('Am I doing something wrong or is he/she?').

If a couple reaches the stage where coitus becomes a prolonged struggle for the impossible, it may be better to abandon the goal of orgasm together in favour of orgasm separately. Oral sex or mutual masturbation may bring the long awaited reward, even though the symbolism of coitus is lost. The very fact of knowing that there are various stages in the sexual response cycle and that each individual may variably prefer any phase opens up the possibility of more leisurely, less performance-oriented sex play. When a sufficient level of excitement has been built up through oral sex or mutual masturbation, coitus can be resumed, or, by mutual consent, bypassed altogether and orgasm brought about by any other pleasurable means, or left until another time. As when dining, it is common courtesy to stay with your partner until he or she has finished. The enjoyment of travelling can surpass the pleasure of arrival.

Different kinds of orgasm?

Is there a difference between so-called vaginal, clitoral, and total orgasm? The answer to this very much depends on whom you ask. One seldom hears the question: Is there a difference between a penile and a scrotal orgasm? What this reflects is a greater variety in the climax responses of women; some women can bring themselves, or be brought, to orgasm by stimulating the breasts, nipples, or urethra, or just by stroking the thighs. What really matters is that sexual partners should communicate their desires and pleasures so that peak moments, however achieved, should not remain elusive.

The original distinction between clitoral and vaginal orgasm came from Freud. He thought that as a woman matures psychosexually she shifts her attention from the clitoris, typically stimulated by masturbation, to the vagina, stimulated by coitus. Today, however, there is little support for the idea that one type of orgasm is more 'mature' than another. Physiologists tell us that the physiological response of orgasm is the same no matter how orgasm comes about. But the primary locus of the orgasm *sensation* varies from woman to women. For most, orgasm is felt most sharply in the clitoris or the vagina. If both clitoris and vagina are involved, which seems to be less common, the sensation is more diffuse, often accompanied by sensations of bodily heaving and holding the breath. Whether consciously felt or not, the rhythmic contractions of orgasm involve, to a greater or lesser degree, the clitoris, vagina, uterus, urethra, bladder, perineum, anus, rectum, and all the other soft tissues of the pelvis, as well as the muscles of respiration. Orgasm also affects heart rate, blood flow, and the whole nervous system.

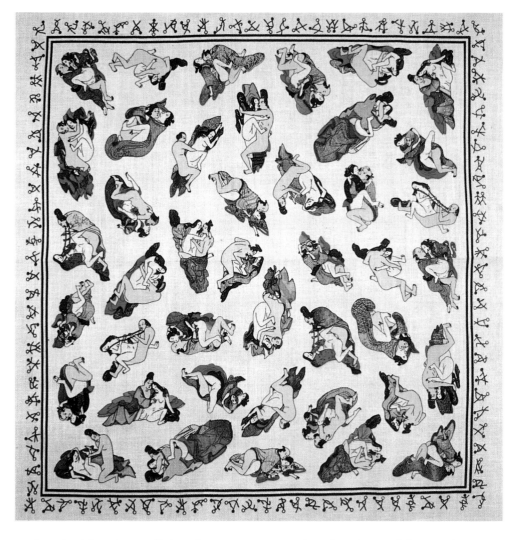

The quality of lovemaking, of the various phases of the sexual response cycle, can vary with the positions used for intercourse. In modern Japan it is not uncommon to give a handkerchief like this, depicting a variety of sexual postures, to newlyweds. At one time 'bridal books' were given instead.

But physiology is not all there is to orgasm, or to the other phases of the sexual response cycle. New ways of looking at the whole area of sexual response are now being called for, in which subjective measures are taken into account. Surveys and research have repeatedly shown that women rate affection and emotional communication as more important than orgasm in a sexual relationship. This being the case, as Leonore Tiefer, the well known sex therapist and researcher, points out, 'it denies women's voices entirely to continue to insist that sexuality is best represented by the universal "cycle of sexual response, with orgasm as the ultimate point in progression".' Sex therapists certainly hear more women complaining about the subjective quality of their experiences than about their bodily sensations.

In India, adepts of tantra and kundalini yoga maintain that coitus gives the greatest erotic pleasure when intromission (penetration) is maintained but orgasm is continually postponed, or even denied altogether; the practice is called *karezza* or *maithuna*. To have an orgasm without ejaculation is to reach nirvana, a high state of bliss.

Obviously the psychological component of orgasm is important because it influences how physiological events are felt and valued. For example, if a woman knows that masturbation is a more reliable means of reaching orgasm she may find difficulty climaxing during coitus or prefer non-coital activities. Loci and intensities of orgasm undoubtedly vary from person to person, and indeed in the same individual on different occasions, but if you believe that one sort of orgasm is more significant or satisfying than another you may, in a sense, begin to narrow your routes to sexual enjoyment. Many people, men as well as women, do indeed say that orgasms brought on by coitus, masturbation, or oral-genital activities feel different. But one can feel great psychological satisfaction whether orgasm occurs or not. Vice versa, physical satisfaction is no guarantee of emotional satisfaction.

Orgasms during sleep are much more common in males than females, typically starting in puberty and occurring most frequently during adolescence. They may continue for many years into adulthood. Generally 'wet dreams' — ejaculation, with orgasm, during dreaming sleep — are more common in single men, which suggests that they may be related to a man's general level of sexual activity. Even so, about 50 per cent of married men say they have wet dreams. Usually these cease by the age of 50 or so. Women can also have nocturnal orgasms, with profuse sweating of the vagina.

Periods of arousal in sleep usually occur during rapid eye movement (REM) sleep, which coincides with periods of dreaming. Even if arousal does not end in orgasm, which it often does not, erection and vaginal wetting take place. The content of the dreams that accompany nocturnal arousal is usually erotic.

Age-related changes

What happens to sexual response as we get older? Almost every mental and physical aspect of each phase of the sexual response cycle changes with age, but the changes are slow and subtle, and vary according to the constitution, health, and mental outlook of the person concerned. With a receptive and active sexual partner, the changes will probably be slower. If sexual opportunities are infrequent, they may be quicker.

Until quite recently it was 'common knowledge' that women past the menopause and men over 50 lost interest in sex. This reflected the convention that tied sex to child-bearing capacity. Until the 1960s sex in later life was a subject for ridicule, carrying the image of the 'dirty old man' and the frustrated old woman. Somehow the idea of senior citizens indulging in sex damaged the dignity that the elderly are supposed to have. Young people are often reluctant to see their parents or grandparents as sexual beings: 'My mother wouldn't do that! And certainly not my grandma.'

Fortunately, as discussion of sexual topics became freer during the 1960s, the assumption that old age is non-sexual or neuter was exposed as a myth. Many researchers reported that while ageing is accompanied by a general decline in frequency of sexual activities, much depends on previous experience, current attitudes, and aspirations for the future. One group of researchers found that 15 per cent of those in their study actually increased their sexual activity as they aged. It seems, in general, that those who arrive early at the party stay late, and those who come late leave early!

There are also psychosocial factors to be considered. After the age of 60 the probability of losing a lifelong partner rises sharply, and the chances of finding another dwindle equally sharply. Interest in sexual activity also diminishes. In a survey conducted by G. Bachman and associates in the United States 32 per cent of women over 60 cited their partner's loss of interest in sex as the reason for their own celibacy, and 25 per cent said that sexual activity had ceased because of their own loss of interest. Also, from other studies in the United States, and in Sweden and Belgium, it seems that couples who are financially better off maintain the sexual patterns of their youth more successfully than those who are poorer.

Age-related changes seem mainly to affect the timing and strength of physical responses. In men, as the years advance, testosterone levels decrease, and this is correlated with a marked decline in sexual activity and capacity during the seventh decade. Erection is slower, coitus less urgent, and orgasm delayed. This more leisurely pace is sometimes seen as an advantage. Each phase and mechanism in the sexual response changes at its own rate. The intensity of orgasm is first to weaken and if one lives long enough it will fade completely.

Erectile ability is next to decline. In some men all physical responses cease for days at a time, as if in an extended refractory period. The ability to be mentally aroused lasts longest, but the stimulus may have to be more extreme than in youth.

Unfortunately, women have to contend with more physical changes as they age than men. This is largely due to the rapid decrease in female hormones at the menopause, which usually occurs between the ages of 45 and 55. This can cause loss of the firm fat pads on the pubis, hips, and breasts, thinning and loss of suppleness of the walls of the vagina, less copious vaginal wetting (infection and certain drugs can also cause dryness), and pain during coitus (although this can usually be overcome by using a lubricating gel). Somewhere between 30 and 50 per cent of postmenopausal women experience one or more such changes. There is also evidence that low oestrogen levels decrease touch sensitivity. Arousal and orgasm also develop more slowly and occur less often. This does not necessarily reflect lack of sexual interest. Indeed, some women find that relief from the burdens of work, family, and home-keeping cause an upsurge of sexual interest in late middle age. Also, an increasing number of women are choosing hormone replacement therapy (maintenance doses of oestrogen, progesterone, and testosterone) as a means of staving off the menopause and preventing osteoporosis.

Partners who face ageing realistically and adjust accordingly find no diminished pleasure in sex, even if frequency and vigour decrease. They are free of the fear of pregnancy, have more time and more privacy than when they were young, and do not expect *grand prix* performance, all of which make for greater relaxation, tenderness, considerateness, and pleasure in all forms of sex play and close body contact.

There are many ways to enjoy a partner's body, pleasure onself, and bring both to peak sensation. As both heterosexual and homosexual couples prove, a penis fits in places other than a vagina, and is not needed for stimulation of the clitoris. For many couples, non-coital techniques — oral-genital sex, simultaneous or not, for example — become those most preferred. It is also true that sexual pleasures are heavily dependent on past experiences and fantasies, that is on the organ that lies between our ears, not between our legs. Indeed the brain is the most sexy organ of all. It is the total person, and not the genital region alone, that makes sexual response meaningful and special.

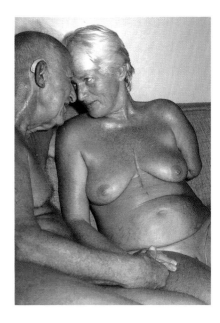

When the feelings are right, age and handicaps are no hindrance to sexual expression.

Chapter 6

Growing up

The declaration 'It's a boy!' or 'It's a girl!' is the first public acknowledgement of a process of sexual development that starts at conception and affects the individual for the rest of his or her life. From birth every child progresses through cultural and sexual training to a maturation at once predictable and unique. It is predictable to the extent that every individual is a product of the forces of family, peers, culture, and biology, yet unique in that these forces are variable in their strength and sometimes conflicting.

In open societies many different sex and gender roles, and many modes of erotic expression, are possible. With love, support, and guidance most boys and girls grow up to be self-accepting adults able to meet the demands of a complex society. Yet many families, societies, and institutions do not allow free choice and stifle individual expression. 'Deviance' may be severely repressed rather than understood and accepted as 'variation'.

As adults we can look back through old photographs, remember childhood friends and games, and see the gradual development of our physical selves. It may be more difficult to recall childhood feelings or the many questions that occurred to us as we grew up. And perhaps we never were aware of some of the vital factors that gave us our sexual identity. After all, sexual development begins long before birth, and it is during gestation that some of the most critical forces make their play.

Inside the womb

Sex is determined at fertilization. The union of sperm and egg not only stamps the future individual as male (one X chromosome and one Y chromosome with one or more genes that will induce testes to develop) or female (two X chromosomes), but endows him or her with 22 other pairs of chromosomes containing half a million genes that will, like a computer program, influence the unfolding, maturation, and even the ageing of that individual.

Both male and female embryos appear similar until about the seventh intrauterine week. Then a series of dramatic events takes place. Between the seventh and twelfth weeks the embryo becomes a foetus, with visible and increasingly distinctive male or female characteristics. Internally a set of testes and male organs, or ovaries, uterus and associated female organs, develop; externally these are matched by a penis and scrotum or a clitoris and labia.

These changes are brought about by the organizing influence of hormones released from the gonads of the foetus. If the foetus is male, the gonads release androgens, male-fostering substances. An absence of androgens, rather than the presence of female hormones, at this critical period will set the foetus on the road to development as a female. The female gonads do not produce oestrogens at this stage so are not comparably involved in the differentiation process. This implies that all foetuses are basically female unless the presence of androgens determines otherwise. Regardless of chromosomal sex, a foetus will develop as a female if gonads are absent or if they do not produce enough androgens, or if, by some biological quirk, the foetus does not respond properly to androgens. In real life it seems that Adam is created from Eve, rather than vice versa.

Sex hormones are known to have dual action. They bring about the foetal changes I have just described and later the changes that mark puberty, but they also sensitize the individual to future sex-linked influences, organizing his or her body so that it is receptive to them.

From the moment of birth a child is labelled 'male' or 'female' on the basis of his or her anatomy, and treated accordingly. Displays of affection towards boy children are often much more boisterous than towards girl children. Most adults are not sure how to behave with a baby who is not obviously a boy or a girl.

Sensitization occurs most markedly in the womb. During gestation, androgens make the foetus responsive to adult beard growth and muscle development; their absence makes the foetus responsive to breast enlargement by oestrogens; at the same time females are given the pattern of the later reproductive cycle (males do not develop such a cycle).

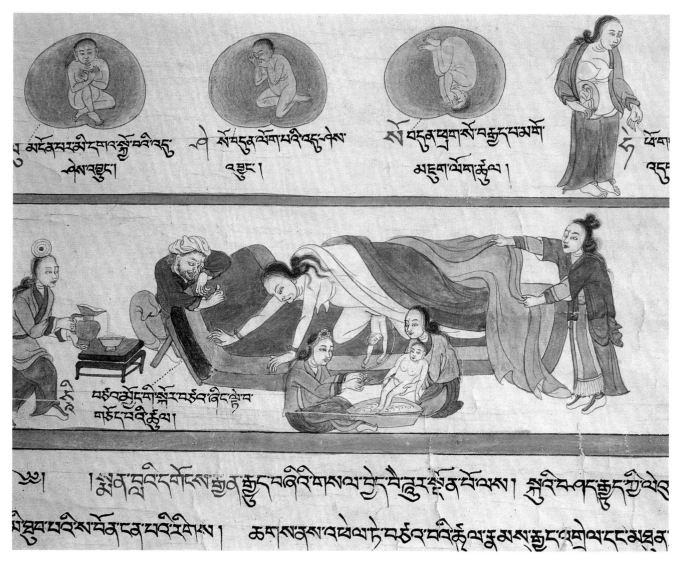

Detail from a Tibetan medical scroll. In Buddhism of course every birth is a rebirth, a return to a cycle of existence that can only end when the individual, by acquiring merit through right thoughts and actions, merges with the universal spirit. The path towards maleness or femaleness begins during the seventh week in utero; until then the foetus is not obviously male or female.

Hormone influences during gestation also affect future responses to erotic stimuli and bias the way the individual will interact with social experience and the way in which sexual behaviour will manifest itself. That is not to say that behaviour is preordained, merely that certain avenues of development are made less or more likely at this time. The opening or blocking of these avenues is closely related to future measures of masculinity or femininity.

Experiments with monkeys have shown that females given androgens at critical periods in their gestation show more masculine behaviour as juveniles and adults than their untreated sisters. They more often engage in rough-and-tumble and mounting displays. Among rat embryos, females nestled like peas in a pod between male embryos and therefore exposed to higher than normal androgen levels behave more like males than females when they reach adulthood. Females surrounded in the womb by other females show more female-like traits and fewer male-like traits when mature.

In humans, females exposed prenatally to male hormones (this can happen if their own or their mother's ovaries or adrenal glands produce too much androgen, for example) are often tomboyish. No matter how they are brought up, they show marked preferences for typical male careers and aspirations. They, more than the average female, enjoy working out of doors or at physically demanding jobs, and rarely look forward to having many children. Human males, if deprived of a normal prenatal androgen supply, are also significantly different from their peers in adolescence and adulthood; they tend to be less physically and sexually aggressive and are likely to be assessed as effeminate.

In humans all major visible changes in the genitals have occurred by the fourth foetal month. The remainder of gestation is essentially taken up with overall growth.

Sexual development

Photographs and ultrasound 'pictures' taken within the uterus show that male foetuses have regular and repeated erections; it is assumed that females have the capacity for vaginal lubrication. Certainly both erection and lubrication are known capabilities from birth onwards, and frequently occur spontaneously. This does not imply that infants are erotic in the same ways that adults are, only that the physiological mechanisms that are part of adult sexual expression exist at birth.

How these capacities are influenced and how sexual behaviour is shaped are matters of passionate scientific and political debate. Many people think that sexual behaviour can or should be carefully shaped and controlled; others believe it is already subject to too many controls, many of them imposed for no better reason than that they are traditional or just socially convenient.

Each individual, as he or she grows up, responds to a myriad of interacting biological, cultural, and social factors. This interaction leads to immense variety, in attitudes and behaviour. However, the individual will always be biased towards a particular sex because of the genetic and hormonal influences that operate before birth and continue operating until death; his or her sexuality will also be biased, by the sexual mores of the environment he or she grows up in. In Western society, for example, a boy who shows traits generally regarded as feminine is likely to be the target of more criticism and ridicule than a girl who acts like a boy. Yet in some societies, among certain American Indian tribes such as the Koniag, the Sioux (of *Dances With Wolves* fame), and the Zuni of New Mexico, and among the Siberian Chukchee, effeminacy in a man was traditionally taken to be a sign of extraordinary powers. Such men, usually referred to as *berdache*, were often looked upon as medicine men (women too could be *berdache* if they displayed what the tribe considered to be significant masculine traits).

Growing up sexually involves more than physical development. In the fullest sense it means evolving as a socially functioning man or woman. The fact that identical twins have much in common physically and mentally even when brought up separately is often cited as evidence that maturation proceeds largely in accordance with biology. Others believe that sexual development proceeds largely in accordance with social forces, with children naturally assimilating the characteristics and attitudes of their elders and peers. Both points of view are correct up to a point, but it is not really a question of nature *or* nurture. To look most meaningfully at physical, socio-sexual, and erotic development, and at the development of sexual identity, we must recognize that innate factors and learned factors operate simultaneously and interdependently. I call these 'interaction effects', the dual influences of society and experience interacting with biological predisposition.

Imagine for a moment that you are a paediatric surgeon and you are presented with a newborn baby in whom the genitals are ambiguous — no vagina or penis, or apparently both. How would you advise the parents? Would the child have a greater chance of happiness being brought up as a boy or as a girl? Or suppose a four-year-old boy came into the emergency ward with his penis completely cut off because of a playground accident or an attack by a deranged adult. Would growing up without a penis be so difficult that it would be better to bring him up as a girl and give him appropriate surgical and hormone treatment? Or would you consider his four years of life as a boy the most crucial factor, in which case it might be better to help him adjust to the loss of his penis? Such cases are not exactly common, but they force us to carefully consider what the major influences on sexual development are.

In surgical terms, it is easier to fashion a functional vagina and female genitals than a functional penis. So to some extent anatomy is used to determine whether an infant is assigned as a boy or a girl. This is the simplest course, though not always the best. However there have been cases of infants having female internal organs but externally appearing more male than female. If these children are reared as boys, physiological and psychological problems appear at puberty when secondary female characteristics — periods, for example — declare themselves. The reverse situation, where the internal organs are male and the infant is raised as a girl because the genitals are ambiguous or female-like, also has its problems. In one spectacular case presented on the BBC and known worldwide in the scientific literature, a male infant whose penis has been accidently burned off was raised as a girl from the age of 18 months onwards. Despite all efforts by family and therapists to help him adjust, he rebelled; as soon as he was able, he sought reconstructive surgery. He now lives as a male.

The male and female brain

Some 40 years ago most American psychologists believed that infants were sexually neutral at birth and could be conditioned to behave as male or female, if necessary in conflict with biology and anatomy. It was also thought that the experience of the first three or four years of life set an ineradicable pattern. This view has now been modified to incorporate a substantial degree of biological predisposition. Acceptance of interaction effects between biology and environment is now general among the scientific community worldwide.

No human being is neutral and without sexual direction at birth. There is no evidence that one can take an individual who is unequivocally male at birth, bring him up as a female, and produce someone who as an adult behaves like a woman. Nor is there any evidence for the converse, bringing up a female to behave like a man. I suggest that there are, from conception onwards, chromosomal and endocrine influences on the nervous system that will manifest themselves no matter how the individual is reared. I suspect it has something to do with the differential development of the two hemispheres of the brain, and the critical timing of this development.

Each of us has a left side of the brain which is verbal, logical, and concerned with imposing order and sequence on experiences, and a right side which is more concerned with emotions, impressions, and pattern recognition. In most of us both sides work in synchrony, but there is also clinical evidence that males and females use different parts of the brain in different ways. For instance, the loci for many functions seem more widespread in females than in

A four-year-old Vietnamese girl cares for her baby brother in a refugee camp in Hong Kong. Is the propensity to nurture programmed into the female brain? Among boys the inclination to play with weapons is more or less universal. Is this also a product of early neural patterning?

males. This is an advantage in some types of surgery, where loss of a particular area of cortex is compensated for by similar function in adjacent areas; in men, loss of a particular area tends to have more drastic effects. The number of nerve fibres connecting the left and right hemispheres of the brain, and the number of synapses between the two halves, are also more numerous in females.

On the grounds that most males in most societies show behaviour rather more obviously associated with the left side of the brain than the right, one can hypothesize that in XY (male) foetuses the left side is imbued with an essential 'maleness', albeit in primitive form. The lessons learned in childhood resonate with this basic predisposition and the individual develops as a male. Similarly, in a female foetus the right side of the brain may carry a primitive 'femaleness'; this too would be developed by upbringing. Most of us develop comfortably using both sides of our brain, utilizing or ignoring parts of our sexual inheritance according to our life experiences. This is still a hypothesis, however. Some researchers argue that it is experience or behaviour that patterns neuronal circuitry rather than vice versa. There are some data that support this when it comes to development of parts of the cortex, but the evidence is scant for this being a major mechanism by which male-female differences develop. These seem to be rooted in the hypothalamus, limbic system, and more primitive areas of the nervous system, areas associated with sexual identity, sexual orientation, reproduction, and basic survival mechanisms. The cortex is the part of the nervous system most susceptible to change by interaction with the environment, especially the social environment, the brain stem least so. Nevertheless there is a continuous swapping of information between higher and lower brain centres; every second of our lives many millions of signals pass between them.

The conflict that occurs in transsexuals — who are convinced that they are trapped inside a body of the wrong sex — may be due to a conflict between those parts of cortex that agree with how the world views genital anatomy and those parts of the brain (probably the hypothalamus and limbic system) responsible for sexual identity. This mismatch might occur if the timing of biological, neurological, or endocrine development was out of phase at a crucial early stage.

Sexual behaviour in infants and children

It is conventional wisdom, but wrong, that infants and children are asexual unless given encouragement by adults. On the contrary, they possess a sexuality that is quite independent of adults. Only recently have researchers begun to explore the subject, and a lot of embarrassment still attaches to it. It is significant, for example, that Freud was castigated more for his courageous attempts to understand childhood sexuality than for any other facet of his work. Even today, childhood sexuality is almost a taboo subject for research or neutral discussion.

Genital and erotic behaviour on the part of infants and children is not allowed in most Western homes, and so it becomes private, secret, hidden, and undiscussed. By word and deed children learn that such activities — going to the toilet, for example — are to be concealed. Discussion of them is limited, evasive, and privileged. Games like 'Mummies and Daddies' or 'You show me yours and I'll show you mine' are played in secret. Like the bulk of the iceberg, direct sexual expression exists with great force and substance beneath the surface of accepted behaviours.

In the United States, Alfred Kinsey and his colleagues recorded what is widely accepted as the most complete set of data prior to 1950 concerning normal sexual behaviour. These records, and some more recent reports from the United States and from Norwegian, British, and Israeli researchers, show that sexual expression by pre-pubertal children in modern industrial societies is common, despite sanctions against it. From early childhood to puberty, sexual activity is largely clandestine.

Little girls and boys very obviously flirt with each other, without any encouragement from adults. Romantic attachments before the age of six are quite common.

Different cultures see masturbation differently. The message in this Japanese advertisement for spa holidays is 'Come and enjoy yourself'. The penis play is seen as unremarkable and of no consequence. Masturbation is a natural way for individuals to learn what gives them pleasure.

Most pre-school children spontaneously show interest in their own genitals. They study, fondle, and exhibit them, and seem to derive pleasure from playing with themselves. Among both sexes the penis seems to attract more attention than the vulva, perhaps because it is more visible. Playing tricks with a penis, such as getting it to erect, or urinating at targets, is seen as good fun. The penis is usually named ('wee-wee', 'willy', 'peter'), but the vulva or vagina is simply referred to as 'down there'; nevertheless the vagina is a source of wonder as a place to stick things in and the vulva is marvelled at as the magic fount of a flow of urine and, for those who are told, the even more magical place from which babies come.

Despite the obvious physicality of a boy's penis, it is girls more often than boys who first investigate their genitals and spontaneously learn to masturbate. As children grow older, the frequency and duration of such activity increases. At puberty boys learn about masturbation from their peers and more than 9 out of 10 have started to masturbate by the time they enter adolescence. Numerous studies of female masturbation have been done among Western populations, but none has shown such a high occurence of self-stimulation.

Masturbation to orgasm is rarely reported in the first years of life, but genital play, obviously pleasurable, starts between 6 and 12 months of age in both boys and girls. By kindergarten age, masturbation for its own pleasure is not uncommon and is occasionally taken to orgasm.

One observant mother who frequently noticed her three-year-old masturbating recorded: 'Lying face down on the bed with her knees drawn up, she started rhythmic pelvic thrusts about one second or less apart. The thrusts were primarily pelvic with the legs tensed...in a smooth and perfect rhythm which was unbroken except for momentary pauses during which the genitalia were readjusted against the doll on which they were pressed...There were 44 thrusts in unbroken rhythm, a slight momentary pause...then 10 thrusts and then a cessation of all movement. There was marked concentration and intense breathing with abrupt jerks as orgasm approached. She was completely oblivious to everything...There was noticeable relief and relaxation after orgasm.'

Pelvic thrusting accompanies many instances of infant play and affection. Mutual kissing, cuddling, and stroking is common. Individual involvement is of course highly variable. In the industrial societies of the West there are marked class differences in the way parents deal with masturbation, working class or blue-collar parents being the most conservative. In general, in North America, Scandinavia, and Western Europe, it is becoming less common for middle or upper class parents to be upset by the fact that their child masturbates. Perhaps with some ambivalence, they are most likely to direct the child not to play with himself or herself in public. One large study of pre-adolescent masturbation by sociologist John Gagnon found that mothers are generally more liberal than fathers in this respect. Other studies, more recent, found that 85 per cent of adult males and females could recall some type of memorable sex play — from kissing and genital stimulation to playing prostitute and client — with peers between the ages of 6 and 12.

A wealth of data reveals that romantic attachments occur before the age of six. Coitus is rare, but coital play and mutual masturbation occur as part of many children's games, whether among children of the same or opposite sex. The scope and likelihood of all these behaviours increase as children approach puberty. Whether these activities are spontaneous experiments or attempts to copy adult models is not clear. Nor is it known to what degree children's erotic sensations and experiences are comparable with adults'. It does seem clear, however, that unless effective prohibitions against sexual behaviour are in force, 'adult sex behaviour rehearsal play', in the phrase coined by researchers John Money and Anka Erhardt, or 'species-typical behaviour', as Paul Okami calls it, is tolerated more often than not throughout the world.

Permissive and restrictive traditions

In some cultures social traditions have evolved that explicitly encourage the capacity of young children for sexual expression. The Muria, a non-Hindu tribal people of Central India, build *ghotuls*, sacred compounds in which toddlers and young children can become accustomed to social interaction. Sexual expression is not only allowed, it is expected. Boys and girls usually lose their virginity by the age of six, and certainly by eight. In some *ghotuls* children are arbitrarily paired off with many different partners to widen their sexual experience. Sexual involvement is not forced as part of an initiation rite, as it is in some other societies; rather it is seen as a natural unfolding of curiosity and learning.

The *ghotul* is not a form of marriage bureau. In fact marriage to a preferred *ghotul* partner is quite rare. As is common practice in India, marriages are arranged to suit parental

In the Southern Highlands of Papua New Guinea women and girls — and pigs — live apart from the men in special meri *houses. Sex segregation is part of the culture; there is no deliberate mixing of boys and girls as there is among the Muria.*

and family considerations. Among the Muria the concept of promiscuity does not exist and premarital pregnancy is rare, probably due to adolescent infertility (see page 90) and to early marriage. The Muria simply recognize that children are sexual beings and, in common with the large majority of non-industrial cultures, put sexual expression in its place as a natural and integral part of childhood. Nevertheless it is thought socially desirable that sexual experience and proficiency should be encouraged.

However the Muria are not unique in their permissiveness. Indeed cultures more permissive than our own are in the majority around the world, although their practices differ. Among the Chewa of Central Africa, children build huts outside the village where they 'play house'. This includes the exchange of sexual partners, and all such activities have parental approval. The Ila-speaking people of Zimbabwe give their young daughters small houses where they are encouraged and expected to entertain boys. The Ifugoro of the Philippines have dormitories for the unmarried, and frequent swapping of sex partners is encouraged.

In tourist-flooded Hawaii there are old-timers who remember being instructed by their elders in ways of pleasing a partner and achieving sexual satisfaction. The traditional way of preparing the penis for healthy sex and also for subincision (slitting the underside of the foreskin) was to blow into the foreskin so that it separated from the glans. This was done daily during infancy and several times a week until the age of six or seven, usually by an older female in the family. (Retracting the foreskin and washing the glans several times a week, as recommended by modern paediatricians, prevents phimosis and serves a function similar to blowing). Individuals I have interviewed tell me that blowing is still done, in secret because it is now against the law. Incidentally, traditional Hawaiian society had more taboos associated with food than with sex. Men and women could have sex together but not eat together. Men cooked with fire, women did not. Which goes to show that when it comes to sex, there are few 'natural' practices. Attitudes to what is natural are determined uniquely by the society one lives in.

Western societies, with the possible exception of Scandinavia and the Netherlands, are among the world's most sexually restrictive cultures. Eroticism and sexual expression among children are not supposed to exist, though everyone knows that they do. Any display of junior sexuality is looked on as deviant, shameful, even sinful. In the West our fear of social disapproval, and perhaps of punishment in a life hereafter, has been manipulated to prevent undesirable sexual behaviours. This repression is still dramatically apparent in some countries, in Ireland for example, where the injunctions of the Roman Catholic Church retain a great deal of force. Some 20 years ago anthropologist John Messenger and his wife reported on the sexual mores of a small Irish island community they called 'Inis Baeg'. The inhabitants of the island evinced no knowledge of such practices as tongue-kissing, cunnilingus, fellatio, or anything other than marital sex for the purpose of procreation. The island's priests threatened to put a curse on sexual wrongdoers and encouraged their parishioners to inform on each other. Even in 1992 a 14-year-old Irish girl, the victim of rape, was prevented from seeking abortion in England — an informant told the authorities of her intentions.

In some societies corporal and even capital punishment is used to keep sexual behaviour under control. In Islamic countries such as Saudi Arabia flogging is not uncommon for even minor infringements of sexual conventions. Women are still castigated for driving a car or not wearing the traditional *chadar*, or head covering. And no woman, unless she is on official business, may be seen in the company of any man who is not her husband or without a married couple present. A few years ago a Saudi princess was decapitated for having married without her father's permission. Women in Pakistan, Iraq, Iran, and other Muslim counties are still being stoned to death, the punishment decreed by Islamic law, for adultery. Even kissing one's spouse in public is considered offensive; foreign films and television programs are 'cleaned up' accordingly.

Let us remember, however, that even in Europe some forms of sexual behaviour were once punishable by death. In the Middle Ages adultery and prostitution were occasionally punished by burning at the stake. Even today, in some European countries, one can be imprisoned for foul language, indecency, and soliciting. In half the cantons of Switzerland cohabitation is illegal (according to British barrister Fenton Bressler, each year in the canton of St. Gallen alone at least a dozen unmarried couples are fined for living together).

Sexual activities between adults and children are considered particularly repellent among most restrictive societies. In the United States anyone convicted of sexual activities involving children, whether they are enjoyed by both parties or instigated by the child, is almost automatically labelled a 'child molester'. Such people are given long prison sentences, and spend most of their time in prison fearful of reprisals from other inmates and extra harassment from prison officials. In the United States, all states now have laws which make it mandatory to report any sexual contact, alleged or actual, between a minor and an adult. This has proved both good and bad, and certainly controversial. It has put a stop to many abusive situations, but it has also prevented abusers from seeking help and created conflict in the minds of those who want to help them. There is little professional agreement as to how to manage such situations for the best.

Forging sexual and gender identity

Depending upon the circumstances and the attitude of parents, a child's emerging sexuality may be seen as cute and appropriate or disgusting and threatening. Certain behaviours will be reinforced, others ignored or punished. Certain aspects of sexuality may become dormant or increasingly expressed, again depending upon the extent to which they are encourage or discouraged. Children whose sexual explorations are severely censored are more likely to become emotionally impoverished adults, handicapped in their general as well as their sexual relationships.

As outward sexual behaviour develops, private and personal aspects of sexuality also form. Between the age of two and six a child begins to express an inner awareness of being male or female. 'I'm a boy and I'm going to be like Daddy' or 'I'm a girl and I want to be like Mummy'. With or without parental encouragement, most children become very interested in exploring adult roles and activites. Games such as dressing up or playing Mummies and Daddies are routine. So is question-asking unless positively discouraged. Parents and society recognize that children need to ask questions, even if some are awkward to answer. Competing with or reinforcing these influences are children's personal experiences, and their observations of the behaviour of peers, parents, and others.

As the individual matures, he or she gradually becomes aware of how well or poorly he or she measures up to social expectations. But a child's sense of discomfort with the gender role imposed by society has to be extremely acute before it is expressed openly. As far as possible, he or she tries hard to please, and strives to reconcile his or her feelings with the actual situation. This is the time of life when 'modelling' is particularly noticeable. Boys want to do what their fathers or other adult males do, girls want to be like their mothers or other adult females.

While asserting the freedom to go topless, these women are just as likely as their more conventional sisters to treat sons and daughters differently. But the message implicit in their lack of self-consciousness will be learnt by their children. Censorious parental attitudes towards sex are far more damaging than openness and honesty.

While not necessarily expressed in behaviour until after puberty, a general sexual preference, an orientation toward males or females, also emerges around the age of five, six, or seven. Adult males who are homosexually oriented often recall being strongly attracted to other boys at around this age, and it is often during these early years that many people become aware of other sexual urges that fit or do not fit in with cultural expectations. Expression of these urges depends on whether society permits or represses them.

By the age of three, most children express a conviction of sexual identity which coincides with biological reality — males see themselves as boys growing into men and

females see themselves as girls growing into women. The social pressures reinforcing such convictions are immense. Every language has separate male and female grammatical conventions and many have separate vocabularies. For example, a Japanese man would use the word *boku* for 'I', whereas a woman would use *watakushi*; other words a man would use would also be more assertive and direct than a woman's. In many Thai expressions, women and men use different suffixes, the women's always more polite. This convention of feminine politeness and masculine directness is almost, if not completely, universal and is of course fostered where there is also segregation at school, at work, and in other areas of everyday life. This is particularly true in many Islamic and Asian societies which are homosocial yet heterosexual. Men and women live and work in separate spheres, coming together for non-sexual reasons only on certain occasions.

In most cultures the clothing worn by boys and girls differs from infancy onwards. The pink and blue colour convention in the West is well known, as is the rigid distinction (except in Scotland and Greece) that only girls wear skirts. Codes of dress at school and work, and uniforms of all kinds, reinforce these stereotypes.

In almost all cultures expectations for boys and girls are different. Boys are expected to be rough and tough, girls to be gentle and sweet. Traditionally, boys are expected to be seekers and doers, while girls are expected to be sought and have things done for them. Males are supposed to be aggressive and assertive, females passive and pacific. While there are cultural variations, these are the expectations that reign in the majority of societies studied, probably because they are biologically biased.

On the Masai Mara of Kenya and Tanzania adolescence is short. Youngsters are expected to start looking after cattle from the age of six or seven.

As children grow up, they learn which behaviours are appropriate for their sex. 'Appropriate' here does not mean desirable or best, but socially anticipated. Although one hears a lot about social expectations and gender roles changing, the changes may be more wished for than real. To quote just one study carried out in California in 1982: 'Despite current presumptions of equality, boys and girls at sixth grade levels still live in totally different worlds, with the classroom and television their only common experience.'

There is no evidence that things have changed. Indeed recent research comparing the way

in which 'feminist' and 'traditional' mothers bring up their children found that the former offer trucks, guns, and dolls equally to both boys and girls, but that neither group insists on their children making sex-typical choices — the children usually make such choices themselves. Both groups speak to boys and girls differently, and expect their aspirations and inclinations to be different.

However the divergent development of boys and girls comes about, it is a fact that by puberty individuals of both sexes are strongly aware of their sexual identity, aware of the behaviours expected of them, and aware of their preferences for relationships with the opposite or same sex. The experiences of puberty and adolescence will strongly influence how these feelings are expressed.

Puberty and adolescence

Both puberty and adolescence refer to extended periods of time rather than to abrupt changes. Puberty is a roughly three- to five-year span between the ages of 9 and 13 in girls and 10 and 15 in boys. During this period the mechanisms organized during gestation are activated toward adult functioning. This is most notable in the workings of the genitals and in sexual behaviour. During these years a constellation of biological processes moves into gear, usually culminating in reproductive capacity, symbolized by menstruation in girls and ejaculation in boys.

In many traditional societies menarche, or first menstruation, is marked by some sort of ceremony. The gorgeous headdress worn by this Balinese girl reflects the importance of the occasion.

While the biological events of puberty are more or less the same for youngsters all over the world, the cultural events that mark puberty vary enormously. Some societies go in for dramatic initiation rites for one or both sexes. Others, at least on the surface, make very little fuss. For some youngsters, puberty may come as a traumatic shock; among the Haviks of India or the Irish of 'Inis Baeg', for example, girls do not learn of menstruation until they start to bleed.

Adolescence is the transition phase between childhood and adulthood. In some societies, in the United States and Europe for example, the transition is protracted. Typically it extends over five years or so, during which the individual acquires the kind of education, training, and social experiences that will equip him or her for economic and social independence. In other societies, the transition is early and abrupt and the demands of adulthood immediate. In many societies marriage at puberty is the custom — Mahatma Gandhi was married at 12. The rigours and hardships of living north of the Arctic Circle or in the Amazonian jungle or the Sahel make it necessary for children to assume adult roles and tasks as quickly as possible. Even so, it is only during the last century or so that the luxury of a long adolescence has become the norm in the industrialized West.

Physical signs of puberty

Puberty first declares itself as disproportionate growth in various parts of the body. Feet usually start to grow before legs, for instance. About two years later — around the age of 12 in girls and 14 in boys — there is a very noticeable gain in height. Temporarily, girls may be taller than their male age mates. This gangling and uneven growth is transitory, but it can lead to lasting sensitivity about looks.

In girls the earliest signs of puberty are changes in body shape. These occur between the ages of 8 and 10. The hips begin to widen and fat deposits soften the skin and round out the body. These events are mainly the result of increased oestrogens secreted by the adrenal glands and maturing ovaries. Oestrogens catalyse the growth of other secondary characteristics such as breasts and pubic hair. The onset of breast development is known as telarche. A year or two later, when the breasts are well shaped and pubic hair is more plentiful, menarche or the onset of the menstrual cycle, occurs. Menarche is brought on by the interplay of several different hormones — hormones from the hypothalamus and pituitary in the brain interact with those produced by the ovaries and these in turn interact with the lining of the uterus (endometrium). Ovulation does not occur regularly until all these hormones and organs have orchestrated themselves properly. Until they have, conception and pregnancy are unlikely. For the first year or so menstrual blood loss varies a great deal — periods may be heavy or scanty, and last one or two days or several; most girls need to be reassured that this variation is quite normal. Prohibitions against swimming, hair washing, or even sexual activity during menstruation are unnecessary.

The onset of menstruation does not necessarily indicate readiness for childbearing, as is sometimes believed. Among some groups, adolescent sterility lasts for a year or longer. Early menstrual patters may be highly irregular and there is no sure, simple way of telling whether a girl is ovulating. Adolescent sterility accounts for the low pregnancy rate among young girls in many sexually permissive societies. Thus one study in Mangaia (one of the Cook Islands in the Pacific) found that only 3 out of 29 women between the ages of 14 and 20 had conceived, despite frequent coitus from pre-puberty onwards. In the West, adolescent sterility appears to be briefer, lasting several months to a year. It cannot be relied on as an alternative to efficient contraception.

Growth of the testes, scrotum, and penis is one of the first signs of puberty in boys. Growth begins around the age of 10 or 11 and the genitals reach nearly full size by about the age of 15, but a great deal of individual variation exists. As the testes grow, the production of male hormones, mainly testosterone, increases. As in the female, hormones activate and fuel most of the changes associated with development of secondary male characteristics — growth of pubic and underarm (axillary) hair, and hair on the chest and other parts of the body, and enlargement of the larynx and deepening of the voice.

Spermarche, the first appearance of sperm in ejaculated fluid, is analogous with menarche. The ability to ejaculate does not mean that a boy is fertile. Unlike ovulation, sperm production is continuous until the seventh decade of life and beyond. A brief period of adolescent sterility is also apparent in males. In the Mangaian study, for example, none of the 30 sexually active adolescent males was a father.

At puberty masturbatory behaviour and wet dreams become increasingly common. Girls also have orgastic dreams, with more vaginal sweating than usual, but apparently less frequently than boys. Adolescent boys quickly become accustomed to their ejaculate and girls to their menstrual flow. For each, however, the first encounter with the other's sex effluents may be distasteful. Like urine, semen and menstrual blood are natural secretions and sterile until they are outside the body.

These obvious physical changes in both sexes are accompanied by a prodigious increase in physical activity, energy, appetite, and social interactions. This is most noticeable in boys, where there is a clear match between physical and social changes; the correlation of testosterone production with erotic activites is dramatic and well established. In girls the transition is more gradual.

A testing time

Socially and sexually, puberty and adolescence are periods of uncertainty, introspection, experimentation, and testing limits. There is a subtle but marked shift away from reliance on the family for support and encouragement. Peer pressures are more strongly felt; it becomes highly important to be 'one of the gang', to be accepted and desired as a friend and sexual companion. Charismatic age mates and other admired figures attract more attention and loyalty than parents or family. The goal of all these behaviours is the development of individual competence and self-reliance.

Puberty is also a time of social testing. The individual is formally or informally put on trial to find out whether he or she is ready to meet the obligations expected of an adult. In societies that have very formal trials — such as circumcision (male or female), certain rituals of dress and behaviour, or tests of skill or daring — the individual emerges from them with his or her merit and self-worth publicly affirmed. Certainly any boy who dives from an 80-foot tower attached by the ankles to overhanging liana vines, as is the custom in the New Hebrides, or climbs a ladder of knives, as in rural China, earns my admiration for courage, as does any girl who undergoes scarification or ritual marking of the skin.

In Western societies the trial may take the form of passing a crucial school exam,

completing a *bar* (or *bat*) *mitzvah*, earning merit badges or other symbols of accomplishment such as a driving licence, reaching voting or drinking age, or being drafted into military service. Even without such outward and visible signs of maturity, many adolescents feel driven to prove their worth to themselves and to a circle of intimates. The result may be some extraordinarily positive accomplishment, or utterly destructive and disruptive. Sexual experimentation leading to pregnancy and various kinds of criminal or antisocial behaviour may, at a deeper level, be a bid for autonomy, a cry for recognition. And whether they realize it or not, most prospective sons- and daughters-in-law are put through a probationary period, often beginning with the traditional and sometimes awesome invitation to dinner 'to meet the family'.

In some parts of the world male rites of passage require great courage. In the Solomon Islands boys are admitted to manhood by jumping from a high platform into the sea. In one of China's remoter provinces would-be men climb a ladder of sharp knives.

Stepping up sexual activity

During puberty and adolescence all pre-pubertal sexual activities increase in frequency and scope, often with a lot of boasting and encouragement from friends. From what we know in the West, for about 6 in 10 boys, masturbation becomes a fact of life by the age of 15; by the age of 20, the ratio is more like 9 to 10. Initially masturbation is done in private or in groups, but eventually it becomes a solitary practice. Girls also increase their masturbatory activity but rarely to the extent of their male peers. By the age of 15 about 1 in 3 girls masturbates; by the age of 20, 6 or 7 in 10 do. It seems that masturbation in girls today is a commoner habit than it was 40 years ago, but the current figures for boys are very much the same as they were 40 years ago.

Homosexual experimentation is also a feature of puberty, but more so for boys than for girls. For the large majority of teenagers, homosexual experiences are transitory and

In Ancient China sex was not necessarily private, as this painting by 11th-century artist Su Shih shows. Nor was there any shame attached to depicting sexual activity. Sex teaching was by example.

never repeated. As we shall see in Chapter 8, one or two homosexual experiences do not make a person homosexual. For the minority of adolescents who prefer same-sex relations, the stage is set for future orientation.

Sex teaching

Sex education for children in most industrial societies consists, at best, of being told about reproduction and menstruation. This is changing, but the pace is slow and the forces of conservative tradition remain strong. Sex education classes seldom teach young adults what to do in bed, how to cope with mental and physical responses to sexual activity, or how to manage relationships and sexual problems. Scandinavian countries are the exception here. The teaching of sex behaviours starts in kindergarten. In 1992 sex education began in all primary schools throughout Japan. Primary school programs began in the United States in the 1970s, with more states coming on board during the 1980s and 1990s. In non-Western countries, however, sex education is very limited, often lumped in with morality teaching, the stated or implied message being 'not until you are married' and then 'only in an approved manner.'

Of course AIDS has had an impact on sex education, and not always for the better. Despite the fact that every poll in the United States has shown that the great majority of parents is in favour of sex education, few state-wide school systems have seized the AIDS-given opportunity to fully and truly educate youngsters about sex. Often they hesitate in response to vociferous minorities who fear that talking about 'it' will encourage 'it'.

AIDS education is not the same as sex education. Saying no to sex may help to prevent the spread of AIDS, but it cannot be called sex education. In an AIDS context, sex is equated with risk and possible death rather than with pleasure and affirmation of life. Although fear of AIDS has undoubtedly lessened sexual experimentation among some adolescents, in general the fear technique has proved ineffective. Youngsters who receive negative, AIDS-oriented instruction generally initiate and conduct their sexual activities at about the same time and with the same frequency as their peers. They just do so with more guilt and apprehension.

In contrast, sex education programs which are more broadly based — which start early in the curriculum, convey the message that sex can be pleasurable as well as risky, put sexual activity in the context of relationships and responsibilities — meet with more success, as measured by first coitus at a later age, fewer out-of-marriage pregnancies, and a lower incidence of sexually transmitted diseases. The crucial factor seems to be that good sex education classes teach students how to analyse situations and how to take sexual decisions for themselves. *They* decide with whom and when to have sex; peer pressure and the excitement of the moment are less likely to dictate behaviour. Conservative parents prefer their children not to make such decisions, but they make them anyway. Who ever asks their parents 'Is is OK to have sex now?'

In the United States, spurred on by AIDS, by the knowledge that the mean age for first coitus occurs during their watch, and by the high incidence of out-of-wedlock pregnancies, some high schools have made condoms available to their students. Unfortunately, the pace of real sex education has not kept up with the needs of most populations anywhere. What is required are programs that start before youngsters become sexually active and include adequate and full preparation for teachers and parents.

Early sex, late marriage

In the last few decades there has been a marked rise in sexual activity among teenagers in the West. Restrictive controls on children began to be relaxed during World War II. The tension of the times, the absence of strong discipline at home, and changing needs and expectations all changed social habits. It became more common for both parents to work to meet economic demands. Movement away from grandparents and the family home in order to attend school or find a job reduced adult supervision. Religious dicta lost their restrictive power. Today, with the immediate threat of nuclear war averted, we face global pollution, depletion of the ozone layer, AIDS, international terrorism, and other brands of man-made doom. How many people today really believe in a future Utopia? Surely, they say, it makes more sense to live for today, to enjoy life while we can. Couple these factors with increased awareness of adult sexual behaviours,

Prolonged education and delayed responsibility are among the factors that have contributed to an increase in sexual activity among adolescents in the West. Boys and girls of 14 and 15 are mature in the reproductive sense but are generally discouraged from forming stable sexual relationships, so the teen years have become a time of sexual experimentation and of testing sexual identity.

higher divorce rates, greater availability of contraception, and the greater exposure of sexual topics in the media, and it is hardly surprising that adolescent sexual activity has increased. Cohabitation, with or without parental knowledge or approval, is also more common. The premarital period is also longer because people are marrying much later than in the past.

I suggest, however, that recent 'permissiveness' is not a new pressure on unwilling and unready youngsters, but rather a release that enables them to follow their natural predilections with fewer inhibitions. As in so many other matters, one's assessment of the importance of such changes depends on the time frame in which one sets them. In Biblical times, adolescence as we know it today did not exist. Adulthood, and with it marriage and sexual activity, arrived very soon after puberty. The time that elapsed between the emergence of sexual drives and the opportunity to satisfy them was relatively short. It remains this way in much of the Third World.

In the industrial world, however, marriage and overt genital expression have been postponed until the individual is capable of making his or her way independently. But the genital activities that Western societies generally think of as belonging within marriage have *not* been postponed. Our protracted system of education and job training has delayed independence, but not sexual curiosity or erotic behaviour. What we are now seeing is a return to more open post-pubertal sexual activities, but no longer accompanied by the custom of early marriage. The advent of modern birth control methods, the automobile, and better and more private housing have provided the necessary technical assistance.

Teenage sex: some facts and figures

In countries where data are available, the incidence and frequency of adolescent genital petting and coital activities have increased markedly since World War II. Virginity before marriage has lost much of its mystique and value. While most premarital coitus still takes place with an intended spouse, a significant proportion of brides and grooms have already had a number of coital relationships. Premarital coitus is now the norm rather than the exception in the United States, Scandinavia, continental Europe, England, Scotland, Wales, Australia, and Canada. Few people in Western society seem to think it worth 'saving themselves' for marriage.

Although hard data are lacking for most of the rest of the world, premarital intercourse also seems to be the norm in Africa, parts of Latin America, and Oceania. Here, by the age of 20, coitus before marriage is more common than virginity. This is probably not the case

These teenagers are still at what might be called the 'group grope' stage. But as confidence is gained, single dating replaces group dating. In the West full intercourse is seldom postponed beyond the age of 19.

in Islamic countries, the Indian subcontinent, and parts of Southeast Asia, where marriages are most often arranged, female virginity is a prerequisite for marriage, prostitutes are readily available for males, and future sexual compatibility is either assumed or not a matter of concern. This is not, however, a Western sexual revolution but an evolution. It is also not a rejection of marriage. On the contrary, marriage is being reserved for more serious matters, such as the rearing of children and lifelong emotional and financial commitment.

Some numbers will help to put premarital sexual activity in the West into perspective. One important study of young adults in England, published in 1973, reported: 'Premarital sexual intercourse is now the normal pattern both for men (80 per cent) and for women (61 per cent).' In 1990 another British study found that 75 per cent of both male and female respondents between the ages of 16 and 24 had had intercourse by the age of 19; among female respondents aged 45–59, first intercourse occurred on average about four years later.

A steady rise in the incidence of sexual activity among teenagers can be seen from the following studies in the United States, where there is probably the greatest wealth of such data. The proportion of teenage American women residing in metropolitan areas who reported premarital sexual experience rose from 30 per cent in 1971 to 43 per cent in 1976, and to 50 per cent in 1979. In 1979, 2 out of every 3 American teenagers had had coitus by the age of 19. L. Rubinson and L. De Rubertis, researching sexual attitudes and behaviours among Midwest college students in 1987, found that the number of males engaging in premarital sex by the age of 20 rose from 75 per cent in 1972 to nearly 90 per cent in 1987; for female students the numbers were 60 per cent and 75 per cent. In 1989 Gayle Wyatt found that the mean (average) age of first coitus among black and white American women was 17, with no significant differences between the races. National probability samples indicate that among females aged 13–19 who have never been married, mean age of first coitus is now between 14 and 16.

If these numbers appear somewhat confusing, let me reiterate a point made earlier. Different researchers report their results in different ways and study different populations. Some investigators give mean ages of first intercourse, while others indicate what percentage of their sample population has had intercourse by a certain age or by marriage. Groups or individuals within a larger population may be quite different from the average; an average of 17 years for first coitus may well mean that some respondents had their first experience at the age of 10 and others at 24. Also, when it comes to teenage sex worldwide, one must keep in mind that in some countries — Yemen, Bangladesh, and Jamaica, for example — marriage typically occurs before the age of 17 and almost always by 20.

A society's attitudes towards virginity and premarital sex, and its expectations of how sexual experience is to be gained, must also be taken into account when interpreting research findings. For instance, a study of university students in Colombia found that the number of females having premarital sex rose from 38 per cent in 1980 to 65 per cent in 1985. Almost all the men in both surveys had premarital sexual experience, 90 per cent with prostitutes in the first study, but only 65 percent with prostitutes in the second study. Sexual initiation with prostitutes was and is common in Latin America, so the implications of the lower figure in 1985 are that prostitutes are being replaced by sweethearts and that female virginity at marriage is becoming less prized. The same is true in other parts of the world.

One of the few countries in which teenage girls seem to be more sexually active than teenage boys is (West) Germany. This was the case in 1976, for females aged 11–16, and again in 1981 — by the age of 19, some 80 per cent of females had had coitus, while the figure for males was just under 70 per cent. In 1966 the figures were only 38 per cent for males and 31 per cent for females. An interesting additional conclusion by researchers Ulrich Clement, Gunter Schmidt, and Margret Krause was that 'married and unmarried students scarcely differ nowadays in their coital and masturbation behaviour; marital status no longer has any marked influence on these aspects of sexuality.'

What of Eastern Europe and the former Soviet Union? It is probably fair to assume that trends in teenage sexual experience are not too dissimilar from those in America and Western Europe. We do know something about Czechoslovakia though. A 1980 report from the excellent Sexological Institute of Charles University in Prague indicated that for 1 in 2 married women born in the 1920s first coitus occurred after the age of 19. For married women born in the 1950s the first experience was before the age of 18; for those born in the 1960s it was no doubt earlier. Interestingly, this same study found that earlier coital experience correlated with more frequent marital orgasm.

In the last few years more data from Asia have become available. Here too premarital sex is on the rise. There has definitely been an increase in teenage sex in Japan since World War II. Between 1974 and 1981, coital experience for male adolescents increased from 26 to 37 per cent and for females from 11 to 28 per cent. Yet Yohiro Hatano, reporting on a series of continuing national surveys by the Japanese Association for Sex Education, found that between 1981 and 1988 there was no significant increase in the number of males or females indulging in premarital sex by the age of 20; by the age of 22, however, 65 per cent of males and 60 per cent of females had had sexual experience, compared with approximately 40 per cent for both males and females by the age of 20. This intriguing jump in sexual activity between the age of 20 and 22 has a lot to do with university entrance exams, which are so stringent that study takes up much of the time that would otherwise be devoted to dating. After high school graduation, a 'release' phenomenon sets in. In Japan, as elsewhere, the majority of those interviewed do not see their behaviour as promiscuous. Most of the girls say they regard intercourse as a reasonable part of a relationship; fewer boys feel this way — they are keener on the sex than the relationship.

Even when youngsters think themselves as devoted and well matched as Romeo and Juliet, the partner is largely a vehicle for self-discovery and exploration. 'Am I attractive?' 'Will she let me feel her breasts?' 'Will he get an erection if I kiss him? If so, what do I do next?' 'Does he enjoy kissing more than I do?' 'What does coitus feel like?' For many people some of these questions recur throughout life.

Although I have concentrated, in the last few pages, on teenage coitus in a heterosexual context, for some societies oral or anal sex are seen as more intimate. Such activities may precede coitus or marriage, often to maintain virginity, or they may be reserved for special or (most often) marital partners. If homosexual activities occur between teenagers, they usually appear before heterosexual ones.

Acutely conscious of their appearance, like teenagers all over the world, Japanese youngsters try out different styles of self-presentation. Early marriage is no longer the expectation or wish of most Japanese girls.

Sexual conflicts

Adolescence is a particularly difficult time for individuals awakening to the idea that they are 'different'. This is certainly true if they are visibly physically or mentally handicapped or significantly less favoured in appearance. It is also a trial for those coming to realize that they are homosexually oriented (sexually attracted to members of the same sex) or transsexual (wanting to be of the opposite sex). A 1989 U.S. Government report indicated that sexually troubled adolescents are two or three times more likely than other adolescents to attempt suicide and may account for up to 30 per cent of completed suicides in the United States (more than 750,000 American adolescents attempt suicide each year). The reasons for these suicide attempts include isolation, low self-esteem, and being on the receiving end of physical and verbal abuse. The message these young people receive from family, peers, and society at large is that they are unwanted, unloved, and undeserving. Without friends or adults to confide in and without knowledge of ways to assert their individuality, they may be scarred for life, unable to develop the skills needed to adjust to adulthood. In Los Angeles, San Francisco, and New York City there are special schools for youngsters with serious sexual conflicts or in need of shelter from the slings and arrows of their peers. In 1988 the National Educators' Association called for every school district in the United States to provide counselling for students struggling with sexual problems. More special schools and programs are needed to deal with the sexual needs of adolescents as well as provide a standard education.

For some, like the physically handicapped, the problem is obvious. For others, like homosexuals, however, it is not, and this means 'coming out', admitting first to themselves and then cautiously to others that they are different, a very difficult revelation. Such coming to terms is usually hardest with parents. To help this situation parents and counsellors have banded together to form P-FLAG (Parents and Friends of Lesbians and Gays).

Confusing messages

Exploring one's capabilities in sex, social skills, responsibility, and love all at the same time can be a daunting agenda, especially in a society where early heterosexual and homosexual relationships are officially taboo. Nevertheless one is expected to know how to manage adult relationships, including sexual ones. For most people, basic sexual knowledge is not difficult to acquire, but knowing what one likes and values in others takes longer, and finding out how to please others takes the longest.

The pace of change today has tended to magnify intergenerational differences. Parents, counsellors, and teachers are routinely caught in the bind of trying to prepare children for a future which is uncertain, unappealing, or incomprehensible. Acutely aware of the procreative capacity of teenagers and the coming pressures of adult life, they often reach for the tried-and-tested recipe of social conformity rather than encourage individual expression or trial-and-error learning. Teaching children about all-important feelings is difficult; it is not easy for adults to transfer the emotional wisdom gained from hard and trying experiences. Also, many parents, especially those who have felt the pain of divorce or been

disappointed in their own relationships, admit that they do not know how to help their children meet the future.

Society's messages to young adolescents are often complex and contradictory. They are told to 'grow up' but only in certain approved ways. Boys are told to curb their sexual drives, but peers — and often fathers as well — exalt when they 'score'. Girls are told to be modest and reserved, yet their peers — and often their mothers — tell them to 'dress up a bit' and act sexy if they want to be popular. The restrictive part of the message seems to be accepted more by girls than boys. Greater pressure is applied to girls than to boys if it is not. Honest parents or helping professionals can at least admit to fumbling teenagers the duplicity of such messages and help them to work out their own feelings and standards.

In an ideal environment children would learn to satisfy their needs and expectations without provoking unneccessary hostility and adults would learn to provide support and encouragement without imposing their own prejudices and fears. Learning is necessary on both sides. Respect for one's parents' views is compatible with developing one's own sexual potential; respect for the individuality of one's children is compatible with following a lifestyle one has chosen for oneself. Parents and children, in mutual respect, can grow together.

Porn comics for Japanese highschoolers are legal and in demand, but protests from parents resulted in the publishers voluntarily withdrawing them. Commercial pressures and adolescent and parental wishes are often in conflict.

Chapter 7

Sexual patterns

As we look around us we see that to a great degree males and females do different things. This is broadly true at home, at work, at play, east and west, north and south, and despite moves to enforce equality between the sexes. In primitive and developed societies, in sophisticated cities and sparsely populated rural areas, men and women behave differently. He drives the car, she packs the picnic. She washes the dishes, he dries. He goes fishing, she goes shopping. These are, to some people, trivial distinctions. But they are indicative of deeper differences that are highly significant.

His job and her job

Men are most numerous in those occupations associated with heavy physical labour, exposure to danger, the distribution of wealth or power, and prolonged absence from home. They run governments, businesses, and industries. Women predominate in those occupations associated with child rearing, clerical work, personal service, in the 'caring' professions, social organization and health. In some primitive societies, the men specialize in hunting, fishing, and raiding, while the women look after the land and the livestock, and gather food. In 'many Third World countries, where women are held in low esteem, these generalities hold as strongly as ever except that women, as well as men, are expected to perform physically demanding and dangerous tasks as a matter of routine.

Well before puberty, in the tradition of our primate cousins, the sexes begin to play apart. Boys tend to roam further from home and form gangs or teams; girls stay closer to home in the company of two or three close friends. Aggression, physical rivalry, and rough body contact are for boys; less active, less exploratory, and less dangerous pursuits are for girls. There are excellent athletes of both sexes, but mostly they compete separately and with different rules and different targets to aim for.

Leaders such as Golda Meir, Indira Gandhi, Margaret Thatcher, and Corazon Aquino notwithstanding, in every society it is typically men who hold key positions in the political hierarchy, and in every society it is women who have the primary responsibility for domestic chores and the daily necessities of family existence. Men provide for prestigious or major acquisitions such as houses, cars, or cows. Men deal with intertribal and international disputes and conflicts. Women adjudicate family squabbles and in-house disputes, but men enforce state or national laws and mete out punishment. 'Just you wait until daddy comes home...' is a threat used by mothers the world over.

Women fight and defend home and family when necessary, but in the main it is men who carry arms into enemy territory. There are exceptions of course. In guerilla warfare, every combatant is needed and there are fewer 'rules', so women *do* become involved in fighting. Women in today's complex hi-tech regular armed forces have been involved and killed in combat, but such incidents are considered to be deviations from the norm and arguments that women should have frontline combat status are strenuously resisted. During the Gulf War there were women in all branches of the U.S. armed forces, but it was not intended that they should play a frontline combat role. A year later, however, a law was passed allowing women pilots to fly combat missions. The U.S. Army and Navy have resisted such changes. The debate, pro and con, is complex, with men and women arguing on both sides.

There never has been a race of Amazons except in mythology, no truly matriarchal society with power and control concentrated in the hands of women. This is a matter of

Women's work, a New York mural. The 'ascent of woman' from the dark regions of childbearing and domestic drudgery into the sunlight of reproductive and occupational freedom is entwined with the symbolism of the 'tree of life'.

Part of a frieze from the tomb of Mausolus (died 353 BC), showing a battle between Amazons and Greeks. The Amazons were a mythical race of female warriors. 'Amazon' means 'without breasts' — legend has it that one breast was removed to allow handling of the bow and sword. The makers of the Amazon myth were more interested in recreating women in man's image than in emphasizing the strengths of femininity.

historical fact. That is what has been, not what might or could or should have been. Remember my third sexwatching axiom in Chapter 1?

In fact the very concept of appropriate gender 'roles', or 'social scripts' as they have come to be called by sociologists John Gagnon and William Simon, encourages the idea that much of life is staged and played out according to the expectations of others. We should therefore ask ourselves how much role play is intrinsic to this or that activity and how much is unconsciously copied from models. Many specifics of any role have to be learned, but it is debatable which and to what degree. In all probability any role or script is appropriate for any individual, having due regard for his or her biological, social, and psychological inheritance and for the fact that people tend to want out from roles that are unfulfilling even though they may be under powerful pressures to stay in them.

Achieved roles and given roles

Some roles are earned. One can work up from stock clerk to company president, displaying appropriate behaviour on successive rungs of the ladder. The same person acts differently and in turn is treated differently at each level. These achieved roles confer status or prestige. Other roles are less easily changed, because they are imposed or accepted rather than earned, felt, or desired. These are ascribed roles and the behaviours that constitute them are fairly rigidly stereotyped.

We ascribe roles to race ('Blacks are good at sport', 'Orientals are shrewd'), to nationality (the Germans are methodical, the French romantic, the British reserved), to age groups ('young people are irresponsible', 'old people are fuddy-duddies'), and most significantly to sex. 'Masculine' and 'feminine' are social and gender roles ascribed on the basis of sex.

But in Paris men wear trousers and in Tahiti they wear *lava lava* wrap-arounds, so what is 'masculine' depends on society, not biology. Nevertheless, many of the things society thinks of as masculine or feminine *are* related to biological attributes. In every society bulging muscles are masculine and smooth curves feminine.

Every individual from infancy onwards confronts the stereotype of his or her sex. If he is male he is under pressure to be masculine and boyish, if female to be feminine and girlish. In a classic experiment observers described babies dressed in blue as 'very active' and the same babies dressed in pink as 'gentle'. When the same babies wore yellow the observers were confused. Many wanted to know the sex of the babies before making judgements about them! Other studies have shown the same thing, that assumptions about the sex of a person dictate behaviour towards that person. Most adults treat boys and girls differently, from infancy onwards, handling them differently, giving them different toys to play with, expecting different things from them.

If adults need external clues about the sex of an infant, infants themselves apparently do not, judging by a study done at Edinburgh University by T.G.R. Bower and his colleagues. In this study, 13-month-old infants were able to tell the sex of other 13-month-old infants despite the removal of all external clues and a great swapping of clothes that had most of the adults involved completely confused. Apparently, certain movements allowed the infants to distinguish boy from girl. Male infants were more interested in other males and females more attentive to other females. Of course societies enshrine their gender stereotypes in many things other than dress — in different first names, different vocabularies, different education, different occupations, different leisure activities, different intellectual pursuits, different marital rights and duties, different sexual and erotic practices, even different burial rituals. Some of these differences have a strong biological rationale, others less or none at all.

Stereotypes: socially or biologically based?

How have these differences in gender roles come about? Soldiering, mining, or tree felling require attributes more often possessed by men than women. And the care and nurturing of young infants require attributes more often possessed by women than by men. But not all behaviours have an obvious physical or biological basis. There are many occupations, especially in a technological society, that cannot be neatly segregated by sex. Any view across different cultures shows how each has various conventions concerning appropriate male and female behaviour. In one New Guinea tribe, for example, the women cultivate sweet potatoes and the men cultivate yams — it would be difficult to think

Almost universally, work traditionally performed by women has low status. Strength is not always the deciding factor. In Japan gangs of women used to be employed on construction sites; here women drive piles for the foundations of a house.

In China fishing is traditionally a male occupation; while the men fish, the women do the family washing.

of a biological reason for a convention like this.

Nowadays many people, especially women, see stereotyped occupational roles as a product of social systems engineered to keep subordinates subordinate and the dominant influential rather than as a product of biological invariants. Some patterns are decreed by civil law — in many countries soldiering is done by men only and midwifery by women only — or by ecclesiastical law — only men are admitted to the Roman Catholic priesthood.

Other conventions

Each culture has its own rules about dress, evolved over centuries, but convention almost everywhere dictates that clothing for males and females is somehow different. Only in particular occupations where the needs of the job outweigh considerations of gender, such as in combat, heavy industry, or special crafts, do both sexes dress alike.

There is a fashion for unisex clothing in the West, but it has a bias. Women find jeans comfortable and appropriate for many different occasions, but men have shown little interest in wearing skirts. Androgynous clothes were popular for a time, but not any more. And even when men make a move in the direction of feminine colours and design, they seldom go as far as wearing a dress. Unisex clothing or not, there is rarely any doubt as to who is what; some aspect of sex-specific appearance is maintained, often in the form of personal decoration.

Masai moran *(warriors) give each other the exotic ochre-and-butter hairdos that are a mark of their status. Non-warriors — apprentice* moran *and women — shave their heads.*

Some societies not only prescribe different dress for males and females but use clothing to distinguish children from adults and married from unmarried, divorced or widowed. Italian widows wear black, Korean widows white. Personal ornaments are also used to indicate social and sexual status. The wedding ring is one of the most widely understood symbols of sexual status. In the West double ring ceremonies are now fashionable, but until about 40 years ago it was unusual for a man to wear a wedding ring. In some societies only women wear wedding rings. In India, among some groups, women wear wedding rings on their toes. A single plain earring is now acceptable for Western men, but an earring in both ears might be seen as feminine.

As far as dress is concerned, there is no obvious link with biology. It might be easier for women to urinate wearing a skirt or a dress, but in rural Turkey, India, and Japan, and almost universally throughout Southeast Asia, women wear pantaloons or trousers. Some forms of female dress make the breast readily accessible to a nursing infant, but social custom may not allow the feeding of infants in public. In many societies dress conventions are dictated more by modesty and style than by convenience. Often the origins of a particular convention may have been forgotten. Of what use is a tie, for example?

Social invention can also be credited with the sex-segregation of first names (why else is Bernard a boy and Eve a girl?), forms of address (Sir, Madam), and gender-based vocabulary ('la table' feminine and 'le taxi', masculine).

When one considers other patterns of sex segregation, the element of social invention is still obvious, but a biological link begins to intrude. In every society the concept of physical aggression as masculine and nurturance as feminine, patterns that are biologically linked, organizes the broad spectrum of social conventions.

The pros and cons of gender roles

In spite of conventional patterns there are individuals who act in ways considered typical of the opposite sex. Does that mean that the behaviour patterns of a great number of men and women will change markedly in the future? I doubt it. Intuitively I would say that if people are allowed greater opportunity to follow their personal preferences the total sum of human experience will be enriched. Greater freedom ought to lead to more fruitful lives and relationships. Denial of opportunity on the grounds of gender seems not only undemocratic and a waste of natural resources, but also an unwarranted blocking of avenues to general happiness and satisfaction.

Nevertheless our expectations of our own sex and of the opposite sex are not excess mental baggage. They are crucial grist from which we form our self-image and solidify our sexual identity. Equipped with that image and identity we develop all our sexual and non-sexual relationships.

Gender roles are the lubricants of social interaction; their images facilitate most social activities. Uncertainty is unsettling and unwelcome for most people. Role expectations, even if later found to be misplaced, provide initial guidelines on how to act and what to expect. Just as we expect different behaviours and reactions from an oil tycoon and a priest, an athlete and a scholar, we have quite different expectations for males and females.

Yet each of us generally prefers and deserves to be judged on his or her own merits rather than on stereotypes. So although sex role and gender expectations have the advantage of shortcutting communication and, when fulfilled, offer feelings of competence and success, they can be disadvantageous. They form mental pigeonholes which limit the exploration and testing of our own abilities and those of others. They build barriers against opportunities to change or expand the nature of relationships. And they stifle communication and creativity. Fortunately, many people successfully negotiate their way out of role stereotypes. Some accept them with comfort. Others explore them, find

All of us prefer to be judged on our own merits. These two women successfully crossed the Atlantic in a catamaran. What is intrinsically masculine about sailing a boat? In fact some consider the boat to be a 'cradle' image and the sea a manifestation of the feminine principle.

them unsuitable, and attempt to make changes. Others neither explore alternatives nor feel free to change; unwittingly, they remain trapped all their lives. This is the sad fate of sexists and bigots, sad for themselves and sad for society.

Throughout the Muslim world homosocial behaviour is the norm. Men socialize with men, women with women. Double standards are also alive and well, as this street scene in Egypt's Port Said shows: womenfolk cover up and do not associate with strangers, but it is OK for men to ogle female tourists and posters of scantily clad houris.

Is there, inside every man, a lustful opportunist waiting to get out? Or does this tatoo recall the fantasies of youth?

Erotic stereotypes

Certain erotic behaviours, because of their private nature, are not easily transmitted from person to person and therefore do not seem to be part of role stereotypes. For instance, even with regular and agreeable sex partners, more males masturbate more frequently than females and men are more often visually aroused to sexual initiation than women. These two findings are only part of a more general pattern that appears to have its roots in biology rather than in social learning: men, more than women, are driven to erotic and genital gratification, experimentation, partner variety, and multiformity (sex in different positions and in different locations); men, more than women, are lustful opportunists, geared towards orgasm, a wider range of sexual practices, and a variety of sexual companions; men, with all their urges to roam, are more sexually jealous (more often driven to murder or separation) and take more sexual risks than women; cultures that practise polygamy are common, those that practise polyandry rather rare; fetishistic desires are common in males, but uncommon in females.

George Bernard Shaw, who had at least two women in his thoughts for most of his life, remarked: 'A man should have one woman to prevent him from thinking about women in general.' Dorothy Parker, in her poem called 'A General Review of the Sex Situation', wrote '...woman wants monogamy; man delights in novelty...count to ten and man is bored.' And consider this reflection by a Kgatla man in South Africa, speaking of his two wives: 'I find them both equally desirable, but when I have slept with one for three days...and when I go to the other, I have greater passion, she seems more attractive...but it is not really so, for when I go to the former again there is the same renewed passion.'

There are many men who would agree that they are more interested in the chase than the consummation: 'Getting a new women to go to bed with me is more thrilling than being in bed.' In contrast, many women claim the opposite. As one of my students said to me: 'I find the seduction dance and game playing most unsettling. But the comfort and warmth with my partner, once having made the decision to go to bed, I find most rewarding.' For men, it is often the challenge that is important, for women the other person.

Typically, it is the male rather than the female who pushes a budding relationship towards genital play. Men constantly test the boundaries of sexual contact. This is still true when the relationship is old and established, when the complications of guilt or shyness have been overcome.

Even without a relationship or challenge to the ego, men are more likely to actively seek sexual satisfaction. The ultimate example of this is rape, which is everywhere almost exclusively committed by men. But it is also exemplified in the use of prostitutes, both female and male, who predominantly service males. In all cultures studied, men are more likely to have extramarital affairs and with a greater number of partners. They are also more likely to form and maintain a relationship primarily to satisfy erotic needs.

In two studies among American college students, 75 and 69 per cent of men propositioned by a female stranger agreed to go to bed with her the same night. None of the women propositioned by a male stranger agreed to go to bed with him. In the first study only 6 per cent of the women even agreed to go to the stranger's apartment, and in the second study none did. In both studies, 69 per cent of males were willing to go to the female stranger's apartment. As investigators Russell Clark and Elaine Hatfield noted, with some surprise, the men they questioned were 'less willing to date than to have sexual relations!'

Many more males than females go to singles bars purely to seek sexual satisfaction, as reported in Shere Hite's books. Even among a population of single, urban, sexually liberated women, she found few who thought casual, spontaneous sex desirable, although many thought they might be happier if they did. In contrast the majority of men she surveyed claimed they did, at least occasionally, desire casual sex. Even against a background of AIDS awareness, this situation has not changed much.

Men everywhere seem to want more sex and a greater variety of sexual partners than women do. In the courts of pre-independence India it was common for princes to entertain several women at once. In this picture the prince is Ram Singh of Kotah, enjoying two women with his hands, two with his feet, and one with his penis. A piece of none-too-discreet flattery?

Novelty versus loyalty

According to Kinsey, the male drive for variety is one of the most common sources of conflict between the sexes. He and his colleagues were struck by the fact that most men readily understand the desire for extramarital coitus, whereas many women find it difficult to believe that a man who is happily married might want coitus with someone other than his wife. To Kinsey this fact was 'the best sort of evidence that there are basic differences between the sexes.' A woman may want sexual relations with a stranger who has special status or appeal or because she is temporarily fed up, sexually or non-sexually, with her current partner. But to a man, the novelty of a new partner may be reason enough for sexual adventures outside marriage or a stable relationship. Affairs do not necessarily reflect dissatisfaction with a current lover, or mean that he or she is no longer loved. As Kinsey noted: '...everywhere in the world it is understood that...the female has a greater capacity for being faithful to a single partner, that she is more likely to consider that she has greater responsibility than the male has in maintaining a home and caring for the offspring.'

Findings recently reported by Albert Klassen, Collin Williams, and Eugene Levitt of the Kinsey Institute give new figures relevant to this discussion. It seems that about four times as many men as women feel that extramarital sex is 'not wrong at all', but that slightly more women than men (90 percent rather than 80 per cent) feel that it is 'always wrong' or 'almost always wrong'.

Double standards

One of the difficulties in making male-female role comparisons is that almost invariably the life, work, and even play of males are awarded more status than those of females. Take the sports pages of newspapers and magazines. Although women are, more than ever, involved in sports at every level, the number of column inches written about them continues at about the same level as 30 years ago. Whether this is the cause or effect of status being largely defined by men is not known but, as many women writers have pointed out, recorded history has usually ignored 'herstory'. Double standards for men and women are universal and almost everywhere the advantages accrue to men. For example, a sexually adventurous man is typically considered worldly, a sexually adventurous woman promiscuous.

Status is not always synonymous with importance. Among many primitive societies the food gathering and gardening activities of women are crucially important for subsistence, but they are not awarded high status. Many people, and not only women, cogently argue that caring for and rearing children is the most important duty anyone can undertake, and yet because it is everywhere mainly done by women it enjoys low status. In most societies, when a marriage breaks up, primary care of the children is usually given to the wife, in the belief that women are more nurturant than men and better suited to the task, even if the woman in question does not want to devote her life to her children. This is changing, but with painful slowness; increasingly, the departing husband, whose income is likely to be higher than his wife's, is being expected to pick up his full share of the costs. These are social conventions and prejudices linked to gender and status. Status resides less in the job or activity itself than in society's view of it as a male or female activity.

Many countries individually, and the United Nations collectively, have made efforts to improve the lot and status of women. The results over the years have been small but they are slowly growing. In industrial societies women are increasingly entering the workforce and the political arena (men's traditional worlds) and leaving the home environment (women's traditional world). Regrettably, in many countries, when women enter occupations typically considered male, the perceived status of these professions suffers. In China and the former Soviet Union women have been encouraged, for idealistic and economic reasons, to enter previously all-male professions, especially medicine. In both countries the status of women has improved, but the prestige of the medical profession has declined.

In tough economic times, with widespread job losses, unless a woman is a professional in her own right she is more likely to return to working in the home than to go out 'looking for work'. In any case, her husband is likely to be better paid for comparable work. Although women's wages have improved in the last decade in the United States, a female college graduate is likely to earn about the same as a male high-school graduate, and as she gets older her pay will not keep pace with his. This is mostly due to pay scale differences between male and female occupations. But, as Carolin Head of the American Association of University Women, says: '...many women don't wish to go into non-traditional, male-dominated occupations.'

Perhaps only in the police force and the military, where women have become increasingly visible, has the status of the job not been materially changed. It is not clear how the entry of men into the previously female worlds of nursing and flight attending has affected the standing of these professions, but the masculinity and sexual orientation of male nurses and flight attendants is often questioned. Women entering 'macho' professions are also suspect, but less so.

Resistance to change

Many women choose to engage in typical male pursuits, but fewer men choose to take on women's traditional roles. A female barrister is more likely to return home to a meal cooked by the au pair than by her husband. Men in Western societies will cook outdoors or on special occasions, but leave women to cook in the home on a daily basis. Men will *help* with housework, but women *get it done*; no matter how prestigious or remunerative their jobs, most working women remain responsible for housework. Clearly there is an imbalance in willingness to exchange gender roles. Despite the economic and social gains won by many women in the United States, their impact on traditional gender roles has been relatively minor.

Generally speaking, if both husband and wife are equally work-centred or career-oriented, the marriage is likely to be strained. The basic issue seems to be one of power, with men reluctant to relinquish any. Married couples, regardless of the wife's earnings, still measure their financial success by the husband's income. In other words, it is up to the man to make the couple's mark in the world. Cohabitors, gay or straight, measure their economic worth as individuals, not as a unit.

It has now become fashionable to argue that there is nothing natural or immutable about gender differences, that they should be seen as anachronistic social inventions, out of place in the modern world. Social inventions, the argument goes, can be changed if institutions and populations work towards such change, and equality of the sexes is worth working for. On the other side of the debate are the sociobiologists, who argue that status and behavioural differences between men and women are not merely cultural aberrations but the result of evolutionary forces designed to ensure the survival of the sexually fittest. While sociologists wonder why males do not play a greater part in the rearing of children, biologists wonder why they take as much interest as they do. That human males are often willing to be monogamous and take direct responsibility for the lives of their offspring runs counter to

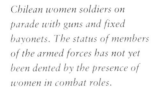

Chilean women soldiers on parade with guns and fixed bayonets. The status of members of the armed forces has not yet been dented by the presence of women in combat roles.

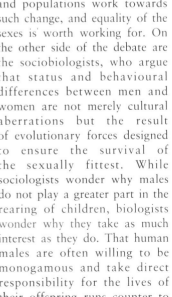

Most young girls still grow up with the idea that planning and preparing meals is their responsibility. According to a recent survey by the European Commission's Employment and Social Affairs Directorate, Spanish husbands top the league for all-round household hopelessness.

patterns of behaviour common in closely related species. To sociobiologists, human sexual patterns reflect both society's conventions and nature's way of maximizing the likelihood that men and women will meet, compete, and then cooperate for sexual and reproductive success.

Sociobiologists see sex-specific behaviour patterns as the predictable outcome of three mechanisms. The first is Charles Darwin's principle of sexual selection, in which males compete with each other for females and each female chooses the male most attractive to her. Second is 'parental investment', as proposed by the theoretical biologist R.L. Trivers; male and female behaviour patterns have evolved so that parents can maximize the chances of their offspring surviving and at the same time minimize their own personal investment in their offspring. The third is 'the selfish gene' theory proposed by Oxford zoologist Richard Dawkins; men and women are 'survival machines...programmed to preserve the selfish molecules known as genes.'

Taking all three mechanisms together, men have evolved to be competitive and will attempt to mate with and impregnate as many females as possible (they can do this because they produce almost unlimited numbers of sperm). They are therefore unlikely to form long-lasting commitments and relationships. In contrast, females (with relatively few eggs, the development of which requires investment and commitment) have evolved as though to maximize their attractiveness to males and to be highly selective in their mating. They are likely to be loyal guardians of their offspring. While modern society seems a strange and unlikely backdrop for the playing out of such primeval disparities, sociobiologists feel that their thesis is wholly contemporary.

For many the debate cannot be neutral. It is fueled by conviction or anger, not only at male-female differences themselves, but at their apparent inevitability and the inequity of the double standard associated with them which gives low status to women. Nevertheless, many studies in the past decade indicate that restructuring certain male and female behaviours is likely to be extremely difficult.

The most significant studies in this area, involving families and twins, have found that the genetic make-up of a child is a stronger determinant of personality than upbringing. At the University of Minnesota, Thomas J. Bouchard, David Lykken, Nancy Segal, and others studied more than 350 sets of twins (many of them brought up apart) over a period of 10 years and found that the traits most fixed by heredity were 'traditionalism or obedience to authority' (the tendency to follow and obey rules, to endorse high moral standards and strict discipline), 'harm avoidance' (the tendency to shun risk and danger), aggression (the tendency to be vindictive or physically violent), and altruism (putting others before self). While one might have expected these aspects of personality to be most strongly imprinted by upbringing, they were in fact shown to be more strongly heritable. (A brief case history is appropriate here. Twin girls were separated soon after birth; one was brought up as the daughter of a wealthy lawyer, the other in a lower middle class family in the East End of London; the lawyer's daughter went to the best schools and 'spoke like the Queen', while her sister, who spoke like a Cockney, left school at 16 and went to work; when they had their IQ tested as adults, they scored within a single point of each other.)

Another series of studies, involving thousands of individuals followed over nine years, came up with similar findings. In the opinion of Paul T. Costa Jr., who along with Robert McCrae conducted one of these studies for the United States National Institute for Aging, such findings sound the 'death knell' for those theories of personality which claim that life experiences can alter and determine personality. Traits such as anxiety level, friendliness, and eagerness for new experiences seem to be quite persistent despite dramatic changes in life circumstances. If traits like these are not susceptible to environmental change, can we expect marked shifts in evolutionary patterns, which are at best conservative?

That does not mean to say that societies should not set themselves humanistic goals. Offering equal opportunities to both sexes, in education and employment and in social, financial, and political spheres, is a worthy aim. In the United States governmental bodies at all levels are working towards laws that will foster parity in appointments.

Of course there will always be many women and perhaps a majority of men who feel that, regardless of the origin of gender role differences, they are basically for the best. They do not see the double standard as necessarily detrimental or reprehensible. Yet change is happening, slowly. In the West, and in parts of Asia as well, more women are entering politics — voters see women as being untainted by corruption, as being outside the entrenched 'business as usual' school of politics — so more and more scrutiny is being given to gender-discriminatory laws. The passing of the Civil Rights Act in the United States in 1991, for example, made sex discrimination illegal in all government departments and, for the first time, gave victims of sex discrimination the right to sue for compensation.

Several countries, notably China, the former Soviet Union, Scandinavia, the Netherlands, and Israel, have made great efforts to give both sexes equal status under the law, and in many respects have been successful. But many aspects of everyday male-female interactions seem to have remained the same. Though the new Japanese constitution of 1946 guaranteed equality of the sexes, women are seldom treated as equals at work or at home. In 1992 a major Japanese publisher was boycotted by women's groups who objected to the publication of a travel guide for single men which listed brothels, massage parlours, and pick-up spots rather than good hotels, restaurants, and tourist sites. And, in a throwback to feudal times, women in rural China are again being sold in marriage or for prostitution. In a rare admission *The People's Daily* reported that, in one province alone, almost 10,000 women and children are abducted and sold every year. This is against the law of course, but laws do not necessarily alter behaviour.

The New Man and the New Woman

While traditionalists and conservatives in the West, and religious fundamentalists everywhere, would like to maintain the status quo or return to stricter times, other forces are calling for new freedoms, opportunities, and directions for both men and women. Despite the relative fixedness of some of the personality traits mentioned above, in free and open societies it is ultimately the individual who determines the path he or she will follow.

The New Man and New Woman are not easy to define. In the past a man was considered adequate if he was successful, but now he must be sensitive ('he should listen, be empathic') *and* successful, as productive and creative in the home as outside it. In the past a woman was considered adequate if she was a good mother, a good housekeeper, and sexually receptive; now she must perform well in a career and enhance the status of the couple. The 'old' man initiated sex and the 'old' woman was always compliant and available. The New Woman takes the initiative and sets the sexual pace, while the New Man willingly lets her do so. In other words, both sexes want it both ways. They want the old stereotypes plus all the latest add-ons!

The first issue of Ms *magazine, in 1972, chose Wonder Woman as the new image for women. Among the topics covered were body hair, the electoral power of women, and earnings for housewives. What has changed?*

The truth is that there is still a wide gap between what each sex wants for itself and for the other. While most men accept that women can have productive and rewarding careers, most are not prepared to give up their own career for the sake of their partner's. Women have always been expected to make that sacrifice. Even when women have comparable earning power, men still expect their own career to take priority. Women's expectations in this area are far less cut and dried. They generally have doubts about being able to reconcile their wish for a home and a family with their desire for a career. According to one of Shere Hite's latest books, *Women and Love*, the 'successful' woman deals with the problem by dispensing with a husband and valuing commitments to friends and lovers instead. However, I doubt whether this is true for the majority of career women.

A backlash against the New Man and New Woman has already set in, even among those who are not conservative or traditional. Men who have conquered their foes at work and have nothing more dangerous to hunt than a steak at the supermarket yearn for the simplicity of a physical challenge. They want their women to accept them as they are. Women who have demonstrated that they can make board-level decisions as well as birth babies and manage a household want a man who can relieve them of decision-making for a while and accept their vulnerability. They too want to be accepted as they are.

Women who operate heavy equipment still attract attention, even though little physical strength is required. Is it their interest in such work that is in question, or their basic sexual orientation?

An adjustment of values

Our society has a value system that equates maturity with personal autonomy and immaturity with dependence or interdependence. That is one reason why the caring professions enjoy less status than professions that create, produce, and control things. Yet many people — I for one — feel that the female tendency to build and protect relationships rather than gloat on performance and material acquisition is humanistic and of great merit; that the female tendency to value feelings over the selfish urge to succeed is of great worth.

Women, more than men, define themselves in a context of relationships rather than tasks, or at least they more readily admit that they do. They also see defence, endurance, and the ability to compromise in the face of adversity as strengths, whereas men tend to stay on the offensive and hate 'giving in'. Even if one accepts that such differences are immutable, the relative values societies give them can be adjusted if enough people wish to do so. It is not nature but society that makes judgements on the value of being male or female. Men and women are different but they are not opposites, nor in fixed relation to each other. They are composites of tendencies that can be maximized for individual and mutual benefit. To paraphrase anthropologist Margaret Mead, men should not be unsexed by failure outside the home and success within it, nor women unsexed by success outside the home and failure within it.

Male tendencies did not evolve in competition with female attributes, but in response to other male tendencies; likewise female tendencies have evolved in response to other female tendencies. Since, for the survival of the human species, males and females must evolve in a way that is mutually beneficial, it is in encouraging the strengths of both sexes that society will gain overall. Some men are naturally tender and nurturing, or learn to be, and some women are aggressive and competitive by nature or when the need arises. Fortunately there are many individuals who manage to combine the most valued traits of both sexes. The aim should be harmony without inequality rather than a battle of the sexes, and harmony cannot be achieved without understanding, respect, and open communication.

I would like to end this chapter with two quotes. The first is from development psychologist Carol Gilligan, who said: '...woman's experience provides a key to understanding central truths of adult life...it gives rise to experiences that illuminate reality common to both of the sexes: the fact in life that there is more than one path to gratification, and that the boundaries between self and others are less than they sometimes seem.' The second is a quote of my own: 'The presence of overly rigid forces (parents or others)...prevents free choice and thwarts the emergence of...natural tendencies.'

The healthiest environment for sexual growth is one that provides the widest possible banquet of experiences and models from which the individual can learn without fear of censure. If each individual is free to act according to his or her sense of sexual identity, preference, and role, then men and women will be truly able to express who they are.

The opportunities now exist — although they must continue to be asserted and fought for — for both sexes to escape from gender stereotypes. However, for reasons of status and income, more women are likely to cross into 'male' territory than men into 'female'.

Chapter 8

On being different

Being unique in a profession is accounted a virtue. Many people yearn to be special — a film maker of rare genius, a top flight pianist, a great chef, a brilliant linguist. If we have a particular talent, we like it to be recognized. Yet in sex most people want to be 'normal', or perhaps slightly better than average. To be different in matters of sex is to be suspect. If a woman shows a keen interest in sex she is labelled a nymphomaniac; if she politely refuses a proposition she is sneered at as frigid. A man is labelled a 'dud' if he shows scant interest in women or a 'stud' if he shows a great deal.

The various behaviours discussed in this chapter demonstrate that the sexual landscape is as broad as it is deep, and full of people quite different from one another. No consensus on 'normal' sexuality exists within or between cultures, or within sub-cultures or even families. Current emphasis in the West is on informed choice, mutual consent, and mutual enjoyment.

The word 'normal' has various implications. In common parlance it means healthy, acceptable, natural. To a scientist 'normal' simply means 'most common', with no connotations of health or sickness, right or wrong. 'Deviant' and 'abnormal', in the scientific sense, simply mean 'unlike the majority'. Used in the popular sense they mean unhealthy, unacceptable, and unnatural. Being different sexually is not easy. Personal habits may be harmless to the rest of the world but nonetheless stigmatized, ridiculed, persecuted, or seen as evidence of mental illness.

While most of us are normal in most respects, many of us are also sexually deviant in some way. We may have coitus significantly more or less often than others of our age, or at times or in places or in positions different from the majority; or be aroused by stimuli others find neutral or repellent; or indulge in fantasies or practices the neighbours would call perverted. Since most erotic activity takes place in private, limited only by anatomy and individual whim, there is probably more variation in sexual behaviour than in any other sort of behaviour. Because it is not seen by others, it provokes neither comment nor criticism.

For a minority of individuals being different is a way of life. Some keep their differences to themselves because of social pressures. At the other extreme are those people whose preferred sexual behaviours must be imposed on or by others to give them the satisfaction they seek. Between the two extremes are those, the majority of the minority, who simply wish to live as the majority of the majority do, free from curiosity, criticism, or condemnation.

A matter of preference

The terms 'heterosexual', 'homosexual', and 'bisexual' refer to behaviours, not to people. They merely indicate the sex of the erotic/love/affectional partners a person prefers, whether those partners are of the same or opposite sex, or either. They say very little about the person doing the preferring. A person's choice of sexual partners says almost nothing about his or her style of dress, occupation, recreational habits, behaviour in public (and that includes mannerisms and speech patterns), marital status, or general happiness. People who

Does this macho demonstration of lesbianism serve the interests of the female homosexual or feminist communities? Many lesbians strongly resist the 'butch' stereotype. Homosexual lifestyles and displays are still profoundly disturbing to the majority of heterosexuals.

prefer homosexual or bisexual relationships are every bit as diverse as those whose preferences are strictly heterosexual — they come in all sizes and shapes and belong to all races, creeds, and social conditions.

Although, increasingly, the term heterosexual is used as a noun, homosexual almost always is, and has been ever since it was first coined in 1851. In fact the label homosexual is too casually used even by those most critically concerned. Often it brackets together those who have regular sexual encounters exclusively with partners of the same sex and those whose tastes are predominantly heterosexual even if they do include fleeting or occasional homosexual experiences or fantasies. Really the term 'homosexual' should be reserved for those whose erotic preference is exclusively, or almost exclusively, for partners of the same sex, 'ambisexual' or 'bisexual' for those who enjoy sexual activity with partners of either sex, and 'heterosexual' for those whose erotic companions are always, or almost always, of the opposite sex. Too often, for statistical or political convenience, people whose sexual tastes are mainly hetero- or usually bisexual are lumped together with those whose tastes are homosexual only. To talk of these groups in the same breath is misleading. One or two homosexual encounters does not make a person homosexual.

Homosexuality

Although some people who prefer homosexual activity openly flaunt their orientation, the majority take pains to remain covert. Their sexual lives are, like those of their heterosexually or bisexually oriented neighbours, private and undisclosed. Their common orientation does not mean that they have any more in common than people of other sexual orientations. A bank manager who is homosexual has more in common with other bank managers than with other homosexuals.

What proportion of the population is strictly homosexual? Not as large a proportion as the media would have us believe. A recent *Newsweek* report quoted former French prime minister Edith Cresson as saying that the reason non-Frenchmen were not interested in women was that the majority of them were homosexual: '...perhaps not the majority, but in the United States there are already 25 percent of them and in England and Germany it is much the same. You cannot imagine it in the history of France.' Male interest in women is alive and well in France! The *Newsweek* writer, eager to put the record straight, added: 'Evidence suggests that about 10 percent of any country's men are homosexual.' Figures like this are often bandied about, but they are not accurate. They are rough extrapolations from the findings of Kinsey and his colleagues, whose sample populations were far from random (they included a high proportion of male prisoners and respondents from homophile organizations).

Newer, less biased studies done in the United States, Britain, the Netherlands, Japan, Thailand, and other countries suggest that the proportion of exclusively or nearly exclusively homosexual men in the general population is about 5 per cent. Bisexuals, male or female, seem to account for an even smaller percentage.

I have just referred to men who are 'exclusively or nearly exclusively homosexual'. As Kinsey recognized, not all individuals are sheep or goats. In order to describe sexual orientation more accurately, he devised a 7-point scale from 0 to 6; individuals rating 5 or 6 were almost exclusively or exclusively homosexual, those rating 0 or 1 were exclusively or almost exclusively heterosexual; a person with a similar number of same-sex and opposite-sex relationships would be 3. He also recorded the *fantasy* orientations of his subjects — a man may have fantasies about sex with another male but be absolutely faithful to his wife. Kinsey then averaged his subjects' real life and fantasy behaviour scores. Most researchers consider that 0 or 1 represents heterosexual, 5 and 6 homosexual, and 2, 3, or 4 bisexual orientation.

Categorizations like this have social and political implications. Some homophobes, and even some gay activists, maintain that anyone who has ever engaged in homosexual activity should be counted as homosexual. Bisexuals, who generally reject the label homosexual, are accused of 'sitting on the fence'. Groups on both sides of the fence abhor grey areas.

Male homosexuality is seldom as visible as this. Most gays are as sartorially conservative as the next man. Those who enjoy wearing women's clothes, often in order to attract the attention of macho gays, are known as 'drag queens'.

But numbers, and the categories of behaviour on which those numbers are based, are important. They could, for example, help to estimate potential growth curves for sexually transmitted diseases, determine the nature and extent of research and treatment programs for HIV disease and AIDS, and shape legislation.

The visibility and social acceptance of homosexual activity has varied with time and place. Although it is often said that homosexuality is now more prevalent than ever before, there is no real evidence that the ratio of homosexuals/bisexuals to heterosexuals is increasing. It is true, however, that homosexual activity is now more visible in the West.

This 14th-century Peruvian drinking vessel depicts two male lovers. Clearly the subject was not taboo, which suggests that homosexual practices were at least tolerated among the Incas.

Bisexuality

Like members of any other group, bisexuals may or may not be monogamous, or they may be monogamous with one sex and promiscuous with the other. They can also be sequentially or simultaneously bisexual.

Bisexual behaviour may be a passing phase or it may represent a transition from heterosexual to homosexual activity, or less usually vice versa. But whereas exclusive heterosexual or homosexual behaviour often commences around puberty, bisexual activity does not usually begin until well into adulthood. This seems particularly true for women. But over a lifetime sexual preference may come full circle — heterosexual may become bisexual, then homosexual, then revert to heterosexual.

Woody Allen once quipped that being bisexual immediately doubles one's chances of getting a date for Saturday night. In fact bisexuals have the same chances as anyone else, no more and no less, for happiness and self-fulfilment. Bisexual women have the most frequent orgasmic outlets, but homosexual men have the greatest number of partners, many averaging more than 1,000 in a lifetime. Nevertheless, in most of the Western world, bisexual activities are as much 'in the closet' as homosexual activities, and suffer from many of the same problems. Although they are more likely to receive acceptance from homosexuals than from heterosexuals, and although, when 'open', they tend to congregate with homosexuals, bisexuals are in a category of their own. They are now calling for recognition as a separate group, with special needs and interests. They don't see themselves as fence-straddlers at all, just as unique and different.

A brief history of homosexuality

Ancient chroniclers such as Juvenal (AD 60–130) described parts of Athens and Rome where boys cruised the streets and worked in brothels for the pleasure of men. Medieval historians wrote of homosexuality flourishing in France and Norman England, and descriptions of Italian cities of the Renaissance contain accounts of homosexual activities. Gay clubs were quite common in eighteenth-century London, and many American cities, notably New York, were hotbeds of homosexuality at the turn of this century. Today almost any major city in any Western country has a gay community and a gay night life. This is less true for the Orient, but holds for the major cities of Japan, India, and Thailand, and for Hong Kong. San Francisco is probably the gay capital of the world, reportedly having the highest proportion of gays of any city anywhere.

Over the centuries, particularly following the rise and spread of Christianity, homosexuality has borne the brunt of many double standards. The Old Testament in the English translation speaks of homosexual activities as 'abomination'. According to the classical historian John Boswell the original Hebrew word meant 'ritually unclean for Jews'; like other prohibitions in the Mosaic code, the eschewing of homosexual activities was a model way of life and a means of distinguishing Jew from Gentile. There was no particular word for homosexual in classical Hebrew or Greek — it was the practice, rather than the person, that was discussed.

For the first 1,000 years of the Christian era attitudes towards homosexuality seem to have been very varied and idiosyncratic. There has been much argument over the interpretation of several New Testament references, and Greek and Roman writers as well as the chroniclers of the early Middle Ages were anything but consistent, lucid, or objective in their writings.

According to Boswell, it was the Roman emperor Justinian who decreed that homosexuality should be punishable by death (which put it in the same category as adultery). From AD 533 onwards this legislation was enforced throughout the Empire. Possibly it gave Justinian an excuse to attack political enemies and confiscate their wealth. Thereafter anyone who engaged in homosexual activities — indeed anyone who was obviously different, such as Jews, astrologers, and unorthodox Christians — became an obvious scapegoat. With or without religious conviction or encouragement from the Church of Rome, Justinian's successors persecuted homosexuality.

Charlemagne (742–814), who considered himself responsible for keeping the Holy Roman Empire Christian, was apparently worried, when he ascended the throne in 771, that there were so few effective anti-homosexual laws and that those which did exist were only half-heartedly enforced. But although he railed against homosexual practices, especially among the clergy, he did not invent any new penalties. In the main, and allowing for a lot of local variation, attitudes towards homosexuality were relatively tolerant in the early Middle Ages.

With time, however, religious and secular leaders became less accepting of sexual 'variations'. Few scholars agree on the forces that brought about this change. Nevertheless the expression 'acting contrary to nature' came to be used for unapproved heterosexual or homosexual acts, and punishments ranged from public ridicule, enforced fasting, and confiscation of property to torture, castration, and even death.

By the time of Richard Lionheart (1157–99), who was not only a Crusade leader and a symbol of chivalry, but also gay, homosexuality was beginning to be regarded as heretical and criminal. The legal description of homosexuality as 'the crime not fit to be named' goes back to the early thirteenth century. The punishments were burning, drowning, or being buried alive. By the time of Edward II (1284–1327), the last openly gay medieval monarch, anti-gay sentiment was widespread. Edward himself was deposed and murdered. The illegal status of homosexual behaviour was retained in English law for another six centuries, although punishments grew less severe. English law was of course the model for the laws of many other countries, including the United States.

In 1895 the brilliant author, dramatist, and socialite Oscar Wilde was brought to trial in London for 'gross indecency', a legal euphemism for a variety of disapproved of sexual acts. He was eloquent in his defence of 'the love that dare not speak its name', telling the world of the deep feelings, noble sentiments, and affectionate companionship he associated with homosexual love. Despite his powerful pleas and his eminence as a public figure, he was found guilty and sentenced to two years in Reading Gaol. His personal ordeal not only caused homosexuality to be named in public but also brought it into open discussion. But it was another 60 years before Britain dropped homosexual acts among consenting adults from its code of punishable offences. To this day the rights of homosexuals under English law do not parallel the rights given to heterosexuals. Sexual activity between two men, even if it is by mutual consent, is illegal under the age of 21; heterosexual activity is only illegal under the age of 16, the 'age of consent' for females. Indeed the maximum gaol sentence under the 'gross indecency' law which convicted Wilde was *raised* in 1967 from two years to five. In America, each state has its own laws regarding homosexuality; in some, homosexual behaviour is illegal and liable to imprisonment, in others it is legal and of no concern to the government.

The designation homosexual was first used in print in 1851 by the German author Kardy Maria Benkart. Theorizing about the origin of sexual arousal, he used the words 'certain male and female individuals with the homosexual urge'. As we have seen, terminology and recognition have trailed well behind private and public practice.

Homosexuality in different cultures

Although no society has ever advocated homosexuality as the predominant mode of adult sexual activity, many have never paid much attention to it, and some have condoned or even encouraged it for certain minority groups. Among the non-Muslim Siwan of Egypt, for example, all men and boys engage in anal intercourse.

Henri de Toulouse-Lautrec painted this portrait of Oscar Wilde in 1895. The tribute of one social outcast to another? It was Wilde's very public affair with the son of the Marquis of Queensberry that led to his conviction and imprisonment.

In many cultures the distinction is made not between men and women, but between men and non-men. Men are those who have married or passed initiation; non-men — unmarried men, uninitiated boys, and unmarried females — are all possible sex partners. This was true in ancient Greece, and is true of the Aranda aborigines of Australia and various groups in New Guinea, who consider homosexual activity necessary for healthy development in young boys. Among the Kaluli of New Guinea all boys are recipients of anal intercourse by the men. Among the Sambia, also of New Guinea, oral-genital practices are believed to encourage the transmission of maleness from man to boy; once they attain manhood, Kaluli and Sambia males switch to heterosexual behaviours.

Latin Americans distinguish between *activos* and *passivos*, indicating that the majority of gay males are either penetrators or penetrated, rarely both. Not unexpectedly in cultures where *machismo* is important, *activos* consider themselves, and are considered, masculine, and *passivos* feminine. These are distinctions which are considered irrelevant or old-fashioned among North American and European gays.

In the traditional Japan of the samurai, homosexuality was a matter of little consequence and remained so until the middle of the nineteenth century, when Western influences made it taboo. Since it has always been traditional for Japanese men to get married, homosexuals (and heterosexuals) satisfy their erotic needs outside marriage. The stigma against homosexuality is still strong, but it is slowly lessening.

In India, with laws inherited from the British Raj, homosexual activites are illegal, but the law is seldom enforced. Nevertheless there has always been a homosexual sub-culture. A gay community is now emerging from the closet, with a voice in *Bombay Dost*, a magazine

Prostitution is part of Bombay's homosexual sub-culture. Here a male Hijra prostitute waits for a pick-up.

that began publication in 1991. In India, as in Japan and many other family-based Asian societies, homosexuality is not viewed as sinful, but it is felt to clash with family interests. In the *Mahabharata*, the classical Hindu epic poem about good and evil, the god Krishna dresses as a woman and gives himself as the first sex experience of the first-born son of Arjuna, the great warrior. Other gods in the Hindu pantheon are openly gay.

In the former Soviet Union homosexuality has been both illegal and politically incorrect, castigated as a product of capitalism. In China, although homosexuality is not illegal, there is strong and widespread homophobic feeling; homosexual activites exist in a furtive underground. In Russia and the other Soviet republics homosexual activities will probably remain illegal for some time to come, but they are becoming more visible and not being prosecuted. An international symposium and film festival in Leningrad in July-August 1991, attended by participants from around the world as well as prominent Soviet artists and politicians, was the scene of an historic public display of homosexual pride and an open call for repeal of anti-homosexual legislation.

Perhaps the most stringent prohibitions against homosexual activities are seen in Muslim countries. Algerian liberals are currently fighting a renewed call by fundamentalists to enforce the death penalty for homosexuality (and adultery). At present, Iran and other Arab countries retain the death penalty.

Erotic album paintings of female lovers are relatively rare in Indian art. It was the custom, in courtly harems, for senior wives to instruct younger wives in the arts of lovemaking.

On a more positive note, the Scandinavian countries, the Netherlands, France, and Brazil have no laws against adult same-sex activities. Each nation, however, has decided that adulthood occurs at a different age. Britain is the most conservative, with 21 for males and 16 for females. In Belgium and Italy the age of consent — the age at which an individual is considered capable of knowledgeably agreeing to sex — is 16 for both sexes; in Poland and France it is 15; in the Netherlands it is 14.

Female homosexuality

Anthropologists say that homosexual activity among females is much less common than among males. However, female homosexuality is overt and accepted among cultures as diverse as the nomadic Chukchee of Siberia, and the African Azanda, Mbundu, and Nama tribes.

From surveys in the United States, Australia, Japan, the Netherlands, and elsewhere, same-sex orientation seems to be roughly half as common among females as among males. International figures are scarce, but those for Caucasians indicate that about 1 in 50 women is exclusively homosexual and about the same number occasionally, or at least in fantasy. The lesbian population is thus even more invisible than the gay male population.

For political reasons homosexual women often prefer to be referred to as lesbians, since it gives them identity as a group. In Victorian times they were referred to as 'romantic friends' and until the 1960s as 'female homosexuals'. The term lesbian is derived from Lesbos, the Greek island home of the poetess Sappho (active around 600 BC), who extolled the beauty of love between two women. Among the millions of lesbians in the United States, Britain, and elsewhere there is a feeling that their existence as a group deserves acknowledgement, even if not all of them wish to declare themselves.

The invisibility of the lesbian population is reflected in English law. Popular legend has it that Queen Victoria rejected the very idea of lesbianism — it was 'impossible' — when the laws on homosexuality were being revised. Lesbianism was also ignored in the report of the Wolfenden Committee in 1957, which led to long-overdue reform of the laws on homosexuality in Britain. (British law has some curious blind spots when it comes to sexual behaviour. For instance, only women can be raped and only females can be prostitutes. American law is 'unisex' in these respects.)

A parallel with the earlier Oscar Wilde case was that of the author Radclyffe Hall. Her novel on lesbianism, *The Well of Loneliness*, published in 1928, was branded as obscene by a London court, and all copies of the book were ordered to be destroyed. Radclyffe Hall was not, as Wilde was, prosecuted for her personal behaviour, though she openly dressed as a man and went about London with her companion Una Troubridge.

While many common needs exist among male and female homosexuals, lesbians have some that are special. In particular, they do not wish to be stereotyped. As with individuals of any other sexual orientation, they can be feminine or macho, conservative or liberal, devout or atheist, orgastically driven or not bothered about orgasm, promiscuous or monogamous, in the closet or out of it, attractive or plain...and their reasons for identifying with the lesbian community are often broader than those for male homosexuals.

By tradition gay day parades in the United States are led by 'dykes on bikes'.

The culture within a culture

A gay lib demonstration in New York. A major goal of gay activists is to break out of the ghetto — tea rooms, coffee shops, baths, bars — to which an oppressive heterosexual and homophobic society has consigned them.

Whereas the term homosexual refers to behaviour, the term gay refers to a sub-culture. Many gay individuals are open about their sexual orientation and can be identified by various mannerisms and activities, sometimes effeminate in the case of males and masculine in the case of females. These may be natural expressions of self or part of highly formalized codes that signal group identity. Many social signals used by homosexuals and heterosexuals are the same, since their purpose is to communicate sexual interest in a way that does not arouse hostility, ridicule, or rejection. Nevertheless, for homosexuals moving in a primarily heterosexual world, certain codes are necessary — subtle uses of tone of voice, stance, code words, and eye contact.

Every large city has contact points — bars, clubs, baths, coffee shops — where those seeking homosexual sex or gay companionship can meet. Formality is minimal and there is plenty of opportunity to openly explore sexual possibilities. Places that cater exclusively for the gay sub-culture are secure oases in an often intolerant world. They provide social support and a setting in which to learn the etiquette and values of the group. Bars for gay males are particularly noted for 'cruising', the picking up of partners solely for sex.

In fact the male gay scene deals with overt sexuality with an ease not found in the heterosexual or lesbian worlds. Immediate sexual encounters are available for the asking in public toilets ('tea-rooms') and baths; however briefly, 'closet' and open gays satisfy their erotic needs. Most often such pick-ups are purely sexual, with no relationship expected or even wanted.

In many societies, and increasingly so in the West, a gay lifestyle is becoming more openly expressed and less frowned upon. Even so, there are different levels of allowable public behaviour. Some people feel uncomfortable when they see a boy and a girl kissing in public. Many more will feel uncomfortable if the partners are of the same sex. Also, overt sexual behaviour is less remarked in a large city than in a small country town.

Coming out and 'outing'

Among the more difficult processes of gay life is 'coming out'. The precise meaning of the term keeps shifting, but essentially it means admitting to yourself that you are homosexually oriented and then revealing the fact to others. Coming out of the 'closet' of denial and secrecy is rather like entering a minefield, and it is a continuing rather than a once-and-for-all process. Friends are usually the first to know; members of the family, parents in particular, are often the last. Do you tell work colleagues, the people you play sport with, your doctor? It depends on how far you want to go. There are no accurate figures for the number of homosexuals who are 'out'. Most gay activists believe that the more people come out, the more difficult it will be for society to remain homophobic, heterosexist, and discriminatory. In the United States and elsewhere National Coming Out Days have been instituted to support this effort. But in the view of other gays and straights (non-gays), one should not have to advertise sexual orientation any more than religion; all tastes should be acceptable.

'Outing' is much more controversial. This is a phenomenon of the 1990s. Seemingly born of frustration at the slow pace of social acceptance, this is the practice of gay activists divulging the alleged or actual homosexual behaviour of politicians, sport or media stars, and others. By doing this, they argue, those ashamed of their orientation are given a variety of successful role models, and the power of those who hide their own homosexuality behind homophobic attitudes or activites is reduced. The counter-argument is that outing is 'philosophical rape', 'psychic violence', and 'ethical blackmail'. Certainly, outing can damage lives and careers. Should it not be up to the individual to reveal as much or as little about his or her private life as he or she likes?

A genetic basis for sexual orientation?

The interacting forces that lead to any type of behaviour are not always clear. Why, for example, do some people find it easy to ignore social conventions and others find it difficult?

Coming out, German style. A gay demonstrator sports the slogan 'Fag come out of the closet'. Some gays are willing to be publicly identified, others not.

At a most basic level, we do not know why the majority of individuals are heterosexual and a minority homosexual. The clues point to genetic predisposition rather than social training.

The strongest evidence for a genetic basis for homosexual orientation comes from studies of families and twins. The classic studies in this area were done in the 1950s by Franz J. Kallmann working with 40 identical (monozygous) and 45 non-indentical (dizygous) pairs of male twins chosen on the basis of known homosexual behaviour on the part of one or other twin. He found, without exception, that if one identical twin was homosexual, so was the other. This was not the case with non-identical twins, where the chances of the second twin being homosexual seemed more or less the same as in the general male population. Kallmann also found that if one identical twin rated 5 or 6 on the 7-point Kinsey scale, the chance that his brother would also rate 5 or 6 were more than 90 per cent. If their ratings were different, they were still within one or two points of each other.

The apparent neatness of Kallmann's findings aroused suspicion and scepticism, with the result that a slew of studies soon followed which showed identical twins who were *not* concordant for homosexuality. In the 1950s and 1960s society preferred to think of human behaviour as a product of free will and social engineering rather than biological destiny. That was Kinsey's view, and Kallmann's conclusions suggested the opposite.

'Nurture' theories of homosexuality remained fashionable until the 1980s. But preliminary reports by myself, and sociologists Fred Whitam and James Dannemiller, and the more definitive work of Richard Pillard, James Weinrich, and others, all based on new studies, now support a major genetic component to sexual orientation.

In their first set of studies, Pillard and his colleagues looked at 186 families in which at least one member was openly homosexual. They also had a set of heterosexual 'index' individuals as controls. Having assessed the sexual orientation of all male and female siblings in each family, they found that if one brother was homosexual the chances of other brothers in the same family being homosexual were between 20 and 25 per cent; if the index brother was heterosexual, the chances of other brothers being homosexual were only between 4 and 6 per cent. Findings for female homosexuality were not so clear.

The most recent report from Pillard and colleagues strongly supports these original findings. In a study involving 110 pairs of twins, they found that 52 per cent of male identical twins of self-identified homosexual men were also homosexual, compared with 22 per cent of non-identical twins, and 11 per cent of non-twin or adopted brothers. In recent studies by myself and Fred Whitam involving 61 sets of twins, we found a concordance of approximately 65 per cent for identical male twins and 30 per cent for non-identical twins. While these figures do not exactly match those of Pillard and Bailey, they indicate that genetic make-up is a large component of sexual orientation. But, and I emphasize it is a big 'but', we also found that when twins are discordant, the divergence is usually large (for example, one twin might be 6 while the other was 0). Why even identical twins who share the same genes and upbringing should differ so markedly is not yet understood. Other factors must be involved.

Lastly, there have been several recent reports from the Netherlands and the United States which suggest that brain structure may have something to do with orientation. Dutch researchers F. Swaab and M.A. Hofman found that a region of the brain called the suprachiasmatic nucleus is much larger in homosexuals than in heterosexuals; American Simon LeVay found that the interstitial nucleus of the anterior hypothalamus is smaller in homosexuals and women than in male heterosexuals. The brains of lesbians have yet to be examined. These findings seem to support a biological component to homosexuality.

Gay critics of sex research are quick to point out that researchers seldom look for causes of heterosexuality. Actually, heterosexuality and homosexuality are two sides of the same coin; learning about one can lead to an understanding of the other.

Ethically, scientists cannot manipulate a person's sexual preferences for the purposes of research, but real life provides plenty of thought-provoking anomalies, such as that of the penectomized boy mentioned in Chapter 6 who was raised as a girl but insisted on surgery to enable him to live as a man and as a heterosexual. The world's scientific literature is full of similar cases The work of J. Imperato-McGinley and her colleagues is particularly instructive in this regard. Among a group of natives in the Dominican Republic some males, due to a genetic quirk, lacked a penis at birth, so their parents raised them as girls. At puberty, however, they developed a penis and scrotum, and switched to living as heterosexual males. Being brought up as girls destined to marry males had minor influence on their orientation as adults. Such cases add grist to the argument that heterosexuality is also a matter of genetic predisposition.

Mother and son? Yes and no. The mother is a male transsexual, a genetic male who has had sex change surgery and now lives as a woman. The children of transsexuals or homosexual parents are no more likely to be transsexual or homosexual than the children of 'straights'.

Children of different parents

To end this discussion of homosexuality I would like to focus on some of the findings of researchers Richard Green, Mary Hotvedt, Jane Barclay Mandel, Brian Miller, and others concerning the sexual orientation of the children of gay or transsexual couples.

Firstly, the children of such parents are no more likely to grow up gay or transsexual than the children of heterosexual parents. Second, gay or transsexual parents do not subject their children to sexual or social harassment or bring them up to be sexually deviant. Their concern for the welfare of their children is quite independent of their own sexual orientation, sexual identity, or sexual lifestyle.

As far as single parents are concerned, matched and controlled studies show that there is no difference between children brought up by lesbian single parents or heterosexual single parents. For single mothers, of any stripe, motherhood, not sexual expression, is the focus of their lives. Similar research on single fathers is not available, but those cases that have been researched fail to show any difference between the children of gay fathers and the children of heterosexual fathers. Generally it is the absence of a parent — usually the father — as a result of death or divorce, rather than the lifestyle of one or both parents, that seems to have the most impact on a child's social development.

Transvestism

People who habitually dress in the clothing of the opposite sex are broadly termed transvestites or cross-dressers (TVs or CDs). The vast majority of transvestites are male and heterosexual. If they are homosexual, they are usually called drag queens (the distinction is critical within such sub-communities). For many heterosexual transvestites, cross-dressing has an erotic function; it is sexually arousing, sometimes to the point of orgasm, with the clothes of the opposite sex acting as fetish objects. But among the 10 per cent or so of homosexuals who cross-dress the erotic fetish element is rare or non-existent. In their case cross-dressing is done to satisfy their feminine feelings or to appeal to other males, though it may also have an element of exhibitionism. Male prostitutes who solicit homosexuals are the most publicly obvious cross-dressers, though by no means all of them wear women's clothes.

People cross-dress for many reasons. Children dress up and put on make-up for the fun of pretending to be someone else or to try out a new image. But cross-dressing among children is rare; if a child repeatedly cross-dresses it is a strong, but not infallible, indication of future homosexual tendencies rather than of transvestism. A study by psychiatrist Richard Green showed that boys who were considered 'sissy' often enjoyed dressing up as girls; as adults, almost all of them were homosexual, although not necessarily cross-dressers.

In adults cross-dressing is more likely to be accompanied by feelings of sexual pleasure, or by the feeling that it satisfies a dimension of personality that cannot be expressed in any other way. For some adults cross-dressing is a compulsion that neither they nor the psychiatric profession fully understand.

A kabuki actor prepares to impersonate the heroine of a tale of illicit love. Most kabuki plays revolve around the conflict between passion and duty. Kabuki theatre became the dominant form of public entertainment in Japan during the 18th century. A visit to the theatre was a special occasion — the audience ate, drank, and talked during the performance.

Cross-dressing is often referred to as 'going in drag'. Originally the term 'drag' was theatrical, and meant the wearing of women's clothes by men impersonating women. Various male entertainers today capitalize on the novelty value of drag; they cross-dress to shock and make fun of establishment stereotypes.

In the history of the West, and among many Oriental and primitive cultures, transvestism has been part of artistic or religious expression. It has had little or nothing to do with eroticism and is highly regulated in form and style. In Noh and Kabuki theatre, classical art forms in Japan, men play all the parts; on the other hand, the dancers and singers of the Takarazuka theatre, a more recent tradition, are all women. In classical Greek and Roman drama and on the Elizabethan stage all

women's roles were played by men.

Cross-dressing was one of the Puritans' main objections to the theatre. They regarded it as a violation of the injunction in Deuteronomy: 'The women shall not wear that which pertaineth unto a man, neither shall a man put on a woman's garment.' One of the charges against Joan of Arc was that she wore men's clothing. In other religions and cultures the opposite was true. Among at least 130 North American tribes there existed a special group of individuals, usually men but occasionally women, who dressed in the clothes of the opposite sex; *berdache*, as they were called, often had high social status and were honoured for their ability to transcend rigid dualities. Homosexuality may or may not have been involved. In Dahomey in Africa cross-dressing was the Sakpota dancers' way of appeasing malign spirits. Among the present-day Yurubas of Brazil transvestism among heterosexuals is well accepted, but usually a private matter; the dressing may be quite elaborate but is not usually displayed outside a circle of trusted friends and relations. Cross-dressing is not uncommon in many parts of Latin America and Southeast Asia.

One famous exponent of cross-dressing was Charles d'Eon, a French spy active in the late eighteenth century. Using the pseudonym Madame Lia de Beaumont, he was sent as a woman to the court of St. Petersburg in Russia and to the court of St. James's in London. His exploits became so well known that 'eonism' became a synonym for transvestism. The British organization for heterosexual transvestites, The Beaumont Society, is named in his honour. He was so convincing both as a man and as a women that members of the London Stock Exchange made wagers as to his true sex and had his body examined in detail after his death.

Transsexualism

Those rare individuals who believe they have been born in a body of the wrong sex are transsexuals (TSs). Theirs is a frustrating existence, in which sexual identity and the image in the mirror are in conflict. Although their genitals are within the normal range for their biological sex, their mental image of themselves often drives them to seek sex change surgery. Cross-dressing is merely palliative, an inadequate substitute for the body they crave. A male transsexual believes he is really a female with the wrong anatomy and usually feels that his orientation towards men as sexual partners is properly heterosexual. No true male homosexual would want to have his penis removed and replaced with a vagina, but this would be the dream of a male transsexual. With a female transsexual the converse would be true. While she may not necessarily opt to have a penis and scrotum constructed in place of her vagina and labia, she does want her breasts removed and her periods to cease, since these are constant reminders of what she thinks she is not. Since sexual identity and sexual orientation are independent, homosexually-oriented transsexuals also exist. Transsexuals very clearly exemplify the distinction between sex, identity, and gender: a male transsexual has the sex (chromosome set, anatomy) of a male but the identity (psychological sense of self) of a female; female transsexuals are born with female anatomy, believe they are male, and want to live as such.

Transsexuals commonly put themselves through a long period of self-testing to see if they can affirm their bodily sex in spite of their mental doubts. A male transsexual might volunteer for the commandos, or a female transsexual work as a stripper, and outwardly be well accepted in those gender roles. But they themselves remain unconvinced. They then turn to trying to convince the world that their inner sexual identity is the real one and that the gender imposed by anatomy and society is false. They try all possible means of altering their appearance and behaviour towards that of the opposite sex. In this urgent desire to transform their genitals and their secondary sex characteristics, they resort to hormone treatment, depilatories, hair transplants, and eventually surgery. The results vary from the amazingly convincing to the pathetic and bizarre. At the last, surgery seems to provide an inner peace not available by any other means.

While homosexuality and transvestism have been known since antiquity, transsexualism seems relatively new, perhaps because the hormone treatments and surgical procedures that can turn wishing into reality are new. Several reputed transvestites of the past may have been transsexuals, the Roman emperor Heliogabalus (ruled AD 218–222), for instance. Wearing a woman's robe, cosmetics, and a tiara, he entered the gates of Rome demanding to be honoured as empress. On another occasion he tried to castrate himself in honour of a Syrian deity.

Female transsexuals, genetic females who make the switch to a male lifestyle, are less numerous than male transsexuals. In this case the transition is very convincing.

Transsexualism hit the world headlines in 1952 when it was announced that an American ex-soldier named George Jorgensen had visited Denmark and returned as Christine Jorgensen. She had had sex change surgery to remove penis and testicles and replace them with labia and a vagina, and had also been given full breasts. Subsequent publicity and open discussion revealed that a surprisingly large number of people felt their true sex was not the sex they were born with. They too wanted sex change surgery. For the first time physicians, psychologists, and psychiatrists worldwide began to realize that sexual identity does not necessarily reflect genital anatomy or gender upbringing, and that it can override both.

Most transsexuals make the transition from one sex to the other without fanfare and quietly melt into their new community. Only few publicize the fact, or the media, always hungry for

The sex change process places enormous strains on an established relationship. This family has survived the process. Husband Kelvin, now Clare (centre), continues to live with his wife and child.

sex stories, do it for them. Jan Morris, the distinguished travel writer, was once James, and described the change in her book *Conundrum*; René Richards, the opthalmologist and tennis star, was once Richard; the musician-organist Wendy Carlos was once Walter; Tula (Caroline) Cossey, the international model who wrote *My Story*, was once Barry.

Female to male changes also occur, but less frequently; the actual ratio is not known, but somewhere between 1 in 4 and 1 in 10 sex changes are in the male direction rather than the female. This is one of the strongest proofs that sex changes are not made for social gain. After all, it is more advantageous in terms of status, income, and other measures to be a man. Society at large more readily understands the wish to change from female to male.

In some Western countries the law simply cannot cope with sex change, despite surgery and gender-appropriate dress. In Britain, for example, despite pleas from the legal and medical professions, transsexuals have been sent to gaol as members of their previous sex and denied the rights of full legal marriage.

Sexual identity — the inner conviction of being female or male — is a separate dimension of sexuality. The way we dress and speak, the jobs we do and the careers we choose, and all our relationships, sexual and non-sexual, are secondary to that inner conviction. Strange as it may sound, the transsexual is really saying: 'Change my body, not my mind'. Our most powerful sex organ is between our ears, not between our legs.

Hermaphroditism

At one time circus side-shows advertised half man/half woman attractions and the mythologies of many ancient cultures celebrate fusions of male and female, but the actual occurrence of hermaphroditic individuals is rare. The word 'hermaphrodite' is a contraction of the Greek names Hermes and Aphrodite; Hermes was the messenger of the gods and

A 2nd-century BC Roman sculpture of a sleeping hermaphrodite. The 'androgyne' (man-woman) theme crops up in the mythologies of Greece, Persia, India, and China, symbolizing wholeness, perfection, the union of male and female, yang and yin, day and night, heaven and earth.

Aphrodite the goddess of love. True hermaphrodites possess both ovarian and testicular tissue. Despite myths to the contrary, and the occasional sensational newspaper report, they could not impregnate themselves even if they wanted to.

Pseudohermaphrodites, however, are not rare. They may appear once in every 100 or 200 births. These are individuals who have one or more sexual characteristics — genetic, genital, endocrine, anatomical — out of keeping with the others. Most pseudohermaphroditic conditions are the result of a genetic anomaly; for example, the individual has an XXY chromosome set and the appearance of a feminized male, or an XO chromosome set and the appearance of a female. Most pseudohermaphrodites live comparatively normal lives with relatives and close friends unaware of their uniqueness, and perhaps unaware of it themselves, although they may bring themselves to medical attention due to difficulties with fertility or low libido or because they feel sexually different.

Incest

In 1979, in Massachusetts, Victoria Pittorino married her brother David Goddu. They had been separated as young children and adopted into different families. On Victoria's initiative they were reunited after 20 years apart and within a few weeks fell in love and got married. Both were brought to court on a charge of incest, instigated by Victoria's adoptive mother. They were found guilty, ordered not to live as man and wife, and to seek counselling in order to re-establish the relationship of brother and sister. A 42-year-old mother in Virginia and her 20 year-old son, reared in a foster home, were not so lucky. Reunited when the son was 17, they married and lived together for a year until a social worker discovered their relationship and brought charges. In 1980 they were banned from meeting again for 10 years. But these cases, though legally tried and judged as incest, are not typical of the popular idea of incest or the features of incestuous behaviour that are most disturbing to Western society.

Most horrific to Western notions of proper behaviour are cases of incest between parents and children, usually father and daughter, where the child is young and unwilling, the age disparity great, and where fear or force is used to maintain the relationship. Much more common, perhaps five to ten times as common, are relations between brothers, sisters, and cousins. These are usually of less interest to the authorities and, if among peers and without coercion, are generally considered part of growing up.

In the West incest is defined as 'sexual activity between individuals prohibited to marry'. Among Roman Catholics, incest extends to first cousins — the marriage of President Franklin Delano Roosevelt to his cousin Eleanor was seen by some as incestuous. Among the Navaho Indians incest extends to all the members of the mother's or father's clan, or 'linked' clans, effectively ruling out hundreds of people as marriage partners. In the Trobriand Islands a girl who marries her mother's brother is committing incest; in Sri Lanka this relationship would be considered an ideal basis for marriage.

Incest has been called 'the last sexual taboo', now that adultery, homosexuality, masturbation, and other behaviours previously swept under the carpet have been acknowledged as prevalent. In fact incest may have been the first taboo of all. In the view of French anthropologist Claude Lévi-Strauss, prohibition of sex within the family was 'the fundamental step...in which the transition from nature to culture is accomplished.' And yet the Mbuti pygmies have no concept of incest, and incest was not only acceptable but a positive duty among royal families in some ancient and not-so-ancient civilizations. The Egyptian queen Cleopatra married two of her brothers to secure the succession. In traditional Hawaii, sib (sibling) mating among *ali'i* (chiefs and others of high status) was obligatory. The offspring of a full brother/full sister mating was considered most sacred: 'The children born of these two were gods, fire, heat, and raging blazes.' A chief born of such a union was so divine he seldom travelled during the day, since all who saw him were obliged to prostrate themselves until he left. But the prerogative was regal only; incestuous relationships were forbidden to commoners.

Until this century, in the West, there were no laws against incest. Legislation more or less coincided with the shift of population from rural areas to towns and cities at the turn of this century, which made incestuous practices more noticeable. Studies have shown that incest is more common within families separated by physical or social distance, hence the belief that it is usually a rural phenomenon.

An often-used argument against incest is that children born of incestuous relationships are more likely to inherit biological defects if both parents contribute similar defective genes. But it is an equally valid argument that incest might enhance genetic assets. Perhaps the strongest argument against incest is that it disrupts standard lines of family authority, puts family members in stressful competition, and subjects them to secrecy, ridicule, and guilt.

Those who want legal sanctions against incest removed say that the law fails as a deterrent and in fact violates personal freedoms of no concern to society at large. They also say that incest by mutual consent may have positive and educative value, and that physical closeness in families is inhibited by fear of the incest taboo.

No very reliable statistics on the prevalence of incest exist. How can they when there is no basic agreement on the definition of incest? It has been crudely estimated that in the United States between 5 and 30 per cent of the population have at some time been involved in incest, defined as everything from petting to coitus between immediate family members as well as cousins and step relations. Figures for other countries are even more difficult to obtain. Not only is research less often done, but record keeping is not consistent since the nature of the concept is not agreed upon. France and Belgium, for example, do not have special laws against incest, and several countries, like England, classify incest under the heading of 'abuse of authority'.

Why be different?

To the ignorant and undiscriminating, homosexuals, transsexuals, transvestites, and others who 'break the rules' are all 'queer'. No attempt is made to understand the distinct characteristics of these different manifestations of sexuality. They are seen as deviant, in the derogatory sense, as sick or evil. The opposite view, slowly gaining ground, is that homosexuals, transsexuals, and others are 'just different'. Some psychiatrists and sociologists argue that such individuals have poor home backgrounds which predispose them to aberrant sexual development, others that particular family constellations — a weak or absent father or an overbearing mother — are to blame, but their arguments are not very convincing. Actually, there is now a great deal of evidence *against* such theories. Children brought up in the same family still go their separate ways, sexually speaking.

It seems that nature has provided us with a maximum of sexual drive, a modicum of bias, and a minimum of direction, and so our fertile minds have found many different ways in which our sexuality can be indulged, expressed, and satisfied. There is no evidence that any of the 'different' behaviours we have been discussing are intrinsically harmful either to the individual or to society, except where social and emotional pressures lead to secrecy and private anguish. But being different does not end there. Individual sexual needs and preferences are more numerous still.

Other sexual tastes

Some sexual practices, such as exhibitionism and voyeurism, require a lack of privacy to be effective. On an everyday level and to a certain extent, almost everyone is both an exhibitionist and voyeur. We like to display ourselves and be thought attractive, and we are naturally curious about other people's sex lives. These are minor sexual indulgences.

Quite distinct are those rare individuals who achieve their major or only erotic pleasure from seeing or being seen in sexual activity. Such people compulsively risk public outrage and even imprisonment by invading the privacy of others. Usually they are more of a nuisance than a threat, and only when such behaviour is regular and compulsive should the clinical terms 'exhibitionist' or 'voyeur' be used. Exhibitionists, or 'flashers', expose their genitals to unsuspecting women, but shy away from pursuing the encounter, even in conversation. They hastily leave the scene after witnessing the shock and attention they crave. They are playing out a fantasy in which self-exposure and the shocked response are the triggers to arousal. A voyeur, or 'peeping Tom', may creep up to the window of a bedroom in the hope of seeing the occupants naked or engaged in sexual activity. The act of flashing or peeping is all that is erotically desired. But those who are flashed or peeped at rarely enjoy the experience.

Almost all exhibitionists and voyeurs are men and their activity sometimes includes masturbation. Flashing and peeping lie at the extreme of a whole spectrum of sexual expression. For most people, seeing or being seen is part of behaviour among intimates or part of fantasies which lead to sexual arousal.

Sexwatchers will be aware of the enormous variety of sexual tastes catered for by the pornography industry. For some, practices such as group sex, rubber, leather, fur, shoe, or foot fetishism, sado-masochism, bondage, and bestiality exist only in magazines and movies, but for others they are fantasies that enliven an otherwise unremarkable sex life. For some of course they are a necessary reality. James Joyce, author of *Ulysses*, enjoyed urine and faeces with his sex play (scatology); T.E. Lawrence (of Arabia) loved to be birched. Perhaps it was part of their genius, perhaps it was apart.

The general attitude towards such practices is disapproving — there is a genuine fear that unwilling participants might become involved if society makes no protest — and so legal or social restraints are placed on advertising and display. For instance, the second largest annual parade in the United States, the San Francisco Gay Day Parade, which attracts some 150,000 participants, is rarely shown on the national evening news, but smaller parades routinely receive national coverage. Advertisements for companionship or mutual activities by

'It's always a pleasure to see young people enjoying themselves', a cartoon published in the French magazine Le Rive *in 1904. Curiosity about the sexual behaviour of others is perfectly normal, but for the voyeur peeping (perhaps with masturbation) may be a more thrilling route to sexual arousal and release than erotic contact with another person.*

many of those who are 'different' are often refused by newspapers and other media that readily carry other advertisements of questionable merit. Legally speaking, an advertisement is not an offer, but an invitation to an offer. If it is consensual behaviour that is being invited, should such advertisements be refused?

No sex please

Lack of interest in sex, abstinence, celibacy — these are behaviours not often thought of as 'different'. In the West, attitudes towards 'no sex' are ambivalent. We accept celibacy as appropriate for clerics, the devout, and the virtuously unmarried, but ridicule it or find it vaguely disturbing in others. In most societies a lack of interest in sex is viewed with puzzlement. Friends and family members feel they 'ought to do something about it'.

There are different types of celibacy. For most people there are times, long or short, when no sexual partner is available. For monks, nuns, priests, yogis, and other ascetics, celibacy is an exercise in self-discipline and self-denial, a means of achieving greater spirituality, union with the deity, greater happiness in the next world or the next incarnation. They abstain from sex on principle as others abstain from alcohol or meat. For others, celibacy simply reflects the lack of suitable or acceptable sexual partners. These individuals, mostly women, live in multiple- or single-person households; for them, sexual opportunities are either lacking or not taken up due to previous disappointments, fear of disease, or fear of gossip. (There are also good demographic reasons for greater celibacy among women; women live longer than men, more women remain unmarried, divorced women find it more difficult to remarry, and very few women resort to male prostitutes to satisfy their sexual appetitites.) There is also enforced celibacy, among mariners and military personnel, for example, and among prisoners. In the Middle Ages absentee husbands locked their wives into chastity belts to enforce fidelity. There are also those for whom sexual or erotic interest is low or non-existent; these women, and fewer men, feel no hardship or loss. They claim that they are never, or only rarely, sexually aroused.

This cartoon, also French, shows a flasher deprived of the shock and horror he was hoping for by dropping his trousers. His lady victim calmly says: 'Actually I rather like the hang of your trousers.' The French pun 'tombe bien' loses something in translation, but if all women reacted like this to flashers there might be fewer flashers.

Loves compared

R ecently I repeated an attempt made some years ago, with the same results. Originally I asked a camera team to roam through the parks and beaches of Honolulu taking candid pictures of people expressing affection. This time I went myself. Honolulu is a destination for honeymooners and has a younger-than-average population, so I thought it would be easy to find couples expressing love — holding hands, embracing, kissing.... I was wrong. Love and affection were indeed there, but expressed much more subtly. Far from being flaunted — and flaunted means different things to different people — love and affection are rarely openly displayed.

How does one recognize love? At its most fundamental, love is a bond, a feeling of attachment between two individuals. It is an emotion that is common, as far as we can judge, to all higher order social creatures. It exists between animals that live in packs or troops and among those in which infancy and dependence are prolonged. It enables individuals, especially young individuals, to learn from their elders and peers. It induces individuals to cooperate for hunting, food gathering, defence, and other important purposes.

Higher social animals show bonds of all sorts — between adults of the same or opposite sex, between parents and offspring, between old and young, between siblings and age mates. Many primates and members of other species act as if they mourn the loss of an infant, parent, or mate who dies or disappears. With that individual, they display behaviour which, in humans, we would call love. The adults of many species, most notably birds and fish, are monogamous and apparently mate for life; when the bond is broken, they do not easily form another. This relationship model, the pair bond, is the one in which humans feel some of their strongest loves and loyalties. In animals and humans it persists after death.

Love, then, is a utilitarian mechanism and not a quirk of nature or the monopoly of humans. It is one of evolution's most significant inventions; long, intimate relationships effectively ensure individual and species survival, and group cohesion. And in keeping with the complexity of the purposes it serves, love is itself enigmatic and complex. In some form or other it exists and has existed in every human society known, yet it has probably never been fully understood by any of them. Also, like many other feelings, it can be communicated in many different ways, or sometimes not at all.

Love denied
Although the propensity to love, to form bonds, is in all of us, we require nurture for that propensity to be realized. American psychologist Harry Harlow and his colleagues found that monkeys brought up in isolation, without the contact of siblings, parents, or human keepers, feared association with others and behaved aberrantly when in company or presented with unfamiliar situations. Harlow raised infant rhesus monkeys in isolation, using wire or cloth 'mothers' equipped with feeding bottles to feed and 'nurture' them. He found that their behaviour was closely tied to the amount of comforting contact they received from their 'mothers'. Monkeys mothered by the wire 'mothers' acted like psychotic children,

Holy matrimony, love sanctioned by church and state, is epitomized in this stained glass window. But the Biblical couple seen here, Sarah and Tobias, are not all they seem: Sarah's seven previous husbands were all carried off on their wedding night by the demon Asmodeus.

131

crouching passively, huddling in corners, crying plaintively without provocation, and rocking back and forth hugging themselves.

When they grew up those monkeys deprived of adequate contact as infants and juveniles failed to relate normally to other monkeys. Males showed very little interest in copulation; if they did, they seemed to have little idea what to do, mounting the female from the side for instance, or thrusting against an arm or leg. Females isolated as infants would not present themselves to males in a normal manner or allow normal males to mount them. Nevertheless the drive to do something was sex-appropriate — the males clearly knew that they should mount, the females that they should be mounted. It was the 'how' that needed learning.

Harlow wrote of his monkey subjects: '...we had developed not a breeding colony, but a brooding colony.' One of the dramatic conclusions from this research was that the ability to bond (love) and perform sexually remains latent unless there are opportunities to socialize, learn,

Everywhere in the world, from sunny Florida (above) to the forests of Zaire (right), skin contact seems to be necessary for normal human development. Without touching, cuddling, and other comforting forms of physical contact, children are likely to grow up hampered in their ability to express affection.

and practice. Another highly significant finding was that if unmothered female monkeys were somehow inseminated and bore infants, they did not know how to mother them. They abused or ignored them to the extent that none would have survived without human intervention. So, for non-human primates, not only is sexual and companionate 'love' something that is learned, but 'mother love' is too. (A series of follow-up studies showed that if isolated monkeys were paired frequently and periodically with younger normal monkeys for six months or more, by the time they reached adolescence they appeared sexually normal.) Is it reasonable to extrapolate from rhesus monkeys to humans?

James Prescott, now Director of the Institute of Humanistic Science in San Diego, California, has reviewed the work of Harlow and others and concluded that during certain critical periods of brain development some kinds of sensory deprivation — an absence of rocking, hugging, and body warmth from a real mother — result in incomplete or distorted development of the neural programs involved in affection. It is his opinion that such studies '...have profound implications for human cultures that raise their infants with low levels of touching and movement. Children in these societies may be unable to experience certain kinds of pleasure and be predisposed to apathy and violence.... In one study of 49 primitive cultures, I found that when levels of infant affection are low — as among the Comanches and the Ashanti — levels of violence are high; where

physical affection is high — as among the Maori of New Zealand and the Balinese — violence is low. I also found that restrictions on premarital sexual affection were associated with high violence.'

In our own society, the evidence from orphanages is that a high ratio of children to care-takers and low levels of cuddling, stimulation, and attention are likely to lead to emotional problems and relationship difficulties in childhood and adolescence.

Ancient loves

In the past it was left to philosophers and poets to probe the love experience. The Greeks of Homer's time wrote of three basic types of love: *philos*, *eros*, and *agape*.

Philos meant supportive, companionate, or brotherly love of the kind that develops between comrades in arms, team mates, or fellow workers striving towards a common goal. It was non-sexual and most often homosocial. This is the love idealized in the relationship of Damon and Pythias, two youths willing to die for one another.

Eros represented erotic love, love born of physical attraction — what we would probably call lust today — but for the Greeks, *eros* did not have negative connotations. It was a healthy and normal sexual response, and could be hetero- or homosexual, and supremely satisfying and joyful. *Eros* certainly provides bliss enough to be called love by many. However, the French-Thai Supreme Court Judge and author-poet René Guyon, in *The Ethics of Sexual Acts*, advises against confusing sexual desire with love: 'How many painful disillusions would be saved if, instead of thinking themselves obliged to say "I love you", men would content themselves with saying "I desire you..."'

Agape was considered to be the highest form of love — the love that is spiritual and altruistic. Love of democracy, truth, science, or God would be *agape*. Martyrs of all faiths have expressed this form of love with their lives. As far as Saint Paul was concerned, *agape* was divine and so sacred that it could not be achieved by mere mortals.

Passionate heterosexual attraction allied to companionate feelings was certainly known in Ancient Greece, but was looked on as a mixture of *eros* and *philos*, or as a sign of emotions that came under the heading of neither. 'Losing one's head' over someone was seen as a sort of craziness, an illness for which no good treatment existed. Yet Plato, coming on the scene some centuries later, spoke of love as admiration of the good and the beautiful, as an asexual kind of *philos*.

Six kinds of love?

Most of us like to think we know what love is. We will recognize it, we say to ourselves, when it happens to us. Yet when we suspect it might be happening, we often ask: 'Is this love?' It is when we think there is only one kind of love that difficulties arise; to think that there is any 'best' kind of love can lead to tragedy.

Canadian researcher John Alan Lee tried to codify love in all its guises and ended up with a 'blending wheel' of six main categories (see next page). He felt these reflected all the loves spoken of by the ancients as well as the feelings of modern men and women. The latter he judged from the responses he got by asking 112 randomly selected adults from England and Canada several hundred questions that requested detailed descriptions of all those experiences that could, in some way, be called love. Summing all these loves he arrived at a list of nine, including *eros* and *agape* and platonic love (*storge*), but also *mania*, *ludus*, and *pragma*.

Mania is the love that is irrational, extremely jealous, obsessive, and often unhappy; it seems to be out of the lover's control. It is the sort of emotion that attracts attention because of its intensity. Psychologist Elaine Hatfield called this 'passionate love', while fellow psychologist Dorothy Tennov coined an alternative word, limerence, to describe it. She defines 'limerence' as

The ultimate expression of agape, *the non-carnal love for which no task or sacrifice is too great, is martyrdom. Antonio Pollaiuolo's painting depicts the martyrdom of Saint Sebastian.*

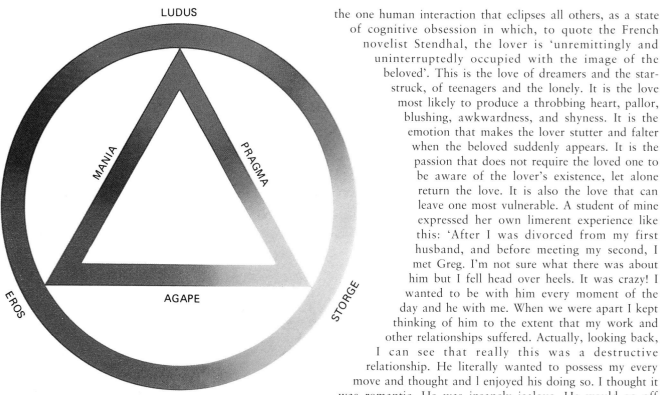

LUDUS

MANIA

PRAGMA

EROS

AGAPE

STORGE

In John Alan Lee's 'blending wheel' of love the circle represents eros (passion), ludus (game-playing seduction), and storge (brotherly/sisterly affection), all subtly shading into one another. The inner triangle represents three different dimensions of love: mania (obsessive love, infatuation), agape (self-sacrificing love), and pragma (practical love). Adapted from Colours of Love, 1973.

the one human interaction that eclipses all others, as a state of cognitive obsession in which, to quote the French novelist Stendhal, the lover is 'unremittingly and uninterruptedly occupied with the image of the beloved'. This is the love of dreamers and the star-struck, of teenagers and the lonely. It is the love most likely to produce a throbbing heart, pallor, blushing, awkwardness, and shyness. It is the emotion that makes the lover stutter and falter when the beloved suddenly appears. It is the passion that does not require the loved one to be aware of the lover's existence, let alone return the love. It is also the love that can leave one most vulnerable. A student of mine expressed her own limerent experience like this: 'After I was divorced from my first husband, and before meeting my second, I met Greg. I'm not sure what there was about him but I fell head over heels. It was crazy! I wanted to be with him every moment of the day and he with me. When we were apart I kept thinking of him to the extent that my work and other relationships suffered. Actually, looking back, I can see that really this was a destructive relationship. He literally wanted to possess my every move and thought and I enjoyed his doing so. I thought it was romantic. He was insanely jealous. He would go off and do his own things, expecting me to be ever waiting for him, and I was. In truth he was "schizy" and I saw it as exciting. Reality came as a shock to me, but at the time he seemed to be everything I could ever desire.'

Ludus is another name for Ovidian love. The Roman poet Ovid (c. 43 BC – AD 17) in his *Art of Love*, wrote of love as a game, the winning of which gives pleasure to the winner and often to the loser. Ovidian love is primarily tactical. Even saying 'I love you' can be a tactic to gain sexual or other favours, an admission fee both literally and figuratively. It was best, Ovid advised, to try to seduce a woman when she was aroused by a gladiatorial spectacle since one type of arousal might well predispose her to another. In modern terms this is called emotional spillover.

The modern Ovidian sends flowers or cooks a special meal. Indeed Ovid's *Art of Love* has been called 'the classic seduction manual of Western literature'. He even included advice as to how men (not women) should conduct an illicit affair. Certainly he would have endorsed the saying 'all's fair in love and war'. Nonetheless tactics and tacticians breed caution. But as philosopher Bertrand Russell once observed: 'Of all forms of caution, caution in love is perhaps the most fatal to true happiness.'

Pragma, as the word suggests, is the accommodation of one person to another for various practical reasons. *Pragma* is the spirit in which arranged marriages are entered into, with compatibility, mutual responsibility, and companionship as their goals. A relationship that starts as pragmatic can evolve into one of great warmth, tenderness, and deep mutual understanding. Or it may start with passion, and then take a companionate course.

My father, close to 90 years of age and 60 years of marriage, expressed his feelings about love like this: 'Love to me is a feeling of closeness, the knowing that she is always there. Even when we argue we know it means we value each other's opinions and respect each other's ideas although we may try to convince each other otherwise. She is my best friend.' My mother, not much younger, said: 'Love is a feeling of wanting to do for another without regard for a return; a concern for the other partner's feelings.' An elderly couple walking serenely arm in arm is almost universally seen as a model of companionate 'true' love. When my mother died, my father said that he was ready to go too, 'to be with her'. Research has confirmed that it is not uncommon for one spouse, more often the husband, to die relatively soon after the death of the other.

Love triangles

While John Alan Lee found the circle a useful metaphor for analysing love, Yale psychologist Robert Sternberg favours a triangle. The side representing the emotional component of love he calls 'intimacy' (the sense of sharing and close understanding); the second side, the motivational component, he calls 'passion' (the drive for sexual fulfilment based on sexual attraction); and the third side, the cognitive component, he calls 'commitment' (the conscious decision to 'make a go' of a relationship). The length of the sides corresponds to the intensity of the intimacy, passion, and commitment felt, and the shape of the triangle to the overall picture. A love containing a great deal of intimacy and passion but little commitment is Romantic Love; commitment and passion without intimacy is Fatuous Love; commitment and intimacy without passion is Companionate Love. Obviously, many loves are blends of all three. In Friendship only the intimacy side of the triangle is present. In Consummate Love the three sides of the triangle are long and of equal length. Does the kind of triangle you draw roughly match that of your partner? Large differences would be a cause for concern.

Other types of love have been described — puppy love, addictive love, dependent love, and certainly mature and immature love. But, of them all, romantic love typically receives the most attention in the West. Is it what 'makes the world go round'? Is it, as the publishers of romantic fiction and television soaps would have us believe, what we all want?

The Garden of Love was a favourite theme of artists in the fourteenth and fifteenth centuries. The garden, secluded from the real world and with echoes of the Garden of Eden, was a metaphor for romantic love. In it all was flowering, beautiful, pleasing to the senses, but also orderly. Romantic love consists of a very carefully constructed and fragile network of fantasies.

Romantic love

Romantic love is seen as an escape from the woes of the real world, as a magic carpet that can soar over such mundane barriers as race, religion, class, education, age, and occupation. It is a state of permanent infatuation which poverty, intolerance, and rotten luck cannot shake or sully. Romantic love fantasizes tenderness, intimacy, privacy, and lust in just the right proportions at just the right time, fantasies in which every action is part of a courtship without end and in which the lovers are sought and desired, seeking and desiring. Sexual consummation is not necessarily achieved, but is constantly anticipated. Romantic love may be fraught with passion and suffering, but the lovers always anticipate a happy ending, if not in the real world, then in some symbolic apotheosis — hence the romantic ideal of double suicide. Romantic love combines the sexual, the erotic, the sensual, and the mystical. It is a brilliantly coloured, surrealistic, and personal painting on a canvas framed by society.

Our modern concept of romantic love has much history behind it of course. As an incorrigible romantic myself, I find it difficult to believe that romantic love was not the reason why Mugga chased Ugga, or Beep 'had a thing' for Bopp, in cave-dwelling times. Nevertheless historians such as Denis de Rougemont date the stirrings of Western notions of romantic love to the twelfth and thirteenth centuries, and specifically to the troubadours of the castles and courts of southern France. Up until that time, in the West at least, the dominant notion of love had been that promulgated by Saint Augustine: the highest form of love was asexual, dedicated to the service of Church, the glorification of God, and the stability of the State.

The troubadours began to sing and write of 'courtly love' and their songs and writings were called 'romances'. In a romance, a troubadour or a knight swore fealty not only to his lord but to his lord's lady. In an age when all social strata knew their place and relationships followed strict expectations, this was a dramatic break with tradition. Traditionally, love was expected to develop within arranged marriages hedged about with rules and roles. Freedom to love by choice was a new idea. In the early Middle Ages even one's choice of friends was limited by class and family.

Courtly love was ostensibly asexual and highly virtuous. The troubadour or knight hero sought favour in his lady's eyes by overcoming all manner of trials and tribulations by self-sacrifice, perseverance, and pious acts. His reward was to wear her token — a ring, a handkerchief — on his travels. Sex he could obtain from any wench or from his wife as a marital right, but from his lady the most he could hope for was permission to lie beside her and chastely caress her naked body (or that was the theory).

Whether this perception of love was spread by the troubadours as an Ovidian ploy to seduce maidens, influence social mores, or reflect current events, is debatable. Yet the model of romantic love inexorably spread. This was non-consummated transcendent love, erotic, heterosexual, and adulterous. It fed on frustration rather than consummation. The troubadours and their audiences were in love with love, consumed more by the desire for the experience or appearance of love than by the desire for a particular person, precisely the kind of love that makes many people put up with totally inappropriate partners. The notion of romantic love also led to the idea that knights in shining armour (or their contemporary counterparts) lurk over every horizon waiting to rescue damsels in distress — a fiction that has wide appeal but cannot be relied upon!

Abelard and Héloise

Quite different from the knights and damsels in troubadours' songs were the lovers Abelard and Héloise. Peter Abelard was a 40-year-old scholar and tutor of great renown and Héloise his teenage pupil. They first met in 1118. Disregarding all social, religious, and legal constraints, their love blossomed and from their passion came a son. Despite their subsequent marriage, the relationship so offended Héloise's uncle and guardian that he forced the lovers apart. Héloise entered a nunnery, at Abelard's suggestion. Abelard was castrated (without anaesthetic) at the uncle's insistence. Their infringement of contemporary social mores and the persistence of their love brought them general condemnation, but it struck a responsive chord in a few hearts. Disciples followed Abelard to his desert refuge to learn his philosophy. Héloise, within her convent walls, continued to consider herself Abelard's lover and intellectual disciple. Over distance, time, and adversity their love prevailed. Abelard's letters advised Héloise to seek solace in God; she did so only because it was Abelard's wish. Her love was constant after the mutilation and separation, and for the 20 years during which she survived him. Legend has it that she asked to be buried with Abelard. When the casket was opened, Abelard extended his arms and they embraced each other for eternity.

This story, in the minds of the ballad singers and poets who spread such tales, was indeed the ideal love. For the establishment of the day, however, it was heretical and dangerous. Sex, and certainly pregnancy, was sinful outside marriage. (Today Abelard might have been

'Knight rescues damsel in distress' is the ostensible theme of Paolo Uccello's famous painting of Saint George and the Dragon. The dragon represents the 'old serpent', Satan, paganism, and heresy. The maiden (who seems rather fond of the dragon) represents pure forces held hostage to evil.

charged with 'abuse of authority' or sexual harassment). Marriage was to be entered into by arrangement, prudently, not on the basis of fanciful notions called love. At the end of the sixteenth century, when Shakespeare wrote *Romeo and Juliet*, the concept of romantic love was sufficiently understood yet disapproved of for the play to be seen as tragic.

In an age when most people lived very close to poverty, illness, disease, and sudden death, it was widely accepted that an emotion as strong as love ought to be reserved for binding a couple together through life's vicissitudes; it was not something to be thrown away or given to the first comer. Sexual favours and virginity, particularly women's, were seen as bargaining chips to be offered in exchange for marriage. Love was to be given, in marriage, to someone who had earned and merited it. Even today, in societies where hardship rather than affluence is the rule, the Western concept of romantic love tends to fall on stony ground. On the Indian subcontinent, for instance, in Pakistan, India, and Bangladesh, the large majority of marriages are still arranged and love has little to do with mate selection. This is not necessarily a function of poverty. As in modern Japan, the old structures and social traditions are still strong enough to keep arranged marriages the norm. I should also add that even in the West romantic and pragmatic notions of love are still in healthy conflict.

Some pros and cons

Although it is difficult to look objectively at something as unobjective as love, it is obvious that each type of love — if one accepts the broad descriptions I have just offered, and not everyone does — has both advantages and disadvantages.

Romantic love requires total commitment, companionate love understanding and give and take. Ovidian love involves planning and strategy, passionate love 'chemistry' and spontaneity. Loves are either stormy and exciting or dependable and predictable. Love either arrives at first sight or develops over time. It is the stuff of dreams or built on substance. It is either lustful or chaste. To some, love is measured by the strength of sexual desire, to others the true depth of love can only be gauged when it is purged of sexual desire; to the former love means sex, to the latter love and sex may be in conflict or have very little to do with each other.

Romantic love is unconditional, selfless, 'made in heaven'; pragmatic love is mutually beneficial, an exchange, something to be worked at. Love, for some, allows the fullest expression of self; for some, it is the melting of two individuals into one; for others, it is too profoundly disturbing to a fragile 'self' to be lived with for long. Love can also be painful,

137

stressful, anxiety-provoking, not always a pleasure.

Despite neat categories and labels, love is an emotional experience that defies easy description. To Socrates, love was a search for something in others that we do not possess in ourselves. To Plato, love was the admiration and contemplation of beauty, the loved one having no obligation other than to exist. To Aristotle, love was a reflection of the self and therefore a form of self-love. To the seventeenth-century poet Dryden, it was 'a malady without a cure', to feminist Ti-Grace Atkinson 'a euphoric state of fantasy in which the victim transforms the oppressor into...redeemer', and to Eric Segal, author of *Love Story*, 'never having to say you are sorry'. In short, even among those who have devoted a good part of their lives to considering the matter there is no common definition. That is because love is not a thing but a very large collection of ideas.

Are attempts to give labels to various sets of ideas within this large collection helpful? In some ways, yes. Labels allow us to look at experiences and feelings and link them to others in ways which are patterned and communicable. We need to express our feeling to others, to tell and be told how we love and how we are loved.

Many of these labels are metaphorical rather than descriptive: love is like 'a bridge over troubled waters', like a madness, like a contract, like a burning and consuming flame, like violins playing, like all the wonderful things in the world rolled into one, longing for someone so much it hurts...and so on. Metaphors freeze feelings, images, experiences, and ideas so that they can be more easily recalled and spoken of. They also help to convey the fact that experiences of love are varied and very personal; they allow us to feel unique. Other people's descriptions of love are not recipes but possible avenues to explore. The other advantage of labels is that they help researchers in their attempts to probe love as they might probe any other complex phenomenon.

Love and science

Can scientists study human love? How do they — and the rest of us for that matter — recognize love and measure its intensity? A very common way of measuring love is to test someone's willingness to have sex: 'If you love me, you'll have sex with me.' But the test can be used in reverse: 'If you love me, you wouldn't ask or you would wait.' Crude as such a test may seem, in many ways it is as good as any. The first version is more often applied by males and the second by females. But although both sexes desire intimate physical contact and orgasm, studies have shown that girls and women are more likely to think they are in love with their partner if they have had coitus than if they have not, although whether coitus is the cause or effect of love is not clear. For men, feelings of love are less likely to be linked to coitus.

Some social scientists claim that love is measurable both quantitatively and qualitatively and that measurement does not necessarily have to involve experimental situations or manipulation. They simply construct questionnaires and ask volunteers to answer them. Here are some sample questions.

On a scale of 1 (not at all true) to 9 (definitely true) indicate your feelings about the person you love/have loved most passionately.

   A Since I've been involved with...my emotions have been on a roller coaster.

   B I take delight in studying the movements and angles of ...'s body.

On a scale of 1 (none at all) to 9 (tremendously strong) indicate your feelings for the person you are most in love with.

   A How much passionate love do you feel for...?

   B How much companionate love does...feel for you?

When most in love I felt as if I wanted to run, jump and scream (circle the appropriate letter): A never   B sometimes   C usually   D almost always

During the time I was most deeply in love some of the things I did were:

....

Using questions like these, different definitions and intensities of love can be compared and correlated with various groups of people. Some social scientists claim that love is measurable. Zick Rubin uses three scales to measure love; one measures attachment (desire for the physical presence and support of the loved one), another caring (concern for his/her well-being), and another intimacy (feelings of closeness and being emotionally in tune). As we saw earlier, Sternberg measured three similar dimensions of love.

Hypotheses about love can be tested by asking people to define and describe love, and say what they prefer in love and why. A study by R. Enis and R. Harper found that university students tended to call a relationship 'love' if it was still in progress, but 'infatuation' if it was in the past. Jon Jecker and David Landy found that givers tend to love recipients more than recipients love givers — the giver of a necklace becomes more involved and has greater investment than the recipient. William Kephart found that, contrary to popular belief, men are usually more romantic than women. When he asked his respondents 'Would you marry someone you didn't love if they had all the other qualities you desired?', few said yes, but more men than women said no. In matters of love women tend to make quite rational and practical (unromantic) decisions.

It also seems that feelings of passionate love begin early. Researchers Elaine Hatfield and Connie Brinton found that the feelings of children and adolescents are every bit as intense as those of adults. They went on to examine whether anxiety and other negative emotional states affected feelings of love, and found (as measured by paper and pencil tests) they certainly did. Michael Liebowitz and others, investigating links between love and the nervous system (anatomy of the brain and substances that affect the nervous system), found that structures within the limbic system of the brain are associated with feelings of pleasure and pain, and that stimulants such as caffeine and theobromine (found in significant amounts in chocolate, for instance) seem to encourage feelings labelled as love; the phenylethylamine (PEA) group of chemicals has a similar effect.

There is now renewed interest among researchers in 'love sickness' and 'love addiction'. The former has elements of limerence and passionate love, but also overlaps with 'addictive' love. The idea that love can be a form of addiction was put forward in the 1970s by Stanton Peele and A. Brodsky. Like addicts of hard drugs, who suffer from dependency, tolerance, and withdrawal, love addicts need

The lady in this 18th-century Indian miniature is prostrated by pangs of unrequited love, against which soothing cordials, drugs, sweetmeats, and massage are of no avail. According to the Kama Sutra *there are 10 stages between loss of love and death; this lady has reached the fourth stage.*

more and more of their love-drug to produce a satisfying 'rush', reduce unwanted anxieties, and cope with the stresses of life. When the love-drug is unavailable or withdrawn, their life goes to pieces — anxiety levels rise, cravings become intolerable, work and other responsibilities go to the wall, they lose sleep, frantically seek a substitute.... How convenient it would be if there were drugs to stop love and desire, true anaphrodisiacs!

Testing the strength of love

Is someone who rates his passion as a 7 more in love than someone who rates her passion as a 6? How many people have had sufficient experience of passionate loves or companionate loves, however defined, to make even personally valid comparisons? And can we rate feelings of involvement with other people on a linear scale, with love at one end and indifference, or even hate, at the other? Perhaps, in answer to the last question, we could, although most love scales do not yet include hate; and yet most murders are domestic, committed by people who once loved their victims. Would a love that is rated 9 today become 3 or even a minus 9 next month? Is climbing two mountains more loving than climbing just one? Is a love accompanied by a 10-carat diamond more intense than one accompanied by a single rose?

'He loves me, he loves me not....'
'Petal plucking' is a cliché, but it is an attempt to rearrange feelings in the direction of greater certainty. Is what we feel for another person, and what they feel for us, love or something else? Should we sit down with pencil and paper instead?

Much of the value of using such arbitrary measures is lost unless great care is taken in structuring the questions and test situations. A major difficulty is that respondents and researchers rarely share a common background and perspective. There is no universal standard, no fixed value system, by which to measure 'the real thing'.

Humanist philosopher Robert Solomon derides the idea of measuring love. He cynically paraphrases Browning: 'How do I love thee? Let me measure something.' The somethings measured, he argues, are seldom meaningful. For example, does the counting of eye contacts between lovers have any more value than the verbal report 'He doesn't look at me like he used to'? Does defining something as 'passion' or 'infatuation' make it any more precise than calling it 'lust' or 'puppy love'?

One thing questionnaires do is obtain information about groups, even if that information is of limited relevance to individuals. If, as philosophers and psychologists agree, love is at least partly a product of social conditioning and learning, tests can certainly mirror what the majority of questionnaire answerers think or have learned. Here Solomon makes a suggestion which I think helpful. He advocates that anyone attempting to investigate love scientifically should, as a matter of course, describe his or her own experiences as well. He says: '...to analyse love, scientifically or poetically, on the sole basis of other people's experience, should strike us as odd, to say the least. The problem, in other words, is not the use of science but a certain emasculation of science....'

I myself find it difficult to follow Solomon's suggestion. While I 'know' I love and want to be loved, I cannot, in my own mind, fix on what would be valid measures of the feeling — perhaps interest, caring, respect, longing, missing the person I love, wanting to be with her, to share things with her. But I have no idea how to adequately scale or test these feelings. Yet I do have some internal gauge which gives me twinges of guilt or anxiety when I feel I'm not loving right. Strangely, it would be easier to list how I would like such feelings to be measured in those who love me: 'If she loved me, she would....'

There is also the question of timing. Other life events — an argument with the boss, illness, a new relationship on the horizon — influence how love is rated. Also, we want to be loved for ourselves, as we are. We may choose to change in order to please a lover, but we don't want to have to change to meet his or her expectations. Also, what one person offers as proof of love may not be accepted as such by the person on the other end of the relationship. Commonly, partners' 'trading items' are different. Many a couple has sat in my office exchanging comments like this:

'You don't love me.'
'Yes I do! I slave overtime at a job I detest to bring home a pay check and keep you and the kids warm and fed.'
'If you loved us, you'd spend more time at home.'

'And if you loved me you'd understand that what I'm doing is for us. You wouldn't put me through this guilt trip.'

'If you loved me, you'd tell me. You always used to.'

'I thought you knew. You never ask straight out. Anyway I thought by now you could take our relationship for granted.'

'I want to hear you say you love me. I want you to show some passion.'

'I want you to take my feelings for granted. Why do I have to keep proving myself to you?'

'We haven't made love in weeks.'

'I love you every day.'

The speakers have obvious difficulties, but they also express feelings and actions that may be considered loving.

Eternal questions

Chekhov once remarked of love: 'When you read a book it all seems so old and easy, but when you fall in love yourself, then you learn that nobody knows anything, and each must decide for himself.' The old, old questions pose themselves anew for each generation of lovers. Is it possible to love more than one person at a time? Is it possible to love someone without being 'in love'? How are sex and love related? Why do some people reject love? Why do some loves persist despite time and distance and adversity? Why do others require closeness and intimacy to keep them alive? Why do some people have one 'true love', and others more than one?

Accepting that there are many types of love and that we ourselves are seldom the same with all people (I like to think we all have different facets that different people see and polish uniquely), the answers to some of these questions become obvious. Certainly one can feel love for several people simultaneously. In fact doing so is common. A man's love for his wife is different from the love he feels for his children or parents or friends. His loves vary in their content from erotic, to companionate, to nurturing, to competitive, to altruistic, and so on. Much depends upon his needs at a given time and the needs of those he loves. As we and our loved ones change, the nature of our love changes.

Some people go through life with only one 'true love'. When the break comes, through death or divorce or for other reasons, the pain can be immense and the hurt long-lasting. Committing, attaching, being dependent, being supportive, being intimate represent a huge investment of self. As with many other traumas in life, time is often the best salve. It may be better not to look for a replacement of a lost love, but for another love with different dimensions. Or not to look at all, but be receptive to opportunities as they arise.

The love between a grandfather and his grandchildren is companionate, practical, even spiritual, and physically affectionate. It is no less love, no less valued, than intense passion.

In our grandparents' day most couples contemplating marriage believed that their love would carry them through the rest of life. But the price of 'one true love' is great loneliness when that love is lost.

Sex with or without love?

One advice columnist received a letter from a woman complaining that her husband 'insisted on making love to me four times. By nightfall I felt physically and mentally abused'. This is a strange mixture of language and feelings. It implies that love and sex may not only be different but antithetical. (I myself refuse to use, and encourage others not to use, the word love when sex is meant, or vice versa. The words love, sex, coitus, intercourse, screw, and fuck have shades of meaning which should be distinguished by the wise sexwatcher.)

The relationship between sex and love is one of the most contentious topics in sexology. There is a growing feeling in the West today, particularly with the spectre of AIDS in the background, that we have moved from the 'sexual revolution' of the 1960s and 1970s through the 'everything up for grabs' and 'me too' paradigms of the 1980s and into the 'caring/sharing' and cautious 1990s. Monogamy and marriage are still held in high regard, but our mental image of what this means, of how much leeway is allowed, has changed. Traditional values have survived the onslaught of 'sex on demand' and for its own sake; 'meaningful' sexual relationships are still sought and valued; we still like to believe that the best and deepest relationships involve sex plus baring of the soul. Our hierarchy of romantic and erotic love is still headed by marriage; next come stable, long-term relationships; then come affairs, flings, and one-night stands; last of all come 'quickies' that take no longer than orgasm. The higher reaches of the hierarchy belong to relationships likely to be based on many, rather than few, of the ideas we call love, not merely on the physical motions we call sex.

Increasingly, however, people are having to settle for less than the ideal in their lives. The stresses of modern life — the pace of social and technological change, tight family and work schedules, inflation, the continuous pressure of information and advertising — lead many people to settle for less love than they probably want. Loves at the bottom end of the hierarchy may help us 'make it through the night' and possibly through the next day, but most of us need more than that.

Both love and sex are forms of communication. To draw a physiological analogy, sex is rather like the nervous system and love like the endocrine system. One is fast and the other is slow. Sex brings about rapid and temporary interactions between people, but love works more slowly and its effects last longer, predisposing the entire organism to an ongoing, evolving relationship. The most 'healthy' situation is when both systems work in harmony.

Many non-Western societies recognize the value of sex uncomplicated by the pressures and problems of emotional commitment. At an intellectual level, so do many respondents to surveys in the West; they agree, in principle, that sex should be available to all, even if it is better with a little love thrown in. And at a fantasy level, so do many married men and women; sex with someone else is a common fantasy, even during intercourse.

It occurs to me that people who object to sex without love may be objecting not so much to sex itself as to having to deal with an intimate relationship that cannot be labelled as love. It is as if they need some emotion strong enough, or some rationale significant enough, to compete with the guilt and stigma that society attaches to sex just for release, or just for ego enhancement, or recreation, or curiosity, or novelty. Though it is often said that women demand love in return for sex, it may be truer to say that they are also interested in many other kinds of personal communication, and not necessarily of the highly involved or demanding kind.

One of the main arguments for sex with love is simply that it is better, more meaningful, more satisfying, a whole experience rather than an optional extra. But sex without love has its own validity. Since partners are chosen mainly for erotic purposes, there is a high likelihood of achieving sexual satisfaction, of fulfilling fantasies. Non-involved partners can make demands they would never dream of making on an emotionally involved other — there is less need to impress, to be consistent, to do the right things at the right time, all of which lessen sexual inhibitions. It doesn't very much matter what the other person thinks. Also, sex for its own sake cuts out the banalities, power ploys, and hidden resentments built into many relationships. If you don't like it, you don't have to continue. It does not impinge on other areas of life, so there is no need for apprehension or regret afterwards. This point of view was well expressed in one of Woody Allen's films in which Diane Keaton says: 'Sex without love is an empty experience.' Allen replies: 'Yes, but as empty experiences go, it's one of the best.'

There are many reasons why people separate sex and love. For a married man or woman a casual affair may be a release from tensions within the marriage, or simply a desire for novelty. Uninvolved sex can also be a transitional phase after a destructive affair or a messy divorce, a way of building new values and repairing self-confidence before making another emotional commitment.

Permission to love

For a minority of people, the opportunity for love or sex never presents itself. The lack of opportunity may be self-imposed of course — all forms of social contact that might lead to intimacy are shunned. But for the mentally or physically disabled, the emotionally disturbed, or for those who are institutionalized (the elderly, for example), the lack of opportunity is often imposed. Often this is purely for organizational reasons, for the convenience of the carers rather than the cared for. But there are many carers — parents, guardians, social workers, psychiatrists — who take the view that love and sex are, at best, emotional time bombs that can only bring hurt and disappointment to their charges. Social worker Harvey Gochros describes groups intentionally deprived of potential sexual relationships as 'sexually oppressed'. One of the reasons often given for such deprivation is that sexual activity would not produce healthy, well cared for babies. Surely, as we have seen, there are many types of love and many ways of expressing love. Certainly there are many ways to stop reproduction without frustrating sex or love. Does anyone have the right to tell another what opportunities, what relationships, what routes to sex and love he or she should be allowed? How societies or individuals decide who shall have access to love or sex says a great deal about their values.

An infinite resource

Too often it is assumed that love is an exhaustible commodity of which there is only so much to go around. On the contrary love is an inexhaustible resource. Leo Buscaglia, or Dr. Hug as his fans can him, is a best-selling author on love. He writes: 'Since love is not a thing, it is not lost when given. You can offer your love completely to hundreds of people and still retain the same love you had originally.' The more one loves the easier it becomes. What I add is that while love might not be inexhaustible, time is. And the demonstration of love takes time.

Every society has its symbols for love. Saint Valentine's day, on February 14, brings an epidemic of hearts and flowers. In Japan the symbol for love is an umbrella over the lovers' names. Here love comes with cakes and sugar icing.

There are those who have never learned to love, in the physical as well as the emotional sense, and those who have learned not to love. There are also those who have learned to repulse love. Love demands a degree of vulnerability with which not everyone is comfortable. Experience, wrongly or rightly, teaches many people not to show love openly, not to risk embarrassment, attack, betrayal, desertion, and pain. To honestly say 'I love you' may be one of life's most difficult decisions, but ultimately one of the most rewarding. And to be able to love another, one must first love oneself. We all know people who belittle themselves at every turn, who reject compliments, who mistake genuine interest and curiosity for condescension and patronage.

For sexwatchers the lesson seems clear. We should savour the eternal dialogue between generation and generation, culture and culture, scientists and poets, experts and raw recruits, for all of them have their different wisdoms. And we should be wary of portraying love in simplistic terms. We would do better to keep an open mind and explore for ourselves the meanings of love and be willing to gamble at love. It is truly 'better to have loved and lost than never to have loved at all'. In loving, the more you give, the more you may get.

Chapter 10

Relationships

One who thinks he can live without others is mistaken;
one who thinks others cannot live without him, is even more mistaken.
HASIDIC SAYING

Curiosity about relationships, particularly sexual ones, and a natural inclination to compare oneself with others turn most people into part-time sexwatchers. The colourful doings of Elizabeth Taylor, Warren Beatty, Cher, Prince Charles and Lady Di, Prince Andrew and Fergie — even the comings and goings of the folks next door — are of more interest to most of us than the musings of Ovid or the findings of obscure scientists. Millions more American citizens cocked an ear to U.S. presidential candidate Bill Clinton's comments about the state of HIS union than listened to President Bush talking about the state of THE Union.

Relationships mirror the values, aspirations, successes, and failures of a culture. Marriage and divorce rates, for example, are seen as barometers of morality and happiness. Relationships are regulated by and reflected in property rights, titles, social responsibilities, and of course laws on marriage, divorce, adoption, and guardianship. Civil or religious law can prevent a union on the grounds of mixed race, mixed religion, incest, homosexuality, or bigamy. In the West two people make a marriage, but four wives are allowed in Muslim countries, and in some southern Indian cultures women are allowed two husbands. In all societies in which polygamy is institutionalized, a man with several wives is a sign of wealth but a woman with several husbands is a sign of poverty.

Categorizing relationships

People are linked in an infinite variety of relationships, ranging from the simple to the complex. The link may be friendship or kinship, great intimacy or brief acquaintanceship, convenience or necessity, contractual or voluntary. Some kinds of relationships are reinforced, others hampered, by the society one lives in. Relationships can be categorized as sexual/non-sexual, homosocial/homosexual, heterosocial/heterosexual, ambisocial/bisexual, or, if one's focus is on marital status, as marital/premarital/extramarital/postmarital/non-marital.

In some societies there is no such institution as marriage. In traditional Hawaii, for example, there was no specific word for 'husband' or 'wife'. He was simply called *kane* (man) and she *wahine* (woman). Individuals stayed together, or not, by choice rather than commitment or obligation. One member of a pair could be monogamous while the other was polygamous. Couples who wanted to sleep together just did. Sex with others was not seen as a cause for separation; jealousy was considered unwarranted. Children of any and all unions were cared for by the society at large. All age mates of any child's parents were also 'parents' and therefore care-takers; everyone of grandparent age was similarly a 'grandparent'. Such patterns were not uncommon among Polynesian cultures.

In contrast, in most non-Western societies today, sanctioned sexual relationships are usually limited to marriage. Boys and girls, and certainly men and women, are often socially isolated from each other. Extramarital liaisons are clandestine, if they are possible at all. In Saudi Arabia, for example, the sexes work and live apart unless they are members of the same family. Even male and female university students rarely attend lectures together; a male professor lectures on closed-circuit television to his female audience in the next room.

A traditional wedding procession, complete with folk musicians and horsedrawn carriage, in Sweden. Even in Scandinavia, where attitudes towards sex are fairly liberal, it should surprise no one that marriage enjoys greater status than other relationships.

Women-only banks exist and one conservative spokesman predicted that women would be more willing to join the workforce if all-female parking lots were provided. The situation is similar in parts of Iran and in both countries things have not changed markedly over the last decade. However, both inside and outside Iran and Saudi Arabia there are forces agitating for change.

Western nuances

In the West there are no such extremes but rather a great number of possible male-female relationships, the nuances of which are not always adequately expressed in English. Here are some of them, in order of erotic involvement: friend (platonic is assumed), boyfriend/girlfriend, intimate, partner, companion, mate, spouse, lover/mistress. I have put lover/mistress after spouse because extramarital affairs usually have a higher sexual component than an established marriage. Referring to someone as a boyfriend or girlfrend usually indicates amorous, if not erotic, involvement, but full sexual involvement is implicit in the other terms. Of all the relationships listed, only spouse, and perhaps mate, imply permanence. In less liberated times, when sex was assumed to occur only within marriage, the terms boyfriend and girlfriend were non-sexual. Today no such correlation is assumed. Many an embarrassing moment can be spent trying to find the right words to define the precise nature of a relationship: 'This is my daughter and her...', or 'My husband and I are separated but I'd like to introduce my....' The United States Census Bureau tried to solve the problem by introducing the classification POSSLQs (pronounced 'poss LQs'), Persons of Opposite Sex Sharing Living Quarters! A more common but equally awkward expression is 'significant other', as in 'All employees and their significant others are invited.'

In every society sexual relationships are taboo within or between certain categories of people. This Benneton advertisement, showing a priest and a nun breaking their vows of celibacy and chastity, caused such a storm of protest that it was banned in certain regions.

For the vast majority of people some type of relationship has to be established before sexual activity occurs. Rarely, except in prostitution, fantasy, pornography, or the anonymous homosexual sex of a tea-room or bath, is sex devoid of any personal interaction. In *Fear of Flying* the novelist Erica Jong described the 'rarer than the unicorn... zipless fuck', the uncomplicated meeting of strangers who, sensing each other's sexual magnetism, melt easily into sexual embrace, without embarrassment, guilt, or fumbling with zippers. Most people who want sex form a relationship in order to get it.

Forming relationships

Traditional societies may seem quaint and restrictive but one advantage of highly structured sex roles is that they remove the trauma and pain the West accepts as the cost of choice and chance. Arranged marriages and chaperoned meetings between young people may frustrate dreams and desires but they protect egos and ensure social approval.

During this century the West has evolved many ways of making meetings between the sexes easier. Initially boy met girl under the watchful eye of the family, or of religious or community organizations. Then coeducation emerged, and instead of entering the labour force at puberty, adolescents were kept at school to gain job skills. In the aftermath of two world wars families and populations shifted, and job opportunities changed. Women, more from necessity than choice, left the home to enter a competitive job market. The extended family, which traditionally provided access to new acquaintances and prospective partners, began to break down. Heads of family, once entrusted with providing social and marriage partners, were no longer reliably in charge. By chance and necessity a freer system of forming relationships evolved. The American sociologist Roger Libby has put forward two models for the formation of relationships within this more open framework. The first he calls the Primrose Path of Dating and the second Branching Paths of Getting Together.

On the Primrose Path, boys and girls share certain notions about romance from a very early age. Today youngsters are likely to be sexually attracted to each other earlier than in the past. According to studies by sociologist Carl Broderick, even 10-year-olds now play teasing and kissing games, though pre-arranged meetings at this age are rare. With puberty, group dating begins. By 17 or 18 single dating is the norm, the assumption being that after a number of random dates one will go out several times with the same person and that will constitute 'going steady'. Initially, sexual activities are bland, but they build in intensity, until heavy petting or coitus signifies that the relationship is 'serious'. Boy and girl strive for different things in a serious relationship, but both are eager for the social status that goes with heterosexual involvement. If one or other is unhappy, the relationship breaks and both look for another serious involvement. The pattern repeats itself beyond adolescence. Fleeting or experimental relationships are gradually replaced by steady ones, which tend to be more and more exclusive, until finally the partners become engaged. When both think the 'time is ripe', because they have made the best match possible, they marry.

Along the Branching Path individuals are, at all ages, less fixed in their expectations and behaviour. To them, exclusivity in relationships is less important and pairing off is more the result of individual needs than obedience to any sex role script. In Branching Path relationships erotic exchanges do not necessarily mean commitment or fidelity to a single partner. Relationships are seen as an ongoing process of change rather than as the fulfilling of a static set of expectations. Marriage is not necessarily the goal and if it occurs it is not always along traditional lines.

For most people in the West the path followed has a lot to do with age and upbringing. Older people, brought up in a less affluent and permissive age, tend to have followed the Primrose rather than the Branching Path in forming their relationships. But stretches of both are not uncommon in any individual's life. And there is no doubt that marriage, and being faithful to one partner, remains the goal for many.

In forging new relationships after divorce, people tend to follow the same path that led to their marriage. For travellers along the Primrose Path, widening of sexual experience occurs through sequential monogamy (or should it be called serial polygamy?). For those following the Branching Path, experiences broaden more quickly and simultaneously.

What do people want?

Psychologist-author Caryl Avery has said: 'Given one wish in life, most people would wish to be...able to reveal themselves entirely to another human being and be embraced and caressed by that acceptance.' It would be nice to have such desires fulfilled, but it is parochial and part of Western romanticism to think they are universal. Twenty years ago, in Japan, a survey of young unmarried adults found that what women desired most was marriage; they also wanted their spouses to be 'manly' and have reasonable incomes (security). The men wanted to marry women who were 'feminine' (willing to care for their home and have their children). Ten years later a repeat survey found that Japanese women put 'kindness' at the top of their want list and men 'independence', 'kindness' meaning understanding of the difficulties of being a wife and mother, and 'independence' the expectation that the woman will go out to work to contribute to a tight family budget. A

The chaperone is no longer part of dating and courting in most of the Western world, but at one time it was unthinkable for a young lady to be seen in public without a female companion or some other responsible person in attendance. Even so, young lovers found ways of stealing kisses. The roles of 'go-between' and 'matchmaker' have also disappeared.

1991 survey showed an even more dramatic change. When asked to name the three things they wanted most, unmarried Japanese women said 'to travel', 'to pursue a personal hobby', and 'to get married', in that order. Idealistic Western notions of a fulfilling relationship were not in high demand. So it seems that the components looked for in relationships are highly time- and culture-dependent.

In England, in 1950, sociologist Geoffrey Gorer found that the husbandly virtues most highly prized by women were understanding and consideration, thoughtfulness, a sense of humour, and various moral qualities, in that order. Men ranked the most important wifely virtues as being a good housekeeper, being attractive in both the social and physical sense, and displaying understanding and consideration. In 1969, nearly two decades later, Gorer found that women put understanding and consideration at the top of their list, but followed them with love, affection, and kindness, and then generosity. Men still put being a good housekeeper first, but raised being a good and affectionate mother to second place, followed by attractiveness.

A *Playboy* survey done in 1982 showed that readers — whether they were single, married, remarried, or cohabiting — felt that love and family life were the most important ingredients of personal happiness. So did divorced women, but not divorced men; they ranked sex as more important than love (which may, of course, have been a factor in their divorce). The study also found that friendship was mentioned as a major requirement by non-marrieds of both sexes. For those without legal ties, friends tended to replace family and recreational sex was important. Even if not possessed, love and family life were still highly valued.

Homogamous relationships, relationships between people of similar backgrounds and interests, are more common than complementary ones. Mixed-race relationships require extra investment and commitment, if only to survive the rougher ride that society gives them.

Do opposites attract?

Aristotle thought of love as representing the search for something lacking in oneself: Chris, who needs affection and reassurance, will be drawn to Sara, who wants to provide them. The traditional stereotyped roles of men and women appear to reflect the idea of complementarity: the man is strong and aggressive, the provider and protector; the woman gentle and conciliatory, the homemaker and mother who needs to be protected and provided for. In many parts of the world where marriages are arranged, much thought is given to partners being complementary and therefore, as a unit, relatively self-sufficient.

The opposite of a complementary relationship is a homogamous relationship, one in which the partners' needs and behaviours are similar. This kind of relationship appears to be becoming more common now that people are freer to choose their own partners. Given a free choice people do tend to marry into a similar background, class, education, and religion. Many studies have shown that most dating partners live within three or four miles of each other (usually indicating a similar socioeconomic background) and end up getting married. Like needing like makes sense. It would be destructive in a relationship if only one partner craved frequent sex, exotic food, loud music, or religion. Marriage bureaux and computer dating services certainly work on the principle of homogamy; they try to match clients' backgrounds, needs, interests, and tastes.

In reality there is no either/or. People relate to each other for both complementary and homogamous reasons, for reasons both rational and quixotic, and these reasons vary with time and circumstance. A partner who fills a particular need at one time may not be appreciated at another, and as a relationship matures, different needs and desires come to the surface.

Trade-offs

Romantics like to think of relationships as predestined. To the more prosaically minded, relationships involve an element of planning and need to be worked at. In fact all of us, whether we are aware of it or not, tend to make and break relationships on a cost and benefit basis; we weigh the costs against the benefits and opt for relationships that bring us most and cost us least. When the benefits fall below an acceptable level, we start looking for a relationship that offers more. This is the so-called exchange theory, or equity theory, of relationships. Interestingly, some psychologists believe that being 'overbenefited' in a relationship can also be bad; it can lead to feelings of guilt and therefore to stress. Of course, we do not always weigh benefits against costs consciously, and even if we do, it disturbs us to think of love and marriage in such mercenary terms.

The most obvious trade-offs between marriage partners are those made in arranged marriages (land, livestock, income). In a romantic 'love match' the idea of a *quid pro quo* may be distasteful, but ultimately, when the passion fades, the relationship must depend on some kind of equity. Unfortunately there is no agreement as to what constitutes equitable trade. As one remarried woman remarked to me recently: 'My new husband is my treasure, but he is his ex-wife's garbage. I can imagine my ex-husband's new wife saying the same.'

When one has invested only a small amount of time, work, or emotion in a relationship, change may occur quite easily. But when a relationship is inextricable from children, an extended family, status, and so on, it is likely to have a solidity and momentum of its own. That does not mean to say that all reactions to adversity or to the possibility of change are based on the investment principle; sometimes they are idealistic rather than realistic, irrational rather than rational.

In judging the quality of a relationship we tend to use such measures as intensity, intimacy, duration, and sexual compatibility, but a high score in one or two of these departments says little about scores in the others. Some relationships last only a few days, yet are so charged with emotion that they are remembered for life. Others, even if they endure for many decades, may never have been close or passionate. Others have wonderful sex, but that is all.

Relationships and sex

Whether free or arranged marriages are the norm, most cultures assume that closeness and intimacy go on developing over the years. Maybe they should, and sometimes they do, but research and common experience show that neither time nor a long-term sexual relationship makes for greater intimacy, or indeed leads to more equity in the relationship.

In any relationship frequency of coitus generally declines with time. Kinsey documented this some 40 years ago and many subsequent surveys, such as the *Playboy* one mentioned earlier and those of R. Dodderidge and colleagues in 1987, have confirmed as much. In 1986 the British National Marriage Guidance Council reported: 'Marriage is a sexless institution for thousand of couples after only a few years of married life.... It is one of the most common problems.... They laugh about it without admitting they're also suffering.' Yet many women say that the quality of coitus, as measured by the likelihood of orgasm, increases as a relationship continues. Feminists say this is because men are more willing to recognize women's enjoyment of sex as a marriage continues, others that women take longer to adapt to coitus but that once they do they become orgasmically more responsive. Another view is that men are learning to take more time and care in coitus. Yet another is that, with age, women become more responsive and men less 'driven' and slower to ejaculate.

In the 1982 *Playboy* survey even the most sexually active respondents reported that after four years with the same partner frequency of intercourse dropped from four or more times a week to between seven and eight times a month. Subsequent surveys have shown that, regardless of the age at which people marry, frequency of coitus in the first year is rarely equalled in subsequent years. The major stimulus to continuing high frequency of coitus between partners seems to be novelty rather than intimacy or love, although other factors within or outside the relationship may also have some effect.

Many studies post-Kinsey have tried to relate frequency of intercourse to overall sexual contentment. One large and particularly thorough study of both married and cohabiting male-female and same-sex couples by sociologists Philip Blumstein and Pepper Schwartz showed a direct correlation between frequency of sex play and degree of satisfaction in a relationship. But an awkward chicken-and-egg problem exists here: the more you like it, the more you do it, and the more you do it, the more likely you are to like it! Nevertheless certain correlations are apparent. Too much sex or too little sex (the definition of too much and too little is a personal matter) makes people unhappy, but at every frequency and in every type of relationship men, more than women, are likely to desire greater frequency. This is most noticeable among single men, but is also true of the majority of married men. Certainly, at some point in a relationship, the woman might desire coitus more frequently than the man (this is particularly true as the couple ages), but she is less likely to complain about it. Only among the divorced and those who are cohabiting do men and women seem equally pleased or displeased with their coital frequency. The *Playboy* survey and the Blumstein and Schwartz study found that once a week was a sort of cut-off point; discontent was likely to set in once frequency dropped below once a week.

A very touchy and common dilemma presented to marriage counsellors is disparity in desire for sex play. The cliché answer is 'Compromise'. This certainly works for some couples, but for many it is a recipe for both partners to remain dissatisfied. To suggest any 'suitable' frequency of coitus is presumptuous and arbitrary, and likely to cause as many problems as it solves. While the overall average frequency of two to three times a week for married couples into their 40s has been around for some time, it is no measure of harmony, nor is it in any way prescriptive or suitable for everyone. Partners must work out their own ways of meeting their own needs, remembering that frequency of coitus, orgasm, or any other aspect of sexual activity is only one barometer of compatibility.

A Hindu wedding in Madras. In all likelihood the bride and groom will have been chosen for each other — on pragmatic, financial, political, and caste grounds — by their respective families. The newlyweds will live with the groom's family.

Marriage on trial

Marriages are entered into for many reasons, sex being only one of them and sometimes not the major one. In fact social and economic reasons predominate if one looks at marriage on a worldwide basis. Marriage is more than a relationship: it is

also an idea, an image, a public announcement of commitment, an institution sanctioned by society, and a package of rights and responsibilities. And in societies in which it is an institution, it is the only relationship approved of as being a proper setting for coitus and the bearing and rearing of children.

It is difficult for most people under 50 years of age in the English-speaking West to accept that only

Official wedding cars in Moscow have two interlocking rings on the hood. Almost half of all marriages in the former Soviet Union ended in divorce before the first anniversary.

several generations ago, among their grandparents and great grandparents, arranged marriages were fairly common. Marriage was regarded as too important to be left to chance. Arranged marriages are still the rule in most of the Islamic world, Africa, Southeast Asia, and even in modern India and Japan. Youngsters in these societies may chafe at such non-romantic practices, yet they continue not only because of cultural inertia but also because they seem to best serve the population's needs. In Japan and India, modern societies by many measures, love marriages are accepted, but they account for fewer than half of all marriages. In parts of the Islamic world, where unrelated boys and girls are not allowed to meet or associate, love marriages are very rare.

The fact that people in the West today are cohabiting more and marrying later suggests that the choosing of a marriage partner, when there is freedom of choice, is no easy matter. The wisdom and accumulated experience of well-intentioned elders has been dispensed with and is not easy to replace. Eligible young men and women feel they need to experiment with alternative lifestyles, 'try their wings', 'live a little' before they finally settle down. Women, especially, want to develop a career before they marry. Marriage records for 1990 show that men and women, on average, are getting married two or three years later than they did in 1975.

Wedding chairs, his and hers, in a Norwegian church. Hers is red, his blue. Western marriages go through their most testing time after 5 to 9 years and again after 20 years, coinciding with the start of having children and their leaving home.

Cohabitation is a solution that fulfils both the sexual drive and the need for affiliation to a 'significant other'. It still carries a stigma — the expression 'living in sin' is still used and still has the power to wound. In the United States, according to the Census Bureau, the number of cohabiting male-female couples rose from about 0.5 million in 1970 to just under 2 million in 1982, 2.6 million (half of whom had previously been married) in 1988, and close to 3 million in 1992. Between 1970 and 1992 the number of same-sex couples living together rose from 1.3 to 1.6 million.

Does the testing of relationships by cohabitation eventually lead to marriage, and does it lead to better or more durable marriages? A 1982 survey among the generally conservative

151

and happily married readers of *The Ladies' Home Journal* found that 25 per cent of those who responded, who had on average been married for 12 years, had lived with their husbands before marriage. Incompatible couples separate before marriage, or marry and then divorce. One cannot help suspecting that those who feel the need to test a relationship extensively before marrying may have valid doubts about themselves or their partner.

Recent studies both do and don't support this thesis. S. Browder in 1988 found that couples who had lived together before marriage had a significantly higher divorce rate than those who had not. R. Watson and P. DeMeo in 1987 found that cohabitation before marriage was *not* a significant factor in terms of marital adjustment. Sociologists Larry Bumpass and Sara McLanahan in 1989 came down on the side of cohabitation leading to longer marriages, but only just. Canadian sociologist James White reported that cohabitors were more than seven times as likely to stay married as non-cohabitors. Unfortunately the couples sampled in these studies were not comparable; they differed in terms of family support, religious beliefs, and many other factors connected with decisions to cohabit, marry, or divorce.

A strong commitment to marriage is perhaps the best index of whether or not a partnership will endure. Most marriage and sex counsellors, as well as married people themselves, say that no matter how long a couple lives together it is not the same as marriage. The institution, with its myths and realities, strengths and weaknesses, pleasures and sorrows, sets in motion special feelings and forces.

Domestic partners and covenants

Domestic partners are a new phenomenon in the United States, almost unheard of a decade ago. Such relationships amount to more than cohabitation but less than marriage. Domestic partners (heterosexual and homosexual) cohabit, have a stable and intimate relationship, and are financially interdependent. They have opted for a new 'family' structure which has some of the civil, financial, and legal bonds and benefits of marriage, but not others. Although domestic partnerships initially evolved to give homosexual unions some of the legitimacy and protection enjoyed by heterosexuals, they now appeal to a much broader community. Those involved may or may not have children, and may or may not have been married before.

Domestic partnerships are presently accepted by only a handful of municipalities in the United States (San Francisco and New York among them), but they are becoming a much larger issue. Individual companies, including the international jeans maker Levi Strauss, are beginning to recognize them. Domestic partners can receive medical and dental benefits, visit each other in hospital, be insurance beneficiaries, take sick or bereavement leave, pass on rental and other privileges — rights usually limited to spouses or family members only. When the first domestic partner law was passed in San Francisco in 1991 about 275 couples registered on the first day.

A personal agreement between two or more unmarried people to live together in an intimate relationship blessed by some religious institution is usually referred to as a 'covenant'. The Metropolitan Community Church, a largely gay-supported non-denominational Christian organization, sanctions such unions, and so, increasingly, do other religious groups in the United States.

If domestic partnerships and covenant relationships are accepted by different states, current sex and marriage laws will be in for a rough ride. Many traditionalists argue that the acceptance of such relationships will further undermine the family and provide models of immoral behaviour. But 'the family', as a concept, has been changing since the origin of humankind. When, in 1990, the Massachusetts Mutual Life Insurance Company asked 1,200 adult respondents to define the word 'family', only 22 per cent chose the legal definition 'A group of people related by blood, marriage, or adoption'. Almost three-quarters of them picked instead 'A group of people who love and care for each other', which definition certainly encompasses domestic parters and covenanted relationships. With the number of people living within marriage declining, at least in the United States, the legal definition of the family may have to change.

In Denmark the definition of the family has certainly changed. On October 1, 1990, Denmark became the first country in the world to legalize gay marriage. In the first 20 days more than 400 gay couples got married. Two restrictions, however, keep gay marriages subordinate to heterosexual ones: gay couples are not allowed to adopt, and the state Lutheran Church refuses to offer homosexual weddings. A national opinion poll found that

64 per cent of those asked supported gay marriage. Similar law changes were proposed for Norway and Sweden in 1991, but have not been carried through. The course and duration of gay marriages will be followed with great interest.

Perhaps one last type of relationship should be mentioned, one that flouts no laws and requires no law changes. I am talking about the kind of arrangement that existed between Jean-Paul Sartre and Simone de Beauvoir; they were in love and committed to each other, but they lived separately. Many less exceptional individuals do the same.

Marriage should be...

The expectation of most people marrying in the West today is that marriage will supply almost everything they need — a comfortable home, sex, affection, companionship, children, security, entertainment, ego support, psychological counselling...and all with the approval of the family and society at large. Marriage is expected to provide a safe harbour from the storms and currents of the world outside. If it truly does provide all these things, why are only 50 per cent of adults in the United States married and living with their spouses when more than 90 per cent marry?

The reality of marriage is very different from the fiction, because it involves two people with different needs, and must accommodate the career and personal development of one or both partners, and the needs of children and other family members.

In Japan, where I lived and worked for several years and which I periodically visit, marriage is surrounded with very few of the expectations typical in the West. Husband and

Building a home together (making a nest for children?) is something most young couples in the West look forward to. But only two or three generations ago few newlyweds could afford to rent or buy a home of their own; often the first years of marriage were spent with in-laws. Rough economic times are forcing a return to the old ways.

wife are expected to occupy separate social spheres, and their sex roles are starkly divergent. In the 1980s marriage was still the primary goal of most Japanese girls. They expected to marry, be responsible for the home, raise two children, and satisfy their husband's needs. In Japan a wife's security and social rank depend (as they still do to a large extent in the West) on how well her husband does. But her emotional support and companionship comes from her original family, her children, and female friends. Her sexual desires and fantasies may be met by her husband, but if not she satisfies them by reading and watching television. Now, however, surveys show that marriage is not uppermost in the mind of many Japanese girls; they are keen to travel and pursue careers and other interests. Marriage can come later in life.

The world of the Japanese husband is very different. His job, not his wife, will occupy the greater part of his life. He will probably relax and enjoy himself with his work colleagues or old school chums and a bar hostess. He will be more willing to share his sexual and other intimate thoughts with an old school friend than with his wife. He will have sexual relations with his wife, but satisfy his erotic fantasies and other sexual needs with a hostess or prostitute, or, if he is wealthy, with a regular mistress. If he is homosexually oriented, he is still likely to marry and seek male partners outside his marriage. Mistresses are no longer as accepted as they were in the past, but they are still part of the fabric of affluent Japanese society. The West certainly has its share of bar companions, prostitutes, and mistresses, but they are part of an uneasy sub-culture, spoken of in embarrassed or defiant tones. The cultures of Korea, Taiwan, Thailand, and other Asian countries are similar. Interestingly, in Hawaii, which has a high percentage of second generation Asians, the split between male and female lifestyles continues. There are more hostess bars per capita in Hawaii, catering to the non-tourist trade, than anywhere else in the Western world.

Adjusting to a sexual relationship

In the West more people are becoming sexually active earlier, and more are having sexual experiences with more than one partner before they cohabit or marry. But these facts tell us little about the sexual sophistication or satisfaction gained by wider and more precocious experience. Even with premarital sexual experience, most people bring to marriage two or three decades of sexually inhibiting influences. Society does not look on the premarital period as a training ground for the gaining of sexual expertise and yet somehow people are expected, when they marry, to become sexually proficient and fulfilled.

Several recent studies suggest that, particularly for women, the earlier in life one starts having orgasms, the more likely one is to have orgasms in a married or stable relationship. And the more one masturbates, the more sexually responsive one will be in such a relationship. However, these findings are not borne out by all studies, and in any case women's overall satisfaction with a relationship correlates only to a minor degree with sexual compatibility, and even less with orgastic satisfaction *per se*. Even regularly orgasmic women (apparently the minority) say that orgasm is no guarantee of sexual satisfaction. Judging by many well conducted studies, for women the consensus seems to be: 'If the relationship is good, the sex will feel good. The better the relationship, the more likely I am to come.' For men the consensus goes like this: 'My orgasm is almost inevitable in any case. And if the sex is good, the relationship will feel good.'

According to a 1990 survey by W. R. Cupach and J. Comstock, sexual satisfaction seems to correlate with how comfortable partners feel about communicating about sex and their relationship. Perhaps the moral to be derived from this is: 'The couple that communicates and has good sex together stays together.'

The other man and the other woman

Among the most ogled sexual statistics are those concerning extramarital sex (EMS). They are looked at with apprehension ('It's almost bound to happen at some time or other, isn't it?'), with regret ('Yes, I was one of those statistics'), with relief ('Yes, it happened to us but that was a long time ago'), with confidence ('Our marriage is too solid for that to happen'), or with pleasure ('It was wonderful while it lasted'). Actually, the likelihood of extramarital sex, or sex outside stable cohabitation, is quite high, as we shall see. And male-female double standards being what they are, more attention is usually paid to her EMS than to his.

A quick run-through of EMS surveys in the United States — *Psychology Today* (1970), *Redbook* (1975), *Cosmopolitan* (1980), *The Hite Report* (1981), *Playboy* (1982), *The Ladies' Home Journal* (1983), and Blumstein and Schwartz (1983) — suggests that male EMS is more frequent than female EMS (between 36 and 71 per cent as compared with between 21 and 57 per cent). A study done by sociologist Annette Lawson in Britain in 1982, mainly through *The Sunday Times*, *The Guardian*, and *Sunday Mirror*, found that overall only 29 per cent of respondents (men and women combined) had no experience of EMS; about 40 per cent of the rest said they had had up to three illicit partners, and about 30 per cent said they had had four or more. The readership demographics here are interesting: only 15 per cent of respondents contacted through *The Sunday Times* said they had never had EMS, compared with 36 per cent of those contacted through *The Guardian* and 42 per cent of those contacted through the *Sunday Mirror*! In the United States only 21 per cent of *The Ladies' Home Journal* readers admitted to EMS compared with 69 per cent of *Cosmopolitan* readers.

Since the early 1980s the kinds of questions asked in large-scale EMS surveys have changed, which makes trends difficult to evaluate. Instead of asking 'Have you ever...?' surveys now ask 'In the last year, have you...? Obviously the latter question will receive fewer 'yes' answers. Sociologist-author-priest Andrew Greeley and colleagues found that 18 per cent of sexually active adult Americans interviewed in 1988 had not been monogamous during the previous year.

How are such statistics to be interpreted? The first difficulty is that surveys rarely make clear just what it is they are asking. A question like 'Have you ever engaged in extramarital sex?' may be interpreted by some to include petting, by others to mean only coitus. Even when the question is 'Have you ever engaged in extramarital intercourse?' some respondents will include homosexual affairs or sex with prostitutes, while others may only mention heterosexual encounters with significant emotional involvement. Also in Western society, extramarital sex is usually clandestine, or the subject of bragging, so the truth of some answers will be in doubt.

The second problem involves the profile of the responding population. The bulk of responses to such surveys come from men and women in their 20s, 30s, and early 40s. But we know that there are significant differences in behaviour among age groups, more so among women. At present, for example, younger women are more likely to have affairs than older women. This raises the female average. On

A time for sober reflection? Statistically 'the other woman' or 'the other man' in an extramarital affair has backed a loser — more marriages survive infidelity than break because of it. Typically meetings are restricted, often hurried, often tainted with guilt and apprehension.

the other hand, since most respondents, male and female, are not yet at the halfway mark in their sexual lives, this tends to lower all averages.

Kinsey's data are now nearly 50 years old. In the early 1940s, when our grandparents and great grandparents were in their sexual prime, heterosexual extramarital intercourse by the age of 40 was the experience of about 50 per cent of married men and 25 per cent of married women. Present estimates of EMS in the United States are that by the age of 60 about 75 per cent of both men and women will had have coitus with someone other than their spouse at some time during their married life. In Britain Annette Lawson found that 74 per cent of the men and 72 per cent of the women who answered her 1982 survey had had sex outside marriage. Actually this should come as no surprise, since between 30 and 50 per cent of marriages end in divorce, many of them preceded by extramarital affairs.

Information about other countries is scarce and probably not comparable. Often the figures reported seem unrealistically low. For example, in a 1969 study of French women by the French Institute of Public Opinion only 7 per cent of respondents admitted to adultery; the investigators felt that at least 22 per cent would have been nearer the mark. A 1980 survey reported that about 15 per cent of Italian women admitted to EMS; another Italian survey found about 40 per cent of Italian men making the same admission. A 1983 survey in Japan found 1 in 40 women had had extramarital affairs compared with 1 in 5 men. Recent figures for EMS around the world are not easily available — journalists and researchers seem to have turned their attention elsewhere — but it is probably safe to say that all countries have experienced increases.

Adultery is the legal term for EMS. In English the word 'adultery' has more moral overtones than 'extramarital sex', and 'infidelity' even more. Both imply a breach of trust and are surrounded by a constellation of words such as 'unfaithful', 'stray', 'cheating', 'fooling around', and so on. However, in many societies adultery is not illegal or clandestine, and even if it is considered immoral, extenuating circumstances are recognized. 'With a drunk of a husband like that, who can blame her?', or 'If I had a shrew of a wife like that, I'd do the same.'

According to Chinese Buddhist beliefs, there are several levels to Hell, one of them exclusively reserved for adulterers. This mural depicts the torments that await the unfaithful.

Context and reasons for EMS

A 1983 review by Anthony Thompson, an Australian psychologist, found that in the United States no particular social class, ethnic group, or educational level has a monopoly on EMS. For women, however, there do seem to be some links between EMS and generation (women born in the 1950s and 1960s are more likely than their mothers or grandmothers to have engaged in EMS), also political persuasion (conservatives are less likely to engage in EMS than liberals), residental area (rural inhabitants less likely), and occupation (those working outside the home more likely). None of these factors is clearly identifiable for men. Nor does the fact of being of one religion rather than another seem to be of importance, for men or women. But devoutness is significant; the devout of all persuasions are least likely, and the religiously unaffiliated or inactive most likely, to engage in EMS. Such findings are not significantly different from those reported more recently by Greeley and colleagues.

However, when it comes to the characteristics of the primary relationship, many reports show clear correlations with the frequency and nature of extramarital relationships for both men and women. EMS is more likely to occur when one or other partner considers the marital relationahip poor and unsatisfactory, and the frequency of coitus too low. However, some authors claim that this does not lead to EMS unless feelings of personal alienation are also present.

For men, the most common reasons for EMS are the desire for novelty and ego enhancement — either or both can be provided by an uncritical and flattering partner. For women, however, the reasons seem to be more varied. Here are some of them: wanting greater emotional satisfaction, a more vibrant and communicative relationship, a release from emotional boredom; wanting higher social status; wanting to retaliate for real or imagined mistreatment, sexual or non-sexual; wanting a new and perhaps more skilful and exciting sexual partner; acceding to the wishes of a respected or valued friend; wanting to assert independence or regain self-esteem by being desired by someone new. In one study the most common reason given by both men and women was 'constant fighting at home'.

The temptations of opportunity

Opportunities for extramarital sex are now greater than in the past. Both men and women have more mobility and more disposable income. Women, now in the workforce in great numbers, spend less time at home. Families live in neighbourhoods where they have relative anonymity. More children are leaving the family nest earlier. Certainly the media, with their frequent focus on extramarital scandals, encourage people to think the grass may be greener on the other side of the fence. Also, in the last three decades, reliable contraception has reduced a major disincentive to extramarital coitus. Significantly, most of these factors have impinged mainly on women — men never have been particularly hampered by children, money, environment, or the fear of pregnancy.

The moral climate has also changed. More so than in the past, people recognize that not all extramarital relationships are wrong or detrimental, that individuality and personal growth may not be totally satisfied by one other person. 'Emotional independence', 'sex role egalitarianism', and 'humanistic expansion' are more than sociological buzz words; they actually mean that more people are doing more of their 'own thing'.

This new sense of individual freedom is not anathema to all religious groups. A 1991 report by the Presbyterian Church questioned the wisdom of regarding form as more important than substance. Why, if it is based on mutual consent, respect, commitment, and an attempt to enhance moral decency, should a non-marital sexual relationship be considered unworthy? 'It no longer makes sense to grant uncritical religious and moral legitimation to heterosexuality and heterosexual relations simply because they are heterosexual. Similarly, it is wrong to condemn non-marital sexual activity as unacceptable simply because it falls outside a particular formal, institutional arrangement....' Such views do not represent mainline Presbyterian thinking or that of other denominations, but many groups are being forced to re-examine their stance on non-marital and non-heterosexual relationships.

EMS: the idea and the reality

Does EMS weaken the primary bond? Does it disrupt trust and intimacy? Might it, in some instances, strengthen some aspects of a relationship? The answer to all these questions is a qualified 'Yes'.

Many couples who live together rather than marry do so on the tacit or explicit understanding that sexual relations with others are 'allowed'. Partners who enter into marriage usually do so on the understanding, again tacit or explicit, that affairs are *not* allowed. In 1980 sociologist Ira Reiss and colleagues found that individuals with happy marriages were less likely to approve of EMS than those less happily married. Nevertheless EMS occurs among those happily and unhappily married, among young and old, newlyweds and old established couples, and the motives for it are many and diverse. When it comes to it, many cohabiting couples find their partners' affairs just as hard to take as married couples do. The reality of a partner's EMS is often more difficult to cope with than the idea.

A significant difference exists, however, between homosexual and heterosexual couples.

Among gay male couples in established relationships, expectations of sexual exclusivity diminish rapidly after the first year together. Not infrequently, homosexual couples will have relationships in which new sexual partners are individually enjoyed or even mutually shared. The term 'comarital' sex would in fact be more appropriate.

More frequently than not, husband and wife become ready for an affair independently. Early in the relationship they may discuss the subject of extramarital sex: 'It's OK when you're on a trip away from home', 'It's OK if I'm out of action or somehow unavailable for a long period of time', 'It's OK as long as you're discreet and I don't know about it', or 'It's OK as long as its just for kicks and you don't get involved'. Nevertheless EMS is seen as a powerful threat. Some 85 per cent of American couples in a major study done in 1979 admitted as much; the breach of trust was seen as fundamentally damaging. Since then, in both the United States and Britain, the indications are that EMS is seen as less threatening; more couples seem to take it in their stride.

When a relationship has endured for a number of years, the idea or the reality of EMS may be more tolerated, especially by those who have already had extramarital experiences. But it is still easier to accept one's own EMS than a partner's. Acceptance may imply that EMS does not represent an impending break to the primary relationship or a lack of care and concern for the family as a whole. 'I know he loves me and the children. If he has a fling now and then, I know it's just that and of little lasting significance.' Many men and women see extramarital relationships as necessary safety valves for the pressures and needs that build up both inside and outside a marriage. The partner having the extramarital relationship may even see it as a way of helping to preserve the marriage. In fact British sexologist Alex Comfort has written: 'It is highly probably that adultery today maintains far more marriages than it destroys....' This may well be the case provided the faithful spouse never gets to hear of it.

In fact most research finds that wives are more tolerant of their husbands' affairs than vice versa. One study of divorced people by Kinsey and his colleagues revealed that only a quarter of those women who knew of their husbands' extramarital activity thought it a significant factor in the break-up; half saw it as a moderate factor. Among the men, however, half thought that their wives' infidelity was the chief reason for the break-up and a third thought it an important, but not the main, reason. An interesting sidelight on the subject came from a 1983 study of some 200 separated and divorced individuals by Graham Spanier and Randie Margolis. More than 80 per cent of both the men and the women in this study felt that their own extramarital relations were the result of marital problems but that their spouses were the cause of such problems. Selective sexwatching indeed! In a poll done for the American magazine *People* in 1986, 20 per cent of those surveyed said they would seek a divorce as soon as they found out about their partner's infidelity, 5 per cent said they would ignore it in the hope that the affair would fizzle out, and the rest said they would try to work things out.

Too often the subject of extramarital relations is first broached when suspicions are already flickering or feelings have already been hurt. Anger and jealousy are stock reactions. Several studies have found that women's immediate reactions to EMS are somewhat different from men's. Women usually try to patch up or improve the primary relationship; they try to 'beat the competition' by making themselves more attractive to their partner. Men are more likely to go out and seek consolation with an affair of their own. Assaults on lovers are not rare, but despite such images as bull elephants charging one another, stags locking antlers, and gentlemen drawing swords at dawn, the emotionally wounded human male in contemporary Western society does not usually confront his rival.

Most husbands and wives avoid confrontation and live with repressed jealousy, hurt, and insecurity until either circumstances force open acknowledgement or the situation resolves itself. Sometimes the *status quo*, the sharing of a partner with another, is preferable to losing a partner altogether. Only for a minority of couples are extramarital adventures acknowledged and accepted as unthreatening.

Gay couples tend to deal with jealousy and sexual competition rather differently. With lesbians the tendency is for the *couple* to deal with the 'competition' and possibly draw closer as a result. Among gay men the tendency is for the primary relationship to break; partners generally prefer to 'switch' rather than fight or work things out.

Open relationships

When both partners feel similarly, they may, by word or deed, contract to allow each other sexual intimacy with others. The term 'open marriage' or 'open relationship' is often used to describe such arrangements. Ideally these are relationships of equals, where neither partner 'owns' the other and both enrich the union by contributing gains from their wider activities, sexual or otherwise. Only 4 per cent of the 3,880 married people surveyed by American sociologist Anthony Pietropinto in 1979 thought open marriage possible or practical, and in my own professional experience I have met few people capable of it for long. Some renegotiation of the contract usually becomes necessary, and the nature or frequency of the outside sex becomes more restricted — only with or not with a certain partner, only during separate vacations or work trips, or not while the children are at home.

What of the threesome, or *ménage à trois*, that so often appears in sexual fantasy? According to Arno Karlen, this is a reality, at least once in a lifetime, for 4 to 5 per cent of American couples. Karlen has observed two main types among individuals who participate in threesomes: 'erotic adventurers' who are sexually active from a young age and enjoy variety, and 'timid late starters' who, for many reasons, feel they have missed out sexually and are trying to catch up. While some threesomes are long-lasting, most are short-lived experiments.

Swinging

Further from the mainstream are couples, known as 'swingers' or 'mate swappers', who engage in mutual and consensual EMS as a form of recreation. Sex may involve a third party, more often female than male, or another couple, or a whole group. For the majority of swingers the stated goal is novelty and sexual pleasure. A small minority participate from a utopian philosophy that society should be free of sexual jealousies and frustrations. In the United States the total number of swinging couples is estimated at between 1 and 5 per cent of all married couples. In Japan the number is nearer 0.3 per cent. Statistics for other countries are not known. In New York, San Francisco, and other major cities there are swingers' clubs where couples, for an entrance fee, disport themselves with others in unabashed sexual games and gymnastics. Where commercial clubs are illegal such activities take place in private homes.

Although accurate estimates are difficult to obtain, it seems that AIDS has not had a major impact on swinging. One investigative reporter, L. McNeil, wrote: '...in 1992 there seemed to be as many swing

In this fanciful 19th-century Indian miniature entitled 'The Swing' the central lovers sit on a swing composed of other amorous couples. Except in their sexual arrangements, swingers do not differ significantly from the rest of the population. Why do most people project all their needs and fantasies onto a single partner?

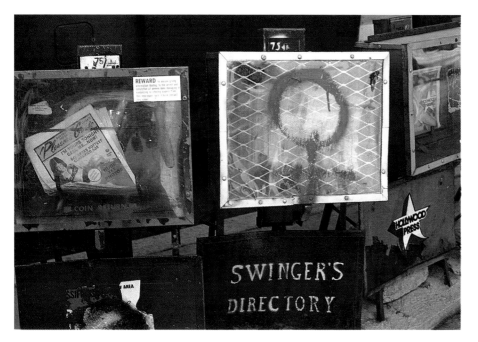

Some people object to anything they feel is 'sexist', i.e. degrading to women (men are still fair game). Here a vending machine for a swingers' magazine has been defaced with the female cross-and-circle symbol.

clubs in the New York City area as there had been at the height of the sexual revolution.' Swingers see themselves as sexually aware and therefore likely to select partners carefully. This may or may not be true, but it is a matter of record that swingers are less likely to indulge in alcoholic excess, inject drugs, engage in male homosexual activities, or have contact with high-risk groups. They are also somewhat racially discriminatory.

Swingers, by the nature of their behaviour, which titillates some and repels others, attract a great deal of interest. Yet most studies have found them to be little different from most of their neighbours, except in their sexual arrangements. In many ways swingers are socially and politically conservative. The majority begin swinging at the husband's urging, or sometimes intimidation, though it seems that wives become more enthusiastic once they get involved. Women can obviously participate longer, with more partners, and without the obligation to 'perform' that men feel. In the past rather biased etiquette allowed single women, but not single men, to join in. Now women are demanding that unattached males should be allowed to take part too.

A 1986 High Court case in England provides an interesting anecdote here. A 30-year-old women sought divorce from her 31-year-old husband after 14 years of marriage on the grounds that he had forced her to swing and take part in threesomes. The presiding judge ruled that if, at the time, she had not liked what was going on, she could have refused. Her petition for divorce was turned down.

The effects of swinging on a marriage are debatable. Participants often say that sharing EMS adventures strengthens their relationship. Researchers are not so sure. Masters and Johnson, for instance, mistrust swingers' positive statements, and say that jealousy is probably repressed. Yet no study has revealed more divorces or more marital battles among swingers than among any other comparable group. Indeed a 1977 study carried out in the United States by Brian Gilmartin found that swingers were generally happier with their lot than most.

Divorce and remarriage

Among modern nations that allow divorce, Italy is the only Western country that does not depend heavily on it as a solution to marital strife. Perhaps it is only a matter of time — divorce did not become legal in Italy until 1974. Italian men reject divorce mainly for financial reasons (alimony awards are high and there are tax penalties). Italian women reject divorce mainly out of fear of ostracism. One woman described the social ordeal of divorce like this: 'I was abandoned by my friends, who were afraid I would seduce their husbands, and chased by their husbands, who thought I would be an easy target. I discovered that a divorced woman in Italy has to renounce both love and sex if she wants to lead a quiet life.' To maintain social networks but resolve marital woes, Italians separate. Not uncommonly the husband moves in with a mistress, whom he has probably been seeing for years, and the wife retains her respectable married status. Divorce is something that happens to less than 2 per cent of Italian couples.

In the United States between 3 and 6 marriages in 10 end in divorce (the proportion varies with the age of the couple, with divorce more likely among younger couples). Often, however, it is the same people getting divorced over and over again who raise the statistics. Researchers A.J. Norton and J.E. Moorman found that the most stable first marriages are those in which the wife is over 30 at age of marriage, and the least stable those in which she is a teenager. Now, however, the divorce rate seems to be levelling out. One of the effects of hard economic times is that couples are more likely to 'tough it out' together than take their chances apart. Or perhaps they are separating without a legal divorce.

Until the early 1970s, in most states in America, adultery was the only justification for divorce accepted by the courts — many a photographer and model made good money providing 'evidence'. This was also true in Britain ('hotel divorces'). Currently, 'no-fault' divorce laws are in force in 48 out of the 50 states ('no fault' is shorthand for 'irreconcilable differences', 'incompatibility', and other socio-legal terms). It is now, for better or worse, almost as easy for Americans to get divorced as married.

In 1980 approximately one third of marriages in the Soviet Union ended in divorce before the first anniversary. In 1990 the proportion had risen to almost half. It is still too early to say what strains and changes the new new order will impose on marriage and sexual behaviour. In Britain the current divorce rate is more than 1 in 3, up from 1 in 4 about 10 years ago, although in Britain marriages tend to last longer.

Sexual problems are not usually the main reason for divorce or the severing of a long-standing relationship. But the importance of sex in a relationship is very relative and subjective. As one of my clients remarked: 'When everything is going right, sex is only 20 per cent of my marriage. When things are going wrong, it's 90 per cent.' More usually, break-ups happen because of a gradual growing apart over the years.

Separation and divorce are seldom easy on the emotions. They provoke feelings of anger, blame, guilt, hurt, and failure. The intention to divorce must be explained to children, parents, friends, and colleagues. But when it actually happens, it is often a welcome escape from hopeless or neurotic entanglement into a brighter, freer world. Some people positively blossom once the initial anguish is over. Though some remain bitter, most eventually look back on their union as a learning experience.

Despite popular belief to the contrary, men are often harder hit by divorce than women, particularly if there are still children to be cared for. They are more likely to get depressed, even suicidal. A divorce typically gives custody of the children to the mother, so she retains her parental role while he loses his, even if he supplies financial assistance. Depending on their age and the character of the marriage before the divorce, children can also be devastated. Is it better for children to live in a conflicted and argumentative family or in a single-parent environment? No one has certain answers.

Divorce is often followed by a period of sexual experimentation and exploration. There may be a frenzy of different sex partners in an attempt to regain confidence and self-esteem, particularly if the problems in the marriage were mainly sexual. Or there may be a desire to make up for lost time. For many divorcees, starting the dating game again is frightening and disheartening. It requires purposeful reintegration into the world of the unattached, a catching up on social and sexual mores which may have changed a great deal in the intervening years. In the 1990s it is not unusual for intercourse to be suggested and actualized on a first date, but someone who has just been divorced may need more time,

Honest communication is as important as sex in maintaining a marriage. People who remarry are generally more flexible in their demands and expectations, more willing to compromise, more prepared to see their new partner for who she or he really is. To paraphrase Freud: 'When two people are in love, there are at least four people present — the two in love and the two they believe each other to be.'

weeks or even months, before they make that jump.

It is a fact that the majority of divorced people remarry and find their second marriage much more satisfactory than the first. Most second marriages seem to avoid the sexual problems that may have bedevilled the first. People enter into second marriages with more amorous and erotic experience, more confidence about making their preferences known and enquiring about those of their partners, more willingness to be adventurous in their love-making. In fact there is more flexibility all round. Second-time-rounders may do things with a lover or new spouse they never dreamed of doing with their original mate. They are more likely to know what it takes to make marriage work and to have learned the spirit of compromise so necessary to all successful relationships.

A shortage of men

Motives for remarriage usually echo those for first marriages: sexual needs, companionship, love and intimacy, desire for commitment, obedience to social pressures, and the belief that it takes two to raise a family. Reasons for not remarrying are lingering bitterness, fear of failing a second time, and fear of hurting children or other loved ones. In the case of divorced women, another reason is the shortage of available or desirable men. Unmarried heterosexual women over the age of 30 considerably outnumber men of similar age, status, and orientation. This is so in most of the affluent nations of the West. Contemporary calculations of the United States' population, for example, show that for 1 in 5 women over 30 no male partner is available, and the disproportion affects black women even more. In fact, two-thirds of those who live alone in the United States are women.

One of the solutions to this disparity of numbers is 'man sharing', a concept described

In the West there are simply not enough men to go around, not if women continue to want exclusive one-to-one relationships with men their own age. Will man-sharing become more common, or will more women settle for celibacy or shorter-term relationships? Women say they get less out of marriage than men do, but 'happiness' often means different things to wives and husbands.

by black sociologist Joseph Scott and well understood among the black community in some regions of the United States where eligible males are often lost to death and institionalization. Women share men because they need the companionship and some measure of financial security, not from choice; if the traditional two-parent family option is not available, a shared man is better than no man at all. Another option, increasingly taken by black and white women alike, with Elizabeth Taylor and Cher as role models, is to choose marriage partners from a much younger age group.

While the male-female numbers crunch is also true in Britain and Europe, it is dramatically different in other parts of the world. In China and India, for example, there is a significant loss of females early in life due to medical neglect and infanticide. In fact it has been estimated that China is 'missing' some 20 million females and India a comparable number. However, this has not resulted in the remaining marriageable women being valued more highly.

After the death of a spouse the move to a new relationship is slow. As with divorce, men seemed to be more depressed and downcast by the experience than women. If there was a great deal of love and commitment, switching to a new partner may be painful; even if there was little love and affection, memories can be powerful and inhibiting.

While most divorced women return to an active sex life, fewer widowed women do so. In contrast, almost all divorced and widowed men under the age of 55 resume some sort of sexual relationship. Statistically, it is easier for men over 50 to find partners. There are also social forces at work here. Women are often expected to grieve longer than men and to relinquish old loyalties more slowly; adults as well as young children have more difficulty accepting their mother with another man than their father with another woman; for many women, not having to take care of an adult 'dependent' is something of a relief; and, more than in the past, women are prepared to settle for companionate and sexual relationships without marriage potential. Widowers tend to feel more adrift than widows, and tend to remarry or form new relationships sooner.

Improving relationships

There is no shortage of advice on how to improve sexual relationships — 'how to' recipes pour out of women's magazines, newspaper advice columns, and television and radio shows. 'Kiss your partner daily on waking', 'Smile when you greet him/her', 'Be open to change', 'Don't welcome your lover with a string of problems' — good pieces of advice all. But a successful relationship is like a chess game, full of nuances and subtlety, the moves of one player influencing the moves of the other, and so on. Even the doyen of behavioural psychology, B.F. Skinner, said of his relationship with his wife Eve: 'There is a problem doing things together. I walk faster and longer than she. She needs entertainment (movies, TV, plays) that I can do very well without. What is a fair deal then? How much should be done to make her happy in spite of the fact that it will make me less happy?' Goria Steinem, the diva of feminism, recently wrote in her book *Revolution from Within*: 'As many women can testify [getting a man to fall in love] is alarmingly easy, providing you're willing to play down who you are and play up what he wants you to be.... The only problem was that, having got this man to fall in love with an inauthentic me, I had to keep on not being myself.' Can we lesser mortals solve our relationship problems any more easily? Can we even agree on what constitutes a good or ideal relationship?

In this chapter I have mainly talked about marriage and long-term relationships. Marriage of course has the support of law, tradition, and convention, and the strength of stated, overt commitment, and its guidelines and obligations, observed or not, are understood by all. But what happens when partners are not married? They have to evolve their own rules. Any relationship, as it develops, undergoes continuous examination and reassessment by the parties to it. What does a cohabiting couple measure or assess their relationship against? In my opinion both cohabitation and marriage need working at, but the former more than the latter. And no one can predict what strains, sexual and otherwise, will accompany domestic and covenanted partnerships as they evolve.

At one level, relationships can be improved by technical measures, such as earning more money, making sure the children are happy, spending more time boosting your partner's ego, reaffirming commitment to the relationship, or making more time for sexual and non-sexual togetherness. But at a deeper level it is not technique alone that will most enhance a relationship but willingness to change attitudes. As one marriage counsellor said to me: 'I can improve a couple's sexual technique and easily solve problems of ignorance, shame, or inhibition. I am most stymied, however, by how to change motivation, attitudes, and basic behaviour.' Couples who go for counselling or who buy 'how to' books usually want to know 'How do I go about changing him/her?' rather than 'How do I go about changing myself?' It is no easier to permamently change sexual behaviour than it is to change smoking or eating habits. Nevertheless people do manage to stop smoking and control their weight, and many people do manage to improve their relationships.

There has been a spate of books recently with titles like *The Myth of Women's Masochism* (P.J. Caplan), *Men who are good for you and men who are bad: learning to tell the difference* (S. Hoffman), and *Women who love too much: when you keep wishing and hoping he'll change* (R. Norwood), all telling readers how to get out of terrible relationships and recognize better ones. They are mainly for women, and most of them say something like this: 'You are too good for your man. Leave him and look for someone who will appreciate you.' This may be galvanizing initially, but there is little real advice to readers on how to change themselves so as not to fall into the same trap again. Men are less likely to look to books for help with relationships. One author who writes for both men and women is Warren Farrel. His book *Why men are the way they are* is a far cry above the others in that it speaks to both sexes and offers a clear perspective of how they might and can understand each other.

Recipes for loving change

The easiest place to start to change a relationship is to *emphasize the positive things* about it. When you are pleased with something, say so. Also, *emphasize your commitment to the relationship.* Don't threaten to walk out or get divorced, and never resort to physical violence. Tell yourself that everything you say and do must build toward improving, not weakening, the relationship.

Give yourself and your partner permission to ask, question, or comment on things that may help you to understand each other better. 'You know, I've told you before, but I'd like you to...', 'Do you know what turns me on/off the most?', 'Which do you like better, ... or ...?'

Perhaps the most important permission is to *allow yourself and your partner to be honest.* Tell each other, clearly and lovingly, what you like and don't like, want and don't want. Don't always expect your partner to take the initiative in the honesty game, and don't expect him/her to

When a relationship goes stale it is no good just hoping it will get better; positive steps must be taken. Taking more time to be erotic and changing lovemaking routines is one way to improve things. 'Getting away from it all' can help too.

know intuitively what you prefer. If you want to try something old, new, or special, give yourself permission to say so. 'Let's do something different tonight. What would you like to do?' or 'You know what we've never tried that I would like?' One of the reasons men most frequently give for visiting prostitutes is that they want sexual favours denied them by their regular partners. Oral-genital play is high on the list. A reason frequently given by women for trying new sexual relationships is that they want a level of intimacy, communication, and patience their regular partner does not provide.

Years of habit may make new practices seem strange and suspect. But novelty in an established sexual context can be particularly pleasing, erotic, and enticing. *Give yourself and your partner permission to say 'Let's spice up our love life a little'*. Said warmly and at the appropriate moment, it should be well received.

Telling your fantasies and erotic desires out loud is a very effective way of initiating new sexual activities. You are not obliged to put them into practice, but neither should you forbid yourself to make them a reality. Even if they only serve to break the ice they will have served their purpose.

Give yourself permission to interact with your parter in different ways. If he always initiates sex, you initiate it instead. If she always asks for a massage, you ask instead. Game playing, flirting, and seductive behaviour can be an exciting return to sexual yesterdays.

Important too is the need to *make time to be together, to be loving and erotic*. Often the excitement of planning and expectancy is lost in a welter of chores and obligations.

A willingness to *improve communication skills* is also important. This means more than speaking with a smile, shrug, sigh, laugh, or frown, messages which are not always as clear as they might be. Often your partner may just want you to suggest something that will make him feel more sexually desired or a more successful provider; or perhaps she may simply want you to listen to a problem, not solve it.

Here are some of the ways in which you can keep communication open and clear. Don't beat around the bush — say what you like and don't like, let your partner know just what you have in mind — but be considerate about his/her feelings. If you want to say no to something, say why and what you would rather do instead. When requesting something you think your partner might not agree to, be patient and understanding if you are turned down — sometimes you have to agree to disagree, but in any case try to find out why he/she feels that way. Don't dwell on past grievances — talk about anticipated pleasures instead. If in doubt about your partner's meaning, intentions, or desires, ask rather than guess — he/she will generally appreciate your interest.

Here are four final guidelines — they require thought and work, but they will pay huge dividends. *Relate to your partner as a person*, not just as a body. *Be willing to please and be pleased. Be flexible, courteous, and considerate. Balance trust, seriousness, and play.*

One of the wonders of human sexual relationships is that satisfaction often comes as much from giving erotic pleasure as from receiving it. The same is true of love. Therein lies a powerful truth: in love and sex the greatest gain may come from the uninhibited offering of oneself, the sweetest feelings from putting aside inhibitions and self-control. Passion and receptivity to passion are potent aphrodisiacs.

Chapter 11

Reproduction and birthwatching

Childbirth, one of life's most significant events, heralded by nine months of advertisement and watchful waiting, typically goes unwitnessed even by the individuals most intimately involved.

In the West, despite the humanization and demedicalization of childbirth, many mothers do not fully witness the moment of birth — they are drugged, half aware, and often lying in the supine position. Nevertheless, in the last decade, in the United States, Britain, and elsewhere, fathers are more frequently present in the delivery room. Increasingly this is not just allowed but encouraged, because it gives the mother emotional support and reinforces family and parental bonds. This has been the norm in Scandinavia and the Netherlands for many years now. But in Latin America, most of Asia, and even in modern Japan, fathers are excluded by hospital fiat, physician's whim, or social custom. Birth typically takes place in the presence of strangers from a select professional class, not in the presence of relatives or friends, and in the anonymity of a hospital rather than in the home. In some cultures, among the Maya of Central America for example, the mother's whole family, including the men and boys, attends the birth. But birthwatching *en famille* is rare. Most societies, even those where medicine is primitive, banish male relatives and children from the scene and leave support and assistance of the mother to an older experienced woman or female relative.

Why the privacy and secrecy? Modesty and embarrassment certainly enter into it, as do considerations of hygiene, but so do mystery and magic. The more the process of bringing new life into the world is seen as something women alone are responsible for the more exclusively it is kept the preserve of women. Among palaeolithic people, who seem to have had only the vaguest appreciation of the male's part in reproduction (as far as we can judge from aboriginal societies still in existence today), birth was a secret female rite, the counterpart of secret male rites. Even in societies that had some understanding of the male's part in reproduction the process of birth tended to be looked on as a physical and spiritual experience proper to women, as a privilege of the female gender; that it took place in secret had nothing to do with sexual shame or modesty and everything to do with the special and fragile magic of the event. Even today some societies believe that at the moment of birth the spirit enters the child's body. It is quite logical therefore that only a few special individuals should be present, and those selected few must have the power to aid the process physically or spiritually. With minor variations and some notable exceptions, societies all over the world admit only the privileged few — midwife, priest, doctor, shaman — to the drama of birth.

In most indigenous South American cultures birth was no secret, as this delightful object shows; it is a flute.

Before birth became organized for the convenience of loftily qualified male physicians, birthing stools were in wide use. In this 16th-century woodcut the midwife kneels in front of the mother. In the sitting, kneeling, squatting, or standing position gravity helps delivery.

The rise and fall of the midwife

In the West this heritage of secrecy and magic has been complicated by two other factors: modesty, and professional jealousy between midwives and physicians. For many centuries it was taboo for women to be seen naked by strangers, even by doctors, and until the eighteenth century almost all births were attended by midwives. Midwives offered, as Elizabeth Nihell put it in her 1760 *Treatise on the Art of Midwifery*, '...a certain shrewd vivacity, a grace of ease, a hardiness of performance and especially a kind of unction of the heart....' Even so, midwives in earlier centuries were often subjected to abuse, and sometimes hanged as witches if they attended a birth where the baby or mother died or the child was deformed.

Today, in the developing world, between 60 and 80 per cent of babies are delivered at home by midwives whose abilities range from the rudimentary and unlearned to the highly skilled and trained, often reflecting the social status of the mother. Even in developed countries like the United States the midwifery profession has been enjoying something of a resurgence, despite the fact that some insurance companies refuse to indemnify or demand huge premiums from anyone who is not a certified obstetrician. Sadly this has left many areas without any birthing service.

The systematic development of obstetrical knowledge can be credited to the Frenchman Ambroise Paré. In 1551 he wrote a treatise on obstetrics, in which he encouraged fellow physicians to master 'podalic version', the manual turning of a foetus to facilitate delivery, an art relatively ignored since the days of Hippocrates. The few physicians who mastered this technique were often called in by midwives when they encountered the not infrequent situation of a baby ill positioned for delivery, its life in danger. Otherwise men were not admitted to the delivery of 'honest' women. In 1522 a German physician, Dr. Wortt of Hamburg, dressed in women's clothes in order to be present at a birth. For the double indiscretion — curiosity and cross-dressing — he was burned at the stake.

In 1663 Louis XIV of France summoned his physician to attend one of his favourite mistresses in childbirth, thus giving royal approval and snob value to male supervision of delivery. The fad soon spread throughout the French aristocracy; the services of an *accoucheur* became a status symbol and physicians were not slow to play the role of male midwife in return for fat fees. This was the beginning of obstetrics as a specialized medical discipline and the beginning of the end for midwifery as the only profession concerned with women during pregnancy and birth. Women were denied access to medical schools and therefore excluded from full knowledge of a process of central importance to their sex.

Calculating the risks

Pregnancy and birth have always been risky. Even today, with modern medical knowledge, the leading causes of death among women aged between 15 and 50 are pregnancy and childbirth. United Nations statistics for the years 1980–85 show that for every 100,000 live births in developed countries such as the United States, England, France, and Israel, about 10 women died from complications during pregnancy, delivery, or puerperium (the period immediately after delivery). Scandinavian countries do rather better because they pay more attention to maternal care. In most other countries around the world fatalities during pregnancy and birth are so high that they are not usually reported accurately. Estimates for some African and South American countries, and for India, Pakistan, and Bangladesh, are that between 3 and 6 women per 1,000 die from pregnancy-related causes, and that more than 1 in 100 infants die at birth or very soon after. In countries that decline to report or, due to poor record keeping, cannot produce such statistics, pregnancy-related maternal deaths could be as high as 1 in 100.

Obstetrics

Obstetrics became a medical speciality precisely because pregnancy and birth can be life-threatening. If a foetus is poorly positioned for birth, the life of both mother and baby may be in danger. Due to quite natural causes, some 4 in every 100 babies get stuck in the pelvis in a position that makes birth impossible without external help. If the baby cannot be dislodged by being turned within the uterus or birth canal (vagina), the lives of mother and baby are in danger. French Huguenot physician William Chamberlin seems to have been the first to develop obstetrical forceps, spoon-like tongs that grasp the foetus in cases where there is no room for hands or where hands cannot get a grip. After emigrating to England to escape religious persecution, Chamberlin and his sons perfected their forceps but kept their use and design secret. In fact they guarded their lucrative monopoly by blindfolding the women they delivered. In 1721 a more public-spirited Belgian barber-surgeon named Jean Palfyne made public to the world, through a speech to the Paris Academy of Sciences, his version of obstetrical forceps, or *mains de fer* (iron hands).

Until the nineteenth century physicians had only the vaguest notion of hygiene or how diseases spread. Most mothers who died in childbirth died of infection contracted during or immediately after delivery. The raw uterus or ripped vaginal canal offers a ready site for infection. By then many lying-in hospitals had been established, but it it was a macabre fact that these facilities brought with them a dramatic *increase* in puerperal fever and death. Hospitals were reservoirs of disease, transmitted from patient to patient by doctors, nurses, unsterilized instruments, and contaminated bedclothes. The magnitude of the problem was such that in the Lombardy province of France in the 1860s few women who gave birth in hospital survived; in the Maternité Hospital in Paris around 1 in 4 women died. Voices such as those of Ignatz P. Semmelweis of Budapest, the Scottish physician Alexander Gordon, and the American author-physician Oliver Wendell Holmes, cried in the wilderness. Without yet comprehending the reality of germs, they surmised that 'contagion' was probably passed from person to person and was not the result of sin or chance. Gordon published his views in 1795 and Holmes in 1843 but the medical world in general closed its ears against contagion theories and pleas for greater cleanliness. Semmelweis, writing in 1861, was even more pointedly rejected when he suggested that everyone attending women in labour, including physicians, should cleanse themselves before entering the labour room, especially if they had been in contact with a diseased or dead person. He advised at the very least washing the hands in a chlorine solution.

It is partly to ensure cleanliness and prevent the spread of infection that non-professionals are excluded from delivery rooms today. The anonymous privacy of modern hospital delivery has a sound medical basis. But there are other reasons for privacy. Delivery is often painful and distressing, something many women would rather go through in private, and which others would rather not intrude upon.

Pain-free birth did not become a possibility until the mid-1800s when the Scottish physician James Simpson demonstrated the use of chloroform during labour. Queen Victoria had chloroform for the birth of her seventh child in 1853 and made the practice socially acceptable. Today we have better methods of pain control, but still the majority of women bear their babies in ignorance of the physiological processes involved and lack the psychological, social, and emotional support that can make childbirth a more positive experience. Ignorance, pain, and psychological isolation are not necessary requirements of birthing; they are the sour fruits of tradition.

Feelings about pregnancy

Birth, or parturition, is the culmination of a growth process that starts nine months (about 260 days) earlier when sperm and egg unite in a process called fertilization. Once the egg has been fertilized it is called a zygote. Most women are not aware that fertilization has taken place until some two weeks later when they miss their period. Missing a period is never a neutral matter; a woman who wants a child will be elated, but if pregnancy is unwanted or unexpected she may be frightened or depressed. Even for women who want children the knowledge of being pregnant often elicits mixed emotions — joy, melancholy, pride, apprehension, an added sense of responsibility. One woman I know, who wanted a child but did not plan her pregnancy, expressed her feelings like this: 'Well, I suppose I ought to feel happy, but right now I feel more numb than elated. I wanted this day to come, but I feel as if I'm somehow becoming part of the establishment, as if I'm approaching middle age earlier

In the West society's attitudes towards pregnancy are ambivalent. The cover of the August 1991 issue of the magazine Vanity Fair, *showing a very pregnant Demi Moore, caused quite a stir.*

than expected. It also means I'm no longer the free spirit I like to consider myself. Yet deep down I know it's what I really want. And I know Larry will be ecstatic.'

While some women say they know immediately that they are pregnant, the only way to be sure of pregnancy is by a home or laboratory test. These tests diagnose pregnancy at various early stages, but their accuracy increases as pregnancy advances. False negatives are possible, as are false positives. If the results of a test are unsupported by other signs, a repeat test about a week later is in order.

To a biologist a pregnancy is first a zygote, then an embryo, then a foetus, and only after birth a baby, but to almost every onlooker and certainly every hopeful parent a pregnancy is a baby right from the start. Every pregnant woman is viewed as a future mother. This social view of a biological event is highly significant. It determines how a pregnant woman is reacted to and how her pregnancy is viewed. She is no longer her 'single' self.

By the seventh week of gestation the foetus' organ systems and appendages are visible, and the genital area has begun to differentiate into male and female. The dark mass in the abdominal area is the liver. The umbilical cord (top right) carries blood to and from the placenta. Alcohol and most drugs cross the placenta — the foetus is especially vulnerable to their effects in the first trimester.

Studies done in many developed and technologically advanced countries reveal that, for more than 50 per cent of women, pregnancy is unplanned. This is not the same as saying it is unwanted; many women plan to get pregnant 'at some stage'. While some women accept unplanned pregnancy fatalistically, an increasing number do not. More and more women are choosing to abort, and in many societies they are supported in their decision. Parental responsibility really begins before pregnancy rather than after, but contraception requires an effort not all people are able or wish to make. In many societies pregnancy is still seen as the natural outcome of sexual activity for women.

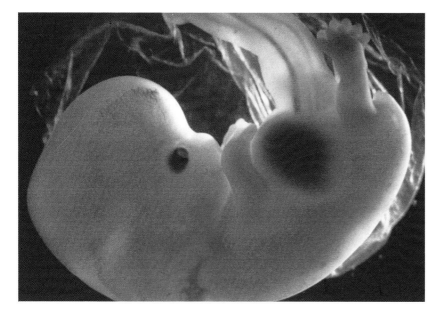

Which sex is the baby?

The units of life contributed by each parent are called gametes. The male gametes are the sperm produced by the testes and the female gamete is the egg, or ovum, produced by one or other of the ovaries. The sex of the zygote, potentially the new human being, is determined at the time of fertilization. Since all ova contain an X sex chromosome, the male's sperm is the factor that determine's the child's sex; if it too contains an X chromosome, the zygote will be female (XX); if it contains a Y, the zygote will be male (XY). For reasons we do not yet fully understand, more male zygotes are produced than female — the ratio is approximately 130/150:100 — but since male zygotes are more fragile, by the time of birth the ratio has fallen to about 106:100 for Caucasian and Asian births and about 102:100 for Negro births. There are also more deaths among infant males than among infant females.

The knowledge that it is the sperm of the male that determines sex is being widely disseminated in countries such as China and on the Indian subcontinent where, traditionally, female babies have been looked on as worthless and wives brutally abused for 'producing' them. Recent reports from China, India, and Pakistan tell of women being burned alive, forced from their homes, beaten, poisoned, strangled, and driven to suicide for the 'offence'

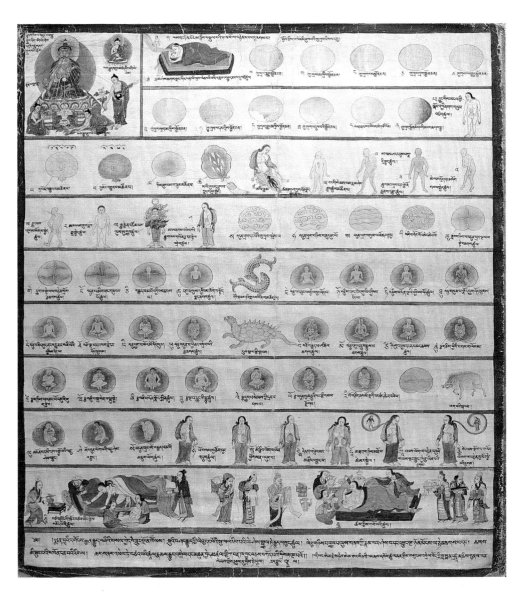

A Tibetan medical scroll showing the whole process of reproduction and birth. Note the squatting position used for the birth, the presence of male and female attendants, and the procession of well-wishers bringing gifts after the birth. Just before birth the baby takes up a head-down position. Anterior presentation (the back of the baby's head towards the mother's front) is commoner than posterior (the baby's face towards the mother's front), but very often the baby turns anterior during labour so that the head slips more easily under the pubic bone and into the birth canal.

of giving birth to girl children. Lessons in elementary biology, and human decency, are sorely needed.

Despite popular recommendations for douching with vinegar or a solution of baking soda, or having coitus in certain positions or at certain times of the menstrual cycle, there is no simple or reliable method of ensuring that a baby will be of the desired sex. Folk nostrums abound because many people would like to choose, and because in many cultures boys are usually preferred to girls. In 1984 I mistakenly anticipated that researchers would have found a way of separating X sperm from Y sperm by now, but they have not. Other than in certain carefully defined circumstances, it is still not possible for parents to choose the sex of their children.

Various hospital methods are now available for determining the sex of a foetus. The most common technique today uses ultrasound to bounce high-frequency sound waves off the foetus through the mother's abdominal wall; the sound echoes are then displayed as an image on a television screen. By this method, which is safe, the presence or absence of a penis can be determined. Amniocentesis, which can be performed from the fifteenth week onwards, is an invasive technique which involves inserting a needle into the abdomen and uterus, and extracting some of the amniotic fluid surrounding the foetus. The cells floating in the fluid can then be analysed to reveal the baby's sex. Although amniocentesis, like uteroscopy, was once a common procedure, it is now reserved for diagnosing more important matters than a baby's sex. Knowing whether a foetus is male or female, and using

171

that knowledge as a basis for maintaining or aborting a pregnancy, is not considered a medical advance by all. For some, it is an affront to God, a tampering with nature. To others it is rational social engineering.

An ultrasound scan is not usually done before the sixteenth week. It can detect obvious physical abnormalities and even neural tube defects. Amniocentesis and foetoscopy use ultrasound to guide needle and laparoscope and the foetus may be monitored during labour using ultrasound. The main organs of the baby and mother appear on the video monitor. As far as we know, the procedure has no adverse effects on mother or baby.

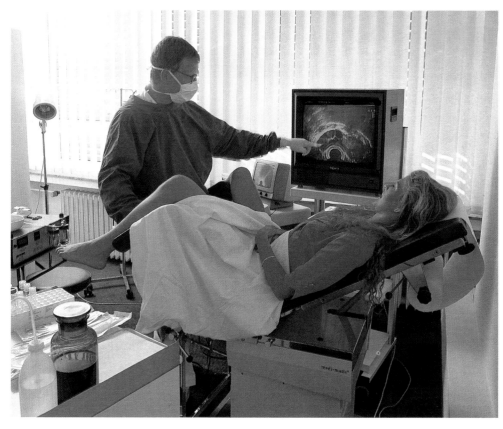

Carp flags, at least one for each male member of the family, flying outside a Japanese home. The carp was a samurai emblem, symbolizing courage, dignity, perseverance, and good fortune. The presence of girls or women in the family is not advertised.

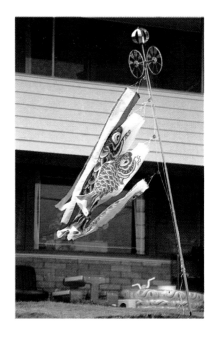

Darwinism in the raw

Neonaticide, the killing of newborn children, has been adopted by some cultures as a way of disposing of children of the 'wrong' (usually female) sex. Sometimes infant deaths are intentional, but they can also be the result of neglect. In China, India, Pakistan, Bangladesh, and Egypt, for example, where resources are scarce for the majority of the population, boys will be sent to a physician when they are ill, but girls will be seen by a local traditional healer. If food is scarce, boys will receive more of it. In countries where diarrhoea is endemic, a son with diarrhoea will be seen as a medical emergency, but a daughter with diarrhoea will be seen as a nuisance. Money will be found for his medicine, but perhaps not for hers. When poverty is extreme, infant girls may be suffocated, buried, drowned, or left exposed to the elements. Ansley Coales, a demographer at Princeton University, estimates that some 29 million females are 'missing' from China, 23 million from India, 3 million from Pakistan, and more than 600,000 from Egypt. In other words the female populations of these countries are 'light' by some 5 per cent. This situation was exposed to the world in a major article in *The New York Times* by Nicholas Kristof entitled 'The missing 100 million women'.

Traditionally, infanticide in such countries was not illegal. Indeed life was so difficult and precarious that a baby was not considered a member of the family until his or her first birthday or until the teeth appeared. In China today an infant does not become a full person until his or her first birthday. The killing of newborn girls was banned in India in 1870 and outlawed by the Chinese after the 1949 revolution (no law was felt necessary for boys). To discourage abortion as a means of regulating the sex of children born, the Chinese have made it illegal for physicians to tell parents the sex of their unborn child. But bribes and tradition go a long way....

The missing millions of China and India reflect the unpleasant reality of poverty,

FAMILY PLANNING—A BASIS NATIONAL POLICY OF CHINA

hardship, and overpopulation. People in these countries must make difficult and undesirable choices to survive. It is not only a matter of boy child versus female child. In many families, contraceptives are not available — they would be used if they were — and babies are not planned. A new baby is more often a burden than a blessing. It is survival of the total family unit that is paramount rather than the survival of any one invididual.

Early days and weeks

Fertilization usually occurs in one or other of the oviducts, the short tubes that lead from the two ovaries to the uterus, rather than in the uterus itself. Soon after fertilization the zygote begins to split (cleave) into two cells, then four, eight, and so on. As it does so it is propelled towards the uterus. Two or three days after entering the uterus, the embryo, as it is now called, implants itself in the uterus wall. On average only 1 in 2 or 3 zygotes gets as far as this; the rest, presumably less healthy, those less likely to survive, disintegrate.

The uterus (womb) is the specialized female organ that carries, nourishes, and protects the developing foetus. Once implantation has taken place, the woman's body becomes aware of its own pregnancy and changes to meet the demands of the developing embryo and foetus. Periods stop and the uterus begins to enlarge. A placenta and other tissues develop at the site of implantation to support the developing embryo, attached to it by an umbilical cord. Nutrients arrive and waste products leave via the cord and the placenta.

The embryo develops most rapidly during the first eight weeks of pregnancy, from a single cell about the size of the dot at the end of this sentence to a mass of cells about 1 inch long and weighing about 10 grams. By the eighth week all the systems the baby will need at birth have started to develop. The brain and nervous system are among the first to develop, hence the disproportionate largeness of the head. From about eight weeks until birth, the head represents 40 per cent of body length; in the adult it represents only 15 per cent. By eight weeks the limbs begin to form. A tail appears during the fourth week, only to disappear by the ninth. This tail is a remnant of the evolutionary history of our species; in

A smiling couple present their only child to an approving father figure (the State). 'One child per family' billboards are seen all over China. Mothers who abort a second child are given considerable community support. Even so the country's population is still growing; in 1970 it was 925 million, today it is approaching 1.3 billion, and by 2100 it will be nearly 1.6 billion.

173

This X-ray/artwork picture shows the female reproductive tract (ovaries, fallopian tubes, and uterus) in relation to the pelvic bones. As pregnancy advances the uterus expands upwards. Composed of three layers of muscle whose fibres run in different directions, the uterus is one of the strongest muscles in the body. In order to push a baby out the top part of the uterus must contract and the lower part relax. Except in emergencies abdominal X-rays are not taken during pregnancy or suspected pregnancy.

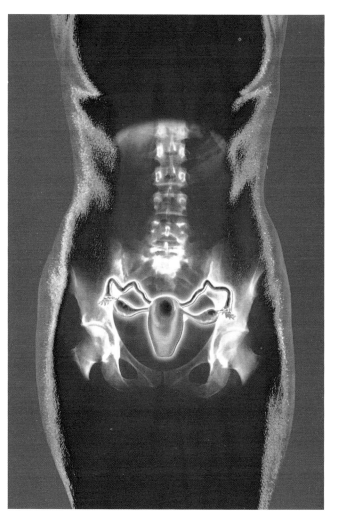

rare cases it remains at birth, but is easy to remove surgically.

By the ninth week the embryo is recognizably human, no longer grub-like. It has now become a foetus. Between the seventh and twelfth weeks the sexual organs and reproductive system begin to develop; up until this time male and female foetuses look alike.

Spontaneous abortion (miscarriage) during the first three months (first trimester) of uterine life is not uncommon; in fact it occurs in 10 to 30 per cent of all pregnancies and, although an unpleasant experience, is probably fortunate, since in most cases the foetus is seriously defective. If a woman does not realize that she is pregnant she may experience loss of the foetus as a late, if somewhat heavy, period, with or without cramps. While miscarriage is not uncommon and is 'nature's way of preventing the birth of a less than perfect child,

A house door in New Guinea decorated with an X-ray style drawing of a pregnant woman.

many women, and their husbands as well, are quite depressed by it and often welcome the support of others who have been through the same experience.

The symptoms of pregnancy

Is it possible to carry a baby to term and not know you are pregnant? Kathy Mountain, a 44-year-old Minnesota woman, did. Apart from noticing a little extra weight around her hips, she claimed she 'never felt anything' to make her suspect she was pregnant. She woke at 3 a.m. in the morning, having done a full day's work as a book-keeper plus four hours on evening call at a women's crisis centre, and realized that the abdominal pains she was having were like the contractions of labour. Shortly afterwards she gave birth to a 7½-pound baby, her sixth child. For most women, however, there are many clues to pregnancy.

Although most women stop menstruating when they are pregnant, 1 in 5 continues to show some bleeding for several months after conception. This is usually light but sometimes sufficient to mask pregnancy if other signs, such as weight gain, nausea, and tiredness, are ignored. Other signs of pregnancy are enlarged breasts and areolae which deepen in colour and develop small bumps, and nipples that are more sensitive to the touch. Some women, soon after conception, say they 'just feel different' for vague, undefined reasons. Morning sickness, a period of nausea, vomiting, or dizziness on waking or at night, occurs in 3 out of 4 women at some time during the first three months. The cause and cure are both enigmatic. Some women link their sickness to car or train journeys, to certain foods and odours, or to being emotionally upset. Eating dry biscuits or toast before getting into bed at night or out of bed in the morning sometimes helps.

Very, very rarely a woman thinks she is pregnant when she is not, and may show some of the signs and experience some of the symptoms. Cases of false or pseudo pregnancy (pseudocyesis) have been known throughout history. Hippocrates reported a dozen cases; in the Middle Ages pseudopregnancy was a state experienced by some nuns who yearned to be true brides of Christ. Mary Tudor, Queen of England from 1553 to 1558, also experienced pseudopregnancy. A contemporary report says: 'Mary, finding herself without her expected baby, imagined herself deserted by God.... During the time of her supposed pregnancy, Mary showed signs of pregnancy and experienced the symptoms of vomiting and enlargement of the abdomen. During this period her favourite amusement, other than attending Mass, was counting on her fingers the number of months she was "gone".' Pseudopregnancy is not a phenomenon easy to investigate scientifically, but it does seem to be associated with intense fear of coitus, intense guilt about having had intercourse when it is forbidden, or an intense desire to be pregnant. A lot depends on the value which the surrounding culture places on virginity. According to Roman Catholic dogma, not only was Jesus born of a virgin but Mary herself was 'immaculately conceived'. Two levels of chastity were obviously thought better than one.

This pottery bowl, decorated with a female figure in childbirth, is from the North American Mimbres culture, thriving at the time of the Norman Conquest. Bowls like this were broken and buried to release the owner's spirit. Did this woman die in childbirth?

From three months to term

During the second trimester the woman's changing shape, and the fact that in the fourth or fifth month the foetus begins to move and the heart starts to beat, confirm the reality of the pregnancy. Most women carry on a dialogue of sorts with the foetus, slowly making it part of their daily lives. Expectant parents, if they have not done so earlier, think up an affectionate name for 'it' — 'marshmallow', 'gumdrop', 'blob', 'monster'. They often enjoy 'listening in' and looking or feeling for signs of movement.

By the end of the second trimester, the foetus weighs about 2 pounds but the mother may have gained 10 pounds. Some women show patches of temporary skin discoloration on the face, stomach, and breasts. A clear yellow secretion (colostrum) may seep from the nipples. These changes are all harmless, but undue weight gain should be controlled.

During the final trimester the foetus continues to grow, gaining about 1 pound a week during the last two or three weeks. By the eighth month all the foetus' systems are well enough developed for it to be capable of precarious life outside the womb. The ninth month in the womb ensures extra strength and better resistance to the traumas of life outside. As the foetus takes up a head-down position in the womb its movements become increasingly noticeable to the mother. As the head enters the pelvis it pushes against the mother's bladder, making urination a more and more frequent necessity. 'Most of the time I feel great, but all I want to do is eat, sleep, and go to the toilet' is a common comment from mothers nearing the end of their pregnancy. 'I've never felt so bloated, tired, and productive all at the same time' is another.

A baby begins to feel real in the fourth or fifth month when the mother begins to feel it moving inside her. It is important for the family to get to know the baby by 'listening in' or feeling for movement.

Countdown to birth

As the foetus enlarges and moves down into the pelvis, the mother's diaphragm is pushed upwards, making her rib cage and breasts more prominent and breathing more audible. As birth approaches, the foetus can be felt pushing down against the pelvic floor muscles and cervix. This is variously called engagement, lightening, or dropping. Gradually the cervix (neck), or exit from the womb, becomes thinner and thinner (a process known as effacement) and the ligaments of the pelvis begin to relax. This makes walking awkward and sometimes painful, but it is part of preparation for birth and a sign that labour will soon begin.

Labour is the passage of the foetus and placental tissues from the womb, via the vagina, to the outside. It is usually described as having three phases: in the first the foetus moves into the vagina or birth canal; in the second it is expelled to the outside (delivery); and in the third the placenta and its associated membranes are expelled (afterbirth).

The process of labour is extremely variable from woman to woman, and even in the same woman first, second, and third labours may be very different. First births generally take longer and are more painful than subsequent ones. Despite cosy assumptions to the contrary, women in primitive cultures do not necessarily have quicker, less painful, or less complicated births than women in technologically advanced ones.

The first stage of labour is marked by contractions of the uterus. These complete the process of effacement of the cervix and cause it to start widening (dilation). Other signals of the onset of labour are the discharge of a plug of mucus tinged with blood ('bloody show') from the cervix and discharge of the fluids ('waters') surrounding the foetus. Any of these signs indicate that it is time to head for the hospital or call in the midwife. Early contractions typically occur at intervals of 10 to 20 minutes and last some 30 to 60 seconds. Contractions may last from 2 to 24 hours but 12 to 15 hours is average for first pregnancies; later pregnancies may take half that time.

When dilation of the cervix is sufficient to allow the foetus to enter the vagina — generally the diameter of the cervical opening is about 4 inches or 'five fingers' in width — the contractions push the foetus through the vagina and delivery occurs. The average newborn baby weighs about 7 pounds and measures about 20 inches from head to toe. A Caucasian baby is considered premature if born before week 36 or if he or she weighs less

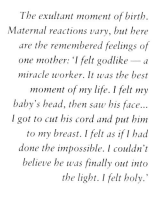

The exultant moment of birth. Maternal reactions vary, but here are the remembered feelings of one mother: 'I felt godlike — a miracle worker. It was the best moment of my life. I felt my baby's head, then saw his face... I got to cut his cord and put him to my breast. I felt as if I had done the impossible. I couldn't believe he was finally out into the light. I felt holy.'

than 5½ pounds at birth. The afterbirth is expelled some 15 to 60 minutes after delivery. In many cultures great magical significance is given to the placenta and umbilical cord. Before the turn of this century, for example, Hawaiian people used to hide the afterbirth (placenta and umbilical cord) in case it fell into the hands of an evil wisher. In the Solomon Islands the umbilical cord was kept safe in the lime-pot containing the mother's chewing nuts.

The assistance the mother receives during labour and delivery depends of course on her own needs and preferences in the matter, but also on local custom and on the physician or midwife in attendance. She may or may not be offered pain-relieving drugs or an episiotomy (a surgical incision to enlarge the vaginal opening). There is no 'best' way to deliver because women and their babies are so variable. No woman should try to live up to some artificial standard of maternal performance. The sole criterion is the best possible physical and psychological health of both mother and child. This includes, if it suits the mother and her physician or midwife, birth in the standing, squatting, or kneeling position, or even underwater. Worldwide, non-supine birth is more common than supine (lying on one's back); in non-supine positions gravity helps delivery.

The couvade syndrome

The phenomenon of husbands suffering sympathetic labour pains and undergoing ritual delivery was a feature of many primitive and ancient cultures. 'Couvade' rituals (from the French *couver*, to hatch) were described by Plutarch in his histories of Greece and Rome and in Marco Polo's tales of thirteenth-century China and India. The custom still exists, though not in societies which regard themselves as modern. Among the Solomon Islanders, for instance, it is still quite common, when the mother's labour pains begin, for the husband to stop work, go to the hut of one of his other wives or neighbours, and sit quietly, refusing to lift anything heavy or handle anything sharp or pointed. All this is supposed to facilitate birth and protect the infant, and may continue for at least three days after the birth. He may then visit the mother's hut to see the child. He may even continue to rest and not go outside the village for another two days. Rituals like this are rooted in a belief in sympathetic magic and in good and evil spirits, but they also establish the father's paternity in a very public manner. A few cynical observers have interpreted couvade as male one-upmanship, or as an attempt to deny women the sole pain and glory of childbirth. Many women would be only too glad to share some of it.

More intriguing are those instances of couvade which are not mere ritual. Many men wish they could take a fairer share in their wife's pregnancy and delivery, but some actually feel real pain and exhibit real physical symptoms. In 1972 the British psychiatrist W.H. Trethowan estimated that the couvade syndrome, in some guise or other, probably occurs in about 1 in 4 or 5 expectant fathers. The American nursing professor Jacqueline Clinton believes the incidence of couvade affects between 22 and 79 per cent of expectant fathers! Common symptoms include nausea, changes in appetite, toothache, indigestion, heartburn, abdominal pains, tachycardia, and general malaise (many of which are experienced by pregnant women). Clinton believes that couvade symptoms reflect stress at a psychological, emotional, and physical level. Though seldom serious, these sympathetic sufferings certainly create a greater bond of concern and care within a family.

Sex during pregnancy

In developed countries most couples continue to have sexual relations during pregnancy, but coitus is generally less frequent, and may cease altogether during the last month or so. Studies of Third World or non-technological societies show that practices are extremely variable. Some societies — the Abelam and Lesu of New Guinea and New Ireland, the American Indian Arikara of North Dakota, the Dahomeans of West Africa, the Nandi of the Sudan, and the Masai of Kenya and Tanzania — expect coitus to stop as soon as the woman has missed one or two periods. More than 30 of the 60 societies studied in this respect expected coitus to cease by the seventh month, but 15 of them had no inhibitions or prohibitions even in the ninth month. Generally, in societies that expect abstinence during pregnancy, it is the woman who is enjoined to abstain, not the man; he can usually have sex with another of his wives or with a prostitute. Even in the West, expectant husbands are disapprovingly allowed a certain licence: 'His wife was pregnant at the time, you know.'

Even today sex during pregnancy is something many physicians refrain from discussing with their patients, apart from a cursory warning about not having intercourse from six weeks before delivery to six weeks or so after. Occasionally there may be contractions ('false labour') in mid-pregnancy: these are harmless. In fact, unless medically contraindicated, there is little reason why a woman cannot continue sex play and even coitus right up to delivery. Indeed the prostaglandins within semen may even facilitate birthing. Left to work things out for themselves, most women 'play safe'.

Modern knowledge tells us that all usual sexual activities may be engaged in until birth without fear of harming the foetus or the mother, as long as there is no vaginal bleeding, the mother has no history of premature deliveries, feels no discomfort, and the process of labour has not started. Having said that, pregnancy quite naturally brings with it certain changes in sexual activity. For most couples during the first trimester it is 'sex as usual'. In the second and third trimesters, though there are exceptions, most couples have intercourse less often, and in the final months they may abstain altogether. Although much depends on previous levels of sexual activity, many women report that they lose interest in sex during pregnancy, masturbate less frequently, and have fewer orgasms.

These changes are due to a variety of factors. As pregnancy advances, women produce more and more of the hormones progesterone and prolactin, which can act to depress libido. Also, many women feel increasingly uncomfortable physically and are afraid of harming the foetus. Husbands can also lose interest in sex; they too may be afraid of harming the foetus or their partner. And there are people who simply find the condition of pregnancy unattractive or feel sexually unsure or frustrated at their partner's lack of interest. This is the situation most likely to cause men to seek casual affairs or visit prostitutes.

As pregnancy progresses, there is a shift from the man-on-top coital position to woman-on-top, or side-by-side, or 'spoons' (rear entry). There is also an increase in oral sex and mutual masturbation. Pregnancy is a time to practice or relearn the value of non-coital sexual contact and non-erotic touching. Both partners want and need and enjoy TLC (tender loving care), especially the woman; despite the great confirmation of femininity that pregnancy bestows, she has to cope with a new self-image as a mother, weight gain, and probably some change in her lifestyle. Interestingly, fathers too have been found to gain weight and alter their lifestyle as pregnancy advances.

Another behavioural change during pregnancy deserves mention. Many expectant parents engage in a flurry of 'nest building'. It seems, all of a sudden, that there is a need to paint, clean, sew, store food, and so on — preparation behaviours we share with many animals.

Some women prefer to give birth in hospital, where there is every emergency facility. There is no medical reason why healthy mothers and babies should be separated immediately after birth; it is not usually necessary for the doctor or midwife to do a complete examination right away.

Natural childbirth

The medicalization of childbirth in the West has often been inveighed against, as have the privacy and secrecy traditionally associated with the whole process. Home deliveries with the whole family in attendance are being experimented with and special birthing centres are being established. In such centres, women have emotional and companionate support, their medical needs are taken care of, and drugs, mechanical restraint, and isolation are not *de rigueur.* There is a lot to be said for traditional obstetric practice, not least its ability to intervene successfully in emergencies, but there are many other ways of giving birth.

It must be said that the modern Western version of 'natural' childbirth is far removed from the fancied 'naturalness' of childbirth in primitive societies, where it is often surrounded with secrecy and ritual. For a start, delivery at home or in a birthing centre is attended by medically trained male or female midwives, with physicians and an arsenal of modern pharmaceutical and intervention techniques available if complications arise. The essence of the modern concept of natural childbirth is that women need not give birth in isolation, fear, and ignorance, and that they should be free to choose whether to have their babies in hospital, at home, or elsewhere.

The natural childbirth movement is not new, but it has been slow to come of age. In England in the 1930s a physician called Grantley Dick-Read challenged his colleagues to make childbirth a great adventure rather than a painful ordeal: 'Childbirth should be accompanied by a sense of maternal achievement and satisfaction and...the mother-child relationship should be enhanced by pride and pleasure and not tainted by resentment or distressing memories.' The first step, he said, was to reduce or remove the ignorance and fear that surrounded birth. How? By offering prenatal information and exercise classes, stopping or minimizing the use of anaesthetics, and resorting to surgical practices such as episiotomy only when absolutely necessary. His first book *Natural Childbirth* (1932) was met with scorn and largely ignored, but *Childbirth Without Fear* (1943) became a public sensation. Predictably it was attacked and disparaged by two strong Establishment forces: doctors too lazy to learn the new techniques or reluctant to see their powers demystified and their fees diminished; and clergymen who thought it only right for women to bring forth children in pain and agony, as they interpreted the Bible. There were also objections from many earnest obstetricians well acquainted with the sufferings of many women in labour and who felt that anaesthetics, episiotomy, and privacy suited their needs best.

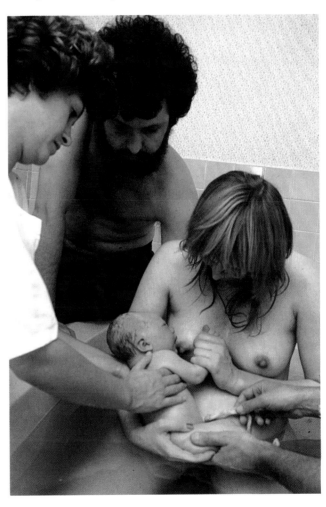

The next major impetus to the natural childbirth movement came in the 1970s from two French physicians, Fernand Lamaze and Frederick Leboyer. Lamaze too had published earlier. In 1956 he wrote *Painless Childbirth*, but his ideas were either derided or ignored. But slowly the movement grew. By the time Leboyer published his book *Birth Without Violence* in 1975 the climate was more hospitable; the public was receptive, although many professionals were not.

Lamaze and Leboyer proposed, as had Dick-Read, that women should be given instruction and exercises to remove fear, ignorance, and trauma during labour and delivery. And, like Dick-Read, both proposed birth in hospitals, but with a minimum of mechanical or technical assistance and little or no use of anaesthetics. Lamaze insisted that fathers, as well as mothers, should attend birth classes and, more controversially, that the father should be present at the delivery to give his wife emotional support and remind her to relax and push and breathe as in the exercise classes. Leboyer was especially concerned with the sensitivity of the newborn infant. In his book he advocated that babies should enter the world with as little trauma as possible. At birth they should be kept warm and secure, treated tenderly, washed in warm water and rocked so that the transition from the womb to the world is as gentle as possible. After delivery, instead of separating mother and baby, the baby is given to the mother for loving and cuddling so that a strong mother-child bond is established as quickly as possible.

The trend initiated by Dick-Read, Lamaze, and Leboyer continues to gain impetus, with valuable contributions from many other imaginative professionals. Perhaps one more natural childbirth approach deserves mention, the Bradley 'relationship-centred childbirth' method.

One woman described the process of water birth like this: 'Nothing seemed to be happening on the bed; it seemed so much easier in the water. I felt kind of open, then I saw my son float out. He was so peaceful and calm. His eyes were open under the water.'

Robert Bradley, a Colorado physician, believed that the couple should work together to improve their relationship in readiness for the arrival of the baby. Couples are taught how to relax and communicate in order to make the birth easier. While the method has a large following, snipers call it the 'no-method method' since there are no specific rules to follow. In the Bradley method the couple rather than the baby becomes the centre of the delivery experience.

Is birth an erotic experience?

All the physicians mentioned above promote maximum concern for the emotional and psychological needs of mother, father, and newborn. But Leboyer went further: 'Childbirth is also passion...an ecstatic experience.' Indeed, the famous Japanese poet-novelist Kazue Morisaki said that birth gave her her best orgasm. Many obstetricians say that the experience of orgasm is not rare in undrugged and uninhibited childbirth. The British anthropologist Sheila Kitzinger, author of *The Experience of Childbirth* (1962) and many other books about birthing, also feels that birth can be a sexual experience. She argues that birth should be returned to the control of the mother so that she can experience all of its manifestations as erotic sensations not unlike those felt during sexual massage, masturbation, and even orgasm. The baby's head pushing through the birth canal and the vagina slowly opening can be 'like the uncurling petals of a rose.' She criticizes the overuse of episiotomy without regard for the painful coitus which often follows.

Sociologist Niles Newton and her obstetrician-gynaecologist husband Michael have also contributed greatly in this area. As they point out, there are remarkable similarities in breathing, vocalization, facial expression, and many other bodily responses during orgasm and uninhibited childbirth. The sensuousness of the experience also has physical advantages. For a brief period in the 1970s and 1980s some practitioners even encouraged masturbation, by the woman herself or by her husband, as an analgesic technique during childbirth. The practice subsided not because mothers did not find it of benefit, but because of prudish criticism from other hospital staff.

In those societies that viewed sex and birth in a relaxed way, birth was a public event and labour relatively short and painless. Such was the case among the Siriono of Bolivia. But among the Cuna of San Blas, Panama, who learned facts and legends about coitus and delivery only after marriage, labour and birth were a long a painful process. It is impossible to say which is cause and which effect. It is easy to be open and public about an ecstatic, pleasant experience and understandable if elders prefer to shield youngsters from matters they know to be potentially traumatic.

No philosophy or method of delivery is best for everyone and not all options are universally available. What is possible everywhere, however, is for each woman to discuss pregnancy and birth with her husband and physician and decide which method suits her best, and work with them to make birth as positive and as fulfilling as possible.

Mother's milk

In most developing countries almost all women breast-feed their children, at least to begin with. In developed countries the practice is far less common, yet it is increasing. In 1970 only about 1 in 4 women in the United States breast-fed their children; today the figure is more than 1 in 2. In fact the practice is now so much in favour with physicians and the public at large that a woman almost has to actively resist the encouragement to do so. Much of this is credited to the Newtons, who strongly advocate breast-feeding from the nutritional and mother-infant bonding points of view. Niles Newton encourages women to feel pleasure in all the reproductive processes, in coitus, parturition, and certainly nursing: '...a mother-infant relationship without enjoyable breast-feeding is in some ways similar to marriage without enjoyable sex.' There are of course those who think that mothers should *not* derive sexual or sensual pleasure from breast-feeding. In 1992 an American mother was charged with child abuse for having nursed her child until the age of two; her accusers felt there was something unhealthy and incestuous about such prolonged nursing. The woman was acquitted, but not without a great deal of embarrassment all round. Although the majority of American women start out breast-feeding, most do not continue beyond the third month, usually because of interference with work. In Britain, the picture is similar.

In general, in the West today, the higher the educational level of the mother, the more likely she is to breast-feed. From a nutritional point of view, breast milk is the best food for infants; no milk substitute exactly duplicates it. It is free, highly palatable, and provides immunological protection. Recent research at the Dunn Nutrition Unit in Cambridge, England, has shown that pre-term infants fed on mother's milk in the early weeks of life develop faster than bottle-fed pre-term infants. Also, by the time they are seven or eight, they have significantly higher IQ scores than bottle-fed children.

Common reasons for not breast-feeding are that it is difficult to fit in with work schedules and embarrassing if it has to be done in public. In Latin American countries the *nouveau riche* prefer to bottle-feed; they regard nursing as a sign of poverty and have no intention of behaving 'like cows'. Health educators are trying to reverse this attitude. Some women also have difficulty, or fear they will have difficulty, in providing enough milk. Actually, almost all women can breast-feed adequately if they allow time for the needs of their body to synchronize with those of their baby.

Occasionally a nursing mother will experience orgasm and frequently a nursing woman will expel milk during orgasm. This is a natural consequence of overlap in the physiological processes involved. Nursing a baby has no particular effect on erotic preferences; nonetheless many couples enjoy 'adult nursing' as part of sex play. It is perhaps not surprising that those who favour breast-feeding are significantly more relaxed about sexual matters in general.

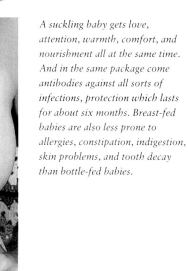

A suckling baby gets love, attention, warmth, comfort, and nourishment all at the same time. And in the same package come antibodies against all sorts of infections, protection which lasts for about six months. Breast-fed babies are also less prone to allergies, constipation, indigestion, skin problems, and tooth decay than bottle-fed babies.

All in all, birthwatching from conception through pregnancy to delivery and nursing can be a highly emotional and rewarding experience for all concerned. Shared knowledge of what is happening, and what can be expected, and loving preparation, are good insurance against fear, pain, and isolation. Properly planned for and understood, birth can be the most exciting of all life's events. The mother, especially, will gain from this approach, but so will the family as a whole. Birthwatching is certainly a major component of sexwatching.

Chapter 12

Sex yes, children no

Since 1960 more than half the families in the world have voluntarily and successfully imposed a limit on the number of children they have. What is more, these changes have taken place in spite of strong opposition from various religious groups, particularly the Roman Catholic Church and Islamic fundamentalists, and political forces as diverse as the Chinese Red Brigades and the Gang of Four, the communist parties of Eastern Europe, and successive pronatalist, anti-abortion Republican administrations in the United States from Eisenhower to Bush. These changes have been both cause and consequence of women's greater sexual and social freedom.

Until 1960 India and China were the only governments willing to consider, let alone adopt, a national policy on family planning. For most governments the topic was taboo. An increase in population was often considered desirable for political reasons; more people meant more fighters and workers ready to defend and support national interests. A few countries gave medals to prolific mothers, and some still do. In the 1950s even the United Nations refused to discuss population control or family planning for fear of irreparable divisions within the organization. Remarkably, the first World Conference on the Environment, held in Rio de Janeiro in 1992, also avoided this crucial issue.

Times have changed, but not for humanitarian reasons. Change has been the result of technology and the realization that economic growth and standards of living are intimately linked to population and family size. By technology I mean the development of oral and depot contraceptives, the improvement of the intrauterine device (IUD) and of techniques of abortion and sterilization, and an explosion in communications. In the 1960s and 1970s television became a worldwide medium. Today even the most remote villages in the Third World have a telephone or radio link to the wider world. News of effective and acceptable methods of birth control can spread quickly.

Before 1960 legal abortions and contraceptives were unavailable or difficult to obtain almost everywhere. By 1975, however, almost every developed country and more than 60 developing countries had made it official government policy to reduce population growth or had expressed government support for family planning. By 1985 the number of developing countries with national family planning goals had increased to more than 80. At a meeting of the United Nations World Population Council in Bucharest in 1974 all but one of the 135 delegates from governments and organizations around the world voted to accept family planning (a less negative term than 'contraception' or 'birth control') as a basic human right. The exception was the Vatican representative, who abstained. Now more than 90 per cent of the world's citizens live in countries that offer some form of family planning. The nations most often held up as models of humane and successful family planning policies are South Korea, Thailand, Sweden, Brazil, Sri Lanka, Colombia, and Indonesia. Their success, achieved with government support, has been due to a combination of good birth control education, effective distribution systems, and a wide choice of contraceptive techniques.

The United States remains one of the few developed countries that has *not* formulated any consistent national family planning policy. Full family planning services are not equally

A selection of contraceptive methods in common use: Pill, condom, diaphragm, sponge, spermicidal foam (in its disposable applicator), and spermicidal pessaries.

available to all. Private bodies such as the International Planned Parenthood Foundation exist expressly to help those thwarted by the obstacle course created by the policies of different administrations. Until 1967, when a U.S. Supreme Court decision changed the law, it was illegal for physicians to offer contraceptives to their patients and illegal to send them through the post. Even today, despite the will of the majority, directives from the Republican administration make it illegal for anyone other than a physician (i.e. not a nurse or a social workers) to discuss abortion with a client in a federally funded clinic.

Contraception and abortion are among the hottest of political and religious hot potatoes. In the United States party attitudes towards the availability of contraceptives and abortion are geared to catching votes at election time. Various countries in Eastern Europe have put the brakes on abortion whenever the rate has threatened to tarnish the national image. Many countries just make up whatever abortion statistics they feel are politically 'correct'. One of the results of the break-up of the Soviet Union has been that individual republics have established their own family planning programs, but between 1989 and 1992, symptomatic of the social, economic, and political chaos of the break-up in Eastern Europe, there was a 50 per cent decline in birth rates due to increased abortion and sterilization.

This Thai New Year greeting card entitles the bearer to a free vasectomy. It also encourages other methods of birth control.

The status of family planning and abortion programs, or 'reproductive options' programs as they are sometimes called, differs markedly from country to country. In China, Sri Lanka, Indonesia, Thailand, Botswana, Kenya, and Jamaica, for example, the government is very involved and supportive; it funds the programs, distributes the contraceptives (often free), and encourages the use of birth control. But in Japan, Nigeria, Colombia, and Paraguay commercial interests play a key role, with the government taking a back seat. This is a political decision, but it also reflects the wealth of these countries and the ability of their citizens to pay. Throughout the world, and especially in Third World countries, cost is a major factor in choosing which contraceptive methods to promote.

In Britain, for instance, family planning supplies and services are available on prescription from chemists and pharmacies, who make a standard, nominal charge for them. In the United States, however, about 75 per cent of women obtain the services and supplies they require direct from their doctor and pharmacy and pay the appropriate fees. In some countries, contraceptives are paid for through medical insurance; this is the case in Egypt and the Philippines, and increasingly in Latin America. This means that family planning is restricted to those who can afford to pay insurance.

Countries also differ in the way they promote family planning. In the United State the mass media have never been used for this purpose; television companies are wary of the controversy that the subject invariably arouses. Indonesia and Thailand, though, because their governments are committed to family planning, make wide use of the mass media. Sales of oral contraceptives, injectables, and IUDs more than doubled in Indonesia between 1989 and 1990 as the result of a mass market campaign funded by the government. In Trinidad and Tobago a family planning centre television commercial, aired for one month, increased the centre's clientele by 30 per cent. In fact the United States is the only major industrialized nation in the world that has actively stood out against population control. China, in sharp contrast, with limited resources and more than 1 billion people to care for, has established and tries to enforce a one-child-per-family policy. Population control is an inescapable part of Chinese life, and all forms of contraception are widely distributed and advertised. The majority of the population now accepts the official line.

Occasionally abortion and contraceptive policies reflect the self-interest of the medical establishment. In India, for example, where the pill was not legalized until 1974, and in Japan, where use of the pill is still restricted to the treatment of menstrual disorders (i.e. not approved as an oral contraceptive), abortion is extremely lucrative for physicians. Sometimes restricted availability of contraception and family planning services reflects the erroneous idea that easy availability encourages promiscuity and social upheaval. There is no evidence for this whatsoever. Most studies have shown that people are already sexually active when they first seek contraception. Fear of pregnancy merely postpones or takes the enjoyment out of coitus; it does not prevent it.

A family planning talk in Lesotho. In most of Southern Africa pressures of people and livestock on the land are acute. Lesotho is an independent kingdom entirely surrounded by the Republic of South Africa and depends heavily on foreign aid. In underdeveloped countries (and in modern ones too) word of mouth is important in supporting family planning.

The governments of most Western states today, whatever their political or religious hue, make consultation with a registered physician a legal requirement for obtaining an abortion. Only in a handful of countries — the United States, Canada, Italy, Yugoslavia, Japan, India, China, and Cuba — is the decision to terminate a pregnancy left solely to the woman herself. In China and India it is not necessary to consult a physician to obtain most methods of contraception, but in every other major country in the world it is.

Choices

Many people, even those well educated, are ill-informed about conception. They do not realize that, while rare, pregnancy can occur from a single act of intercourse or that the few drops of fluid that sometimes appear at the tip of the penis during the excitement or plateau phase contain sperm which can be transferred by hand or penis to the vagina. Nor is it widely recognized that ovulation, though cyclic, is often irregular. Whenever a woman is ovulating there is the possibility of conception. And contrary to popular belief, ovulation can occur even during menstruation.

Family size can be controlled at any stage of the reproductive process, before or after conception, or after birth. Celibacy and virginity are one solution. Social approval of virginity, especially for females, has traditionally postponed reproduction until marriage. In many countries, in India, Spain, and most Islamic and Latin American countries, for example, young men and women are discouraged from spending time alone together before they are married; it is not 'proper' for an unmarried woman to be seen in mixed company in public. Later marriages have also had a powerful population-decreasing effect. This was especially true in Europe and Japan in the first half of this century and has been true in a number of Asian countries since World War II. In China young people are advised to postpone marriage until after the age of 25. Abortion and infanticide are late and drastic preventives, but for centuries they have been the main method of limiting family size, and abortion still is.

Not everyone feels comfortable about using contraceptives. Many women, and some men, prefer to think of sex as spontaneous and unplanned: 'I don't like to seem prepared because he/she might think I'm promiscuous/presumptuous.' For some, thoughts of contraception intrude on thoughts of love. Others just pray and hope. Nevertheless the most reliable temporary methods of contraception are those used with confidence and consistency, and until effective and acceptable male oral contraceptives are invented it is women who will continue to be mainly responsible for not getting pregnant.

Certain contraceptives are seen as inconvenient, aesthetically unappealing, or likely to spoil sexual concentration. Condoms and vaginal creams come into this category. Condoms can be awkward to slip on and creams messy to use, but if contraception is seen as a shared responsibility they can be made part of sex play, an opportunity for erotic stimulation. Condoms can be sensuously applied by the woman and the man can erotically insert foam or a piece of sponge. Actually, for many people, the worst distraction from sexual enjoyment is fear of pregnancy itself.

The ideal contraceptive is well known: it is completely reliable, inexpensive, can be used by both sexes at any time, lasts as long as required, and has no detrimental side/residual/long-term effects. Unfortunately it is still waiting to be discovered.

All currently available contraceptives have some drawback or other, but by and large the disadvantages are trivial compared with the advantages. Pregnancy and childbirth are far riskier for women than any standard method of contraception, and having a child is too large a responsibility to be left entirely to chance. Contraception means less risk, more choice, and freedom from unnecessary anxiety. Factors such as ease of use versus reliability, convenience versus possible long-term side effects, aesthetic appeal versus low cost are seen differently by different poeple.

Rhythm methods

Abstinence is the only contraceptive that is free and available without legal or medical restriction, and periodic abstinence, the so-called rhythm method, is the only method of contraception sanctioned by the Roman Catholic Church, which considers all other methods unnatural. Coitus is avoided at times when conception is likely (the 'unsafe period'), and reserved for times considered safe. But determining these periods is difficult. It requires the woman to keep a very careful check on her menstrual cycle. The two most reliable rhythm methods require that she checks, daily and without fail, either her body temperature on waking or the nature and amount of mucus around her cervix. Both methods are highly unnatural practices for most women and require not only a regular and predictable lifestyle but also a strong degree of motivation and discipline; unfortunately sexual desire rarely coincides with the calendar or with other events in daily life. These routines are inconsistently used even among Roman Catholics.

The temperature method cannot be relied upon until the woman has recorded her temperature daily for a minimum of six months; she then has to determine when, within each cycle, there is a consistent rise in temperature following after a consistent low. Three days after the rise has peaked, coitus is allowable until the onset of the next period. The cervical mucus method monitors daily discharges from the cervix. A day or two before ovulation mucus taken from the cervix turns from cloudy and sticky to clear and stringy. The so-called safe period starts four days after the clear mucus appears and lasts until the onset of the next period, after which the mucus changes back to cloudy.

Another method of determining the safe period is to monitor the menstrual cycle for 6 to 12 months and then, assuming that subsequent cycles will be similar, 'guesstimate' the danger zone, usually from 10 to 19 days before the start of the next period. The remainder of the cycle is 'safe'. Unfortunately, predictability is poor since most women's menstrual cycles are affected by stress, illness, nutritional factors, and weight changes.

It is difficult to evaluate the relative reliability of these methods since more depends on the user than on the technique. Best estimates are that, regardless of the method used, within a year between 2 and 4 in every 10 women will get pregnant.

Rhythm couples, despite the quip that 'abstinence makes the heart grow fonder', generally find that enforced abstinence dampens sexual ardour and increases anxiety. It also decreases the spontaneous expression of love and affection that helps to keep a marriage fresh. Anxiety rather than pleasure often accompanies intercourse. Some women remain obsessively concerned with pregnancy. But the really serious drawback is that rhythm methods are very unreliable and result in many unplanned and unwanted pregnancies.

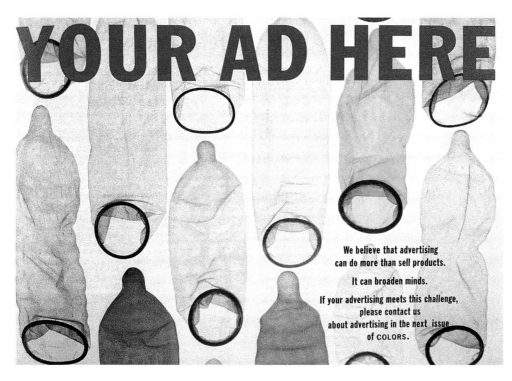

With admirable social consciousness, the clothing company Benneton gave condoms a boost by donating this advertising space for the use of others. Both Benneton clothes and condoms come in attractive colours.

Condoms

For the earliest scientific reference to a sheath for the penis we are indebted to the Italian anatomist Gabriello Fallopio, after whom the fallopian tubes, or oviducts, are named. In a treatise written in 1574 he describes a linen sheath moistened with lotion as a protection against sexually transmitted diseases. The origin of the word 'condom' is not known; it may honour the French town of Condom in Gascony, or a Colonel or Doctor Condom said to have perfected the device to protect King Charles II of England from the rapacious claims of mistresses and illegitimate children. The French picturesquely call the condom *le redingote anglaise* or *le capote anglais* (the English riding coat or overcoat) and the British retaliate by calling it the French letter.

Japan is the world leader in condom use — 69 per cent of all couples use condoms, which are sold, like cosmetics, from door to door by women to women. Condoms are also popular in Denmark, Finland, and Sweden, where more than 20 per cent of married women are regular users. In most other developed countries condom use accounts for between 5 and 15 per cent of contraceptive use. However, with more efficient contraceptives having become available in the last decade, their use has dropped. Fear of AIDS is increasing condom use again, but for the protection against disease rather than the prevention of pregnancy. A 1990 study estimates that, worldwide, between 30 and 40 per cent of condoms are used outside marriage.

Condoms have been in use in one form or another for hundreds of years. The modern condom, to which no one has ever laid a patent claim, is made of latex rubber or plastic, though versions made from animal intestines are still used and, until the advent of AIDS, were considered rather special. Skin condoms are adequate for contraceptive purposes, but not for AIDS, since the HIV virus is hundreds of times smaller than sperm and can therefore pass through the pores in the skin membrane.

A condom prevents sperm from entering the uterus, and also acts as a partial barrier to

infection. It has to be unrolled or pulled over the erect penis, but should not be stretched so tight that it splits from coital friction. After coitus it must be carefully removed to prevent leakage of semen. Carelessness on both counts can lead to unwanted pregnancy. Some couples claim that condoms reduce sensitivity, an effect welcomed by men who ejaculate quickly. But the major drawback of the condom is inconsistent or careless use. Otherwise it is safe, reliable, inexpensive, convenient, and one of the few methods for which men can take the major responsibility.

The history of modern use of the condom is interesting. Initially condoms were developed to combat venereal diseases. Only later were they promoted as a means of preventing pregnancy. Then they were prohibited as contraceptives (in the United States, until the 1960s, condoms were labelled 'Sold for the prevention of disease only'). Then the tide changed again and they regained their popularity as contraceptives. Now, in the 1990s, they are used for contraception *and* disease prevention. The message today is 'Use a condom' if you have sex with a new partner, unless he or she is definitely known to be disease-free, because the risk of infection is greater than the risk of pregnancy. Since the late 1980s, in response to the wide range of penis sizes around the world, condoms have been available in different widths; they can be unrolled onto the penis to different lengths.

The female condom was introduced in 1992. Like the condom for men, it is a

This is the Femidom, a brand of female condom. It is still too early to say how well female condoms will be accepted.

disposable tube or pouch made of plastic film or latex, and has thin, flexible inner and outer rings to maintain its shape. It is inserted manually into the vagina and fits loosely to allow free movement rather than snugly like a male condom. In tests in the United States users said it offered a 'more natural' feeling than the male condom, but a study among prostitutes and their clients in Thailand found that both groups preferred the male condom. Loose-fitting condoms for men are also under development.

Cervical caps and diaphrams

These are also barrier devices made of rubber or latex, but to be maximally effective they need to be used with spermicidal vaginal jelly. The idea of placing a device in the vagina so that it covers the cervix, the entrance to the uterus, is not new either. One of the recommendations of the great Casanova (1725-98) was to squeeze the flesh from half a lemon and insert the cup of rind over the cervix; any juice (acidic) remaining in the lemon acted as a spermicide. The Egyptian Petri Papyrus (1850 BC) advises the use of a vaginal pessary of crocodile dung and honey, or fumigation of the vagina with smoke from burning wax and charcoal. From India and Asia there is also evidence of early barrier devices made from small wads of feathers, sponges, lint, or cloth soaked in acacia extract, honey, or citrus juices. The German physician C. Hesse, under the pseudonym Wilhelm P.J. Mensinga, seems to have been the first to write about a rubber version of the diaphragm. That was in 1882. Thereafter use of the diaphragm spread from Germany to Holland, and then to England, where it is still known as the Dutch cap. Actually a cap and a diaphragm are different. A diaphragm is a very flexible saucer-shaped barrier between 5 and 10 centimetres in diameter which covers the cervix and upper end of the vagina, and a cap is a less flexible dome-like covering between 2.5 and 4 centimetres in diameter which fits over the cervix alone.

Giacomo Casanova de Seingalt, 18th-century Italian adventurer and author of licentious memoirs, being introduced to the Duchess of Northumberland. Was 'reproductive responsibility' part of his charm or part of his seduction strategy?

Spermicidal jelly is applied to a cap or a diaphragm before it is inserted into the vagina. Correct size and fit should be determined by a physician or a trained nurse, and correct placement is crucial or either may get dislodged during coitus. Either can be inserted some hours before coitus, and a cap can be left in place from the end of one period to the beginning of the next, although this is usually not advised. With both, jelly should be applied each time intercourse is likely to occur. A diaphragm should not be left in place for more than 24 hours, nor should it be removed until at least six hours after coitus. This allows time for the spermicide in the jelly to do its work.

Caps and diaphragms do not suit all women; they are often considered 'messy' and unaesthetic and some women dislike the idea of having a device specially fitted. Nevertheless they can be inserted well in advance of intercourse, are highly reliable, and do not interfere with any body functions. Use of the cap is quite common in Britain and Europe but less so in the United States, where the diaphragm is overwhelmingly preferred. Used with spermicidal agents that also contain preparations such as nonoxynol-9 (which kills viruses), protection against sexually transmitted diseases and AIDS is greatly enhanced.

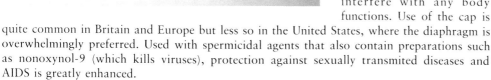

Several sizes of diaphragm, a cap (smaller), and two brands of spermicidal cream commonly used with diaphragms and caps. Both devices have their pros and cons. A cap can be more difficult to insert than a diaphragm if the vagina is long, and a diaphragm can become uncomfortable if its anterior rim presses on the bladder. After use both should be washed in warm soapy water, rinsed, dried with a clean towel. Before each use a diaphragm or cap should be inspected for holes.

Mention must also be made of vaginal rings, another new type of female contraceptive. These are soft, compressible rings about 5 or 6 centimetres in diameter which contain synthetic hormones that diffuse into the bloodstream through the wall of the vagina. Inserted manually and pushed to the back of the vagina where they do not interfere with coitus, they can be left in place for up to three months, removed with ease, and inserted again as necessary.

Creams, foams, jellies, and suppositories

These are chemical contraceptives that either kill sperm or make conditions inside the vagina hostile to them. Inserted with the fingers or with a simple applicator, they are applauded by women as the only female birth control method that does not require medical supervision. Many couples feel they interfere with sexual pleasure because they have to be inserted shortly before intercourse and most of them taste bad, which makes oral sex unpleasant. On the other hand they are easy to obtain and insert and need not be used on a permanent basis. They also provide extra lubrication and, as mentioned above for caps and diaphragms, a degree of protection against certain types of infection. They do not have to be removed after coitus, and their spermicidal action is obviously reduced by douching too soon after coitus; several hours should be allowed to elapse before douching.

Researchers have now developed a modern version of the small natural sponges soaked in citrus juice that Egyptian, Roman, and Hebrew women used in Biblical times: small plastic, disposable sponges permeated with a common spermicide. Initial tests show these to be as reliable as the diaphragm or cap and pleasant to use. They can be left in place for about 24 hours and do not need additional applications of spermicide no matter how often coitus occurs. They kill and absorb sperm, and prevent their passage into the uterus.

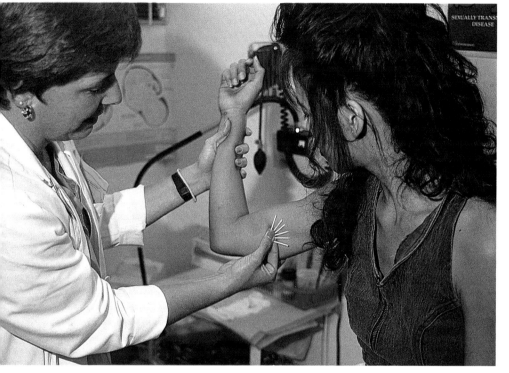

The effects of Norplant being discussed in a family planning clinic. Norplant bacomes effective within 24 hours of insertion and delivers the daily equivalent of two or three progestogen-only pills during the first 18 months and one thereafter. It can be removed on request, all traces of progestogen leaving the body within about seven days. Since some types of progestogen have been linked with congenital birth defects it is important to check that you are not pregnant at the time of implantation.

Injectables and implants

These are hormone preparations that are given in a single injection, become effective within 24 hours, and provide 99 per cent effective contraception for six months to a year. Also available are implants effective for up to five years. The hormones injected or implanted are long-acting artificial progesterones, known by such names as Depo Provera or Norplant, which inhibit ovulation and increase the viscosity of the cervical mucus so that sperm find it difficult to enter the uterus. Norplant consists of three or six silicone rubber matchstick-size capsules containing a synthetic progesterone called levonorgestrel. These are inserted in fan-like fashion (women refer to Norplant as 'the fan') just beneath the skin of the inner arm above the elbow. The procedure takes about 15 minutes and is done under local anaesthetic. In Indonesia, where gold used to be inserted under the skin as a good health charm, such implants are called *susuk* ('gold'). After removal, normal fertility usually returns within several menstrual cycles.

Depot contraceptives are relatively new but have gained rapid acceptance, especially in rural and less technologically advanced societies. This undoubtedly has something to do with the mystique of total effectiveness attributed to any treatment given by needle or syringe, but it is also the result of not having to bother about remembering and counting days and pills. In areas where a woman's only access to medical care is when she delivers a baby, a single injection or implant immediately afterwards can provide months or even years of protection against another pregnancy. The advantages of depot contraceptive have not been lost on women in advanced countries either. In the United States distributors cannot keep up with demand.

Injectables and implants are now in use in more than 90 countries, especially in Latin America and Southeast Asia. In Europe they are available just about everywhere. They are also popular in the United States. Initially it was feared that such long-acting contraceptives would have damaging effects on women themselves or lead to congenital deformities in foetuses exposed to them. But with three decades of clinical experience behind us, there is as yet no basis for these fears. The main disadvantage of injectables and implants is that they can upset menstrual patterns, which is not harmful *per se* but is often disturbing. After two years of use about 40 per cent of women lose their periods altogether and may gain up to 9 pounds in weight.

Many more types of injectables and implants are under development. Some are completely biodegradable (i.e. they do not need to be removed once they have ceased to be contraceptively effective). Some are made to last for specific periods, from between three months to two years. Many of these will be available before the turn of the century.

Various injectables have been tested on men. While they are effective at reducing sperm production, they have many undesirable side effects, including breast development, dizziness, nausea, and a decrease in libido and potency. However, research continues. Most promising seems to be a long-acting androgen that tricks the male brain into shutting off the pituitary hormones responsible for sperm production (female oral contraceptives work in a similar way). To date only repeated weekly injections have achieved the desired result, but scientists in China, Germany, France, Australia, and the United States are still working along these lines. Some years ago gossypol, a derivative of cottonseed, was the focus of great interest when it was found that cottom farmers in China had low levels of fertility. Gossypol showed promise as a contraceptive, but it was also associated with liver damage, potassium depletion, and unwanted permanent sterility in 10 to 20 per cent of the men it was tested on.

Intrauterine devices (IUDs)

These are plastic or metal devices that are placed in the uterus and stay there for a period of months or years. They come in many shapes — rings, bows, Ts, Xs, coils, 7s, shields — and would probably work even if they looked like tiny spoons or toy battleships. The elongated S-shaped Lippes loop is no longer marketed but is the standard device against which other IUDs are compared, but each shape has its pros and cons. Attempts to make the perfect IUD have now produced 'active' lUDs, with added copper or hormones. The knowledge that foreign objects in the uterus prevent conception is not new; camel drivers in the Middle East traditionally inserted pebbles or peach stones into the uteri of their mares. How intrauterine devices work is not clear, but their effect is to reduce the likelihood of the zygote implanting itself in the uterus wall. Somehow they make the intrauterine environment more hostile to sperm and also alter transport mechanisms for both eggs and sperm (i.e. increase or decrease the time it takes for an egg to travel from oviduct to uterus or sperm from uterus to oviduct, with the result that the zygote arrives in the womb when the endometrium is not ready to receive it).

The IUD, in more or less its present form, was developed in Germany in the late 1920s by Ernst Grafenberg (later of G spot fame) and in Japan in 1934 by T. Ota. It was enthusiastically received at first, but then storms of protest erupted from the medical profession in both countries; it was feared that unnatural devices kept in the body for long periods would be harmful. In 1936 the Japanese government prohibited lUDs and in Europe pioneering stopped when Grafenberg and others fled from the Nazi regime. Reluctance to revive its use continued until 1959, when new and favourable trials were conducted in Israel and Japan.

The main attraction of the IUD is that it is easy to insert into the uterus, cheap, does not interfere with body chemistry, and can be left in place for long periods and forgotten about except for the occasional check. It is also easy to remove if pregnancy is desired. It can be put in place immediately following delivery or abortion, or just after a period. One of the main reasons for its popularity in Third World countries is that anyone can be trained to insert an IUD; the procedure does not have to be done by a physician.

The thread attached to the IUD hides inconspicuously in the vagina and makes it easy to check that it is still in place. For some women an IUD is not suitable because it causes heavier than usual menstrual bleeding, occasional cramps, and, in a few cases, interferes with sexual activity. Some women, and their partners, say they can feel an IUD during intercourse and orgasm. Though it is unusual, an IUD can be spontaneously expelled during a period or vigorous sexual exertions. When this occurs, it is typically during the first few months of use by women who have never been pregnant. It seems to be an adjustment reaction by the uterus to the presence of a foreign body. In exceptional cases an IUD can

The Saf-T-coil (seen here greatly enlarged), an 'inert' IUD, ceased to be manufactured because it was not profitable enough. Copper IUDs, still available and popular, are 'active' devices; the copper wire wound around them actually kills sperm. The newest IUDs are also active, containing progestogen, a synthetic form of progesterone. Women who have a history of ectopic pregnancy, pelvic inflammation, or very heavy periods should not use IUDs.

become embedded in the wall of the uterus, or even perforate it.

Once very popular in the United States, the IUD has now fallen in favour. An occasional complaint against various brands is that they cause heavier than normal menstrual bleeding. One brand in particular, the Dalkon shield, has been associated with pelvic infection, and even a few deaths from infection. Dalkon and some other manufacturers have discontinued sales in the United States rather than face the astronomic cost of court battles and insurance claims. IUDs are inexpensive and long-lasting, so the profit margin is low anyway. Now that newer progestin and copper IUDs are available, however, the IUD market in the United States is picking up again. However, it must be said that the vast majority of women using both old-style and new-style IUDs have been and are perfectly happy with them. If there is an increased risk of infection it has much more to do with sexual behaviour than with the simple fact of having an IUD. Women with multiple partners, and therefore at greater risk of infection, should use a different contraceptive method.

IUDs are popular among all age groups in more than 50 countries, including the United States, England, Wales, and Scotland, and particularly in Norway, the Netherlands, Korea, and Jordan. Where there are problems they seem to be associated with particular clinics, which suggests that it is poor health worker technique or an unsuitable clientele that is responsible for most difficulties. Interestingly, one study among sexually active female physicians by E. Zbella and colleagues in 1986 found that the IUD was the most preferred contraceptive method among obstetrician-gynaecologists. Provided one is alert to signs of infection or any unusual bleeding, the advantages are thought to outweigh the risks.

Oral contraceptives

What could be easier than swallowing a pill or a potion to prevent pregnancy? The modern pill is the fulfilment of thousands of years of wishing. The Chinese *Book of Changes*, dating from 2700 BC, advises drinking fried mercury on an empty stomach, and other ancient writings encouraged prostitutes to take potions containing lead. In fact metallic brews have often been recommended for contraceptive purposes — in AD 540 Aetius of the Upper Tigris described a drink containing copper, and in the Middle Ages women in the Alpine region of Austria swallowed concoctions of arsenic. Such preventives did more than stop conception; they often killed those desperate enough to try them.

Almost every society has its folk contraceptives, foods, or herbal preparations traditionally supposed to prevent pregnancy, and modern pharmaceutical companies and research institutes continue to investigate them in the hope of discovering the ideal contraceptive. In fact most modern oral contraceptives are based on diosgenin, a synthetic progestogen extracted from wild barbasco root, a plant native to Mexico. Attempts at large-scale cultivation of barbasco root have not been successful so far, but there is a fortune waiting for the shrewd farmer who achieves predictable yields.

Development of the pill, now the most widely used form of temporary contraception in the world, came about through dogged research and concerted effort rather than any sudden, chance discovery. The research that ultimately proved successful was encouraged and supported by Margaret Sanger, a pioneer advocate of birth control, and was funded by Katherine Dexter McCormack of the McCormack tractor family. Gregory Pincus, H.C. Chang, and John Rock of the United States put in place the final crucial pieces of the puzzle contributed to by researchers all over the world. In essence their work involved close analysis of the female reproductive system and the mechanism of ovulation. They realized that during pregnancy, when ovulation and periods cease, levels of oestrogens and progesterone in the blood are naturally elevated. If they could induce a state of pseudopregnancy by giving extra doses of these hormones, ovulation could be prevented and conception would not occur. They then had to work out how to make these hormones active when taken by mouth and establish a safe and convenient dosage. In 1960 their work culminated in the launch of Enovid (a mixture of synthetic oestrogens and progestins, manufactured by Searle and Co.). Now there are hundreds of different contraceptive pills in use worldwide.

Provided it is taken regularly for a fixed number of days within a 28-day cycle, the pill is almost 100 per cent reliable. It is inexpensive, separates contraception from coitus, and very rarely has any adverse effect on sexual activity. Some women feel side effects such as nausea or changes in menstrual flow. Thrombosis is a rare side effect and it is women who are confirmed, long-time smokers who are most at risk; this is why smokers are advised to come off the pill after the age of 35. In fact the pill is not normally recommended to any woman after the age of 40. But, as British investigator J. Guillebaud has pointed out, there are some interesting paradoxes here. A women over 35 is half as fertile as she was at 25, but her fear of unwanted pregnancy is greater. Perhaps she should stay on the pill, which is almost 100 per cent effective. Also, although women are advised to come off the pill after the age of 35 or 40, several years later they may be advised to take supplemental hormones to reduce menopausal symptoms. Perhaps this whole area needs a good rethink.

All in all, pregnancy and birth are much riskier undertakings than using oral (or any other) contraceptives. There is no evidence that the pill encourages breast or cervical cancer; on the contrary it may actually reduce such risks. This protective effect, partly the work of progesterone, seems to last for at least a decade after the pill is discontinued and is most noticeable in women who have never borne children, the group most at risk of these types of cancer. Recent research has also shown that sexually active women aged between 18 and 44 who are on the pill have a 50 per cent reduced risk of developing pelvic inflammatory disease (PID), a leading cause of morbidity, hospitalization, and infertility.

Nevertheless many women still have doubts about the pill. In this connection I would like to quote from the 1990 edition of the British Department of Health's *Handbook of Contraceptive Practice*: 'There are a number of advantages in taking the pill. Women with painful, heavy or unpredictable menstrual periods will usually benefit from the change to a regular, pain-free and lighter interval blood loss. Use of the combined pill reduces the risk of ovarian and endometrial cancer. Benign breast tumours are less likely in women after prolonged use of the pill and conditions such as endometriosis may be rendered quiescent...[the pill may also] contribute to the mental and social well-being of women...[its] effect on acne varies with different combinations, but oestrogen-dominated formulations generally tend to improve this condition...[researchers have also] reported lower incidences of functional ovarian cysts, rheumatoid arthritis and possibly thyroid disease...the symptoms of premenstrual tension may be reduced.'

A delay of two or three months in getting pregnant is not uncommon when the pill is discontinued; a similar time delay occurs with discontinuation of non-oral hormonal contraceptives too.

The Chinese, among whom birth control research has high priority, have been active in developing many new types of oral contraceptive. One is an edible paper permeated with hormones; the women chews a piece the size of a postage stamp each day for 22 days in 28. Another type is a large-dose pill, the 'visiting pill', for use by women who see their partners infrequently; one pill provides protection for about three days. Another large-dose pill works for a month. No prescription or visit to the doctor is needed for any of these contraceptives. They are available free to married people at their place of work.

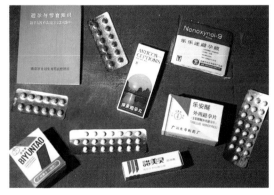

In China contraceptives are supplied free to married individuals. Those pictured here are, clockwise from top left, spermicidal film, once-a-month pills, daily pills, condoms, and 'day after' pills.

Withdrawal and other methods

These usually involve withdrawing the penis from the vagina just before orgasm so that ejaculation does not occur in the vagina. The technical term for this is coitus interruptus. But even if withdrawal is properly practised, there may be sperm in the fluids released from the penis prior to ejaculation and therefore the risk of pregnancy. The only advantage of withdrawal is that it is better than nothing. With practice it is also possible to refrain from ejaculating but allow orgasm to occur inside the vagina. This is called coitus reservatus. Most men know when ejaculation is about to occur, so both methods are feasible. Unfortunately, the experience of witholding ejaculation or withdrawing before orgasm is often, though not always, intensely frustrating. Even with the best of intentions, neither method always prevails over the excitement of the moment.

Other behavioural methods, such as oral or anal intercourse, are much more effective, although they too cause frustration and are not to everyone's liking. With AIDS awareness, such methods are now more widely discussed. In parts of the world where the cost of contraception is a major factor they are common birth control techniques. Anal sex has been more closely associated with increased risk of HIV and other sexually transmitted diseases than oral sex, probably because the lining of the rectum is more fragile than the lining of the mouth and more likely to be injured in vigorous sexual activity.

Breast-feeding is sometimes regarded as a method of birth control too, but it is highly

unreliable. At best it can help to space pregnancies. In most women breast-feeding postpones ovulation and therefore the possibility of conception for about six months after childbirth. Another pregnancy commonly follows if nursing is the only method relied on.

Douching is a useless contraceptive procedure; by the time it is done, many sperm have already entered the uterus and begun their journey towards the oviducts.

Sterilization

Though sterilization has been technically possible for many years, it was not widely or confidently recommended until the late 1960s. Now, worldwide, it is the most effective and most popular method of controlling fertility, twice as popular even than oral contraceptives. In both developed and developing countries more than one third of couples who plan their families do so by means of sterilization. In about 75 to 80 per cent of cases it is the woman who has the procedure, and in 20 to 25 percent it is the man. Even in the United States, sterilization is the most used method of birth control for women over 30. There is even increasing acceptance of voluntary sterilization in Islamic countries, where it is no longer seen as conflicting with religious teachings. The only factors limiting the wider use of sterilization seem to be cost, availability, lack of trained physicians, or lack of government support. It is something that ordinary people accept. In China and India sterilization is fashionable among all classes, rural and urban. In many Third World countries sterilization procedures are carried out by mobile clinics.

Sterilization methods differ for men and women, but in both sexes they usually involve cutting and tying the tubes leading from the gonads, the vasa deferentia in men and the oviducts in women. A trained doctor can do the operation in less than 20 minutes. After vasectomy men are advised to take it easy and refrain from intercourse for several days, but otherwise they can go back to work or continue with their usual routine within hours. Since live sperm remain in the vasa and urethra for some time after vasectomy, contraception must continue to be used for at least 20 or so ejaculations or until the ejaculate is free of sperm. Recently 'no-scalpel' vasectomies have been developed which are relatively simple to perform — the scrotum is pierced with special forceps — and well accepted.

Sterilization procedures for women are a little more complicated, and several days' to two weeks' rest are usually advised, depending on the method used. During this time intercourse must be refrained from.

Hysterectomy, surgical removal of the uterus, is now a common procedure and is usually done for reasons that have nothing to do with contraception — abnormal or heavy bleeding, prolapse of the uterus, or tumours or growths within the uterus. The end result is of course sterilization. Psychologically, hysterectomy can be difficult to come to terms with; unlike

It's thumbs down to breastfeeding and douching as means of birth control. Breastfeeding has some contraceptive effect because the hormones that stimulate lactation inhibit ovulation, but it cannot be totally relied on beyond four or five weeks postpartum because ovulation can occur even before menstruation has re-established itself. Vaginal douching is next to useless. Buyers of syringes 'pour la toilette intime', as described in this turn-of-the-century French advertisement, would have been better off using them to spray the roses.

sterilization, it is usually a matter of necessity rather than a matter of choice. If a hysterectomy is suggested, a confirming second opinion should be sought, and the exact nature of the operation should be discussed.

Sterilization should be regarded as a once-and-for-all procedure. It is not generally reversible, although there have been more successes with reversing vasectomies. For couples who have decided that their reproductive days are over it is the ideal answer. Although it is a safer and simpler procedure for men than for women, more women are sterilized than men, which is not surprising since women bear

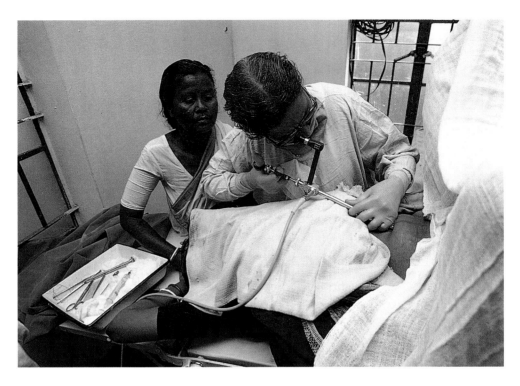

the burden of pregnancy. Feelings of inadequacy or depression after sterilization are not unusual. After all, fertility is a strong symbol of femininity and masculinity. Unfortunately, for some couples the erroneous belief that sexual drive fades after sterilization becomes a self-fulfilling prophecy.

Researchers are now developing sterilization techniques that do not involve surgery. The sterilizing agent may be a vaccine which incapacitates sperm and eggs or makes the woman immune to sperm (by producing antibodies to a particular protein found on the heads of sperm). Either of these techniques could prevent fertilization. Another technique might be to inject a substance which causes constriction and closure of the tubes leading from the gonads. A technique I worked on for several years involved the drug quinacrine, also used in the treatment of malaria. In liquid or paste form, quinacrine can be injected into the uterus or oviducts via a tube passed up through the vagina. Once inside the uterus it causes the oviducts to close, preventing the passage of eggs or sperm. Other tissue adhesives are now being used in China for male sterilization; injected into the vasa deferentia through the thin skin of the scrotum, they cause them to close, preventing the passage of sperm. Mechanical plugs and clips have also been developed which do the same thing, block the passage of sperm from testes to penis or of eggs from ovaries to uterus. Some of all of these alternatives to surgery should be widely available within the next 10 years.

A woman in a Calcutta clinic being sterilized by laparoscopy. One incision is made below the navel and another just above the pubic hair. A laparoscope (an instrument with a light on the end of it) is inserted through the top incision and the abdominal cavity is pumped up with carbon dioxide so that the surgeon can get a good look at the fallopian tubes. Another instrument is passed through the suprapubic incision to tie, clip, or cauterize both tubes so that eggs cannot reach the uterus.

More pluses than minuses

The links between contraception and sexual activity are complex, but whichever method is used, it should be used consistently and properly. Condoms used sporadically or oral contraceptives taken only when remembered or coitus is anticipated are destined to fail. Diaphragms can get dislodged with vigorous sexual activity, particularly with the woman on top. The taste of foams and jellies puts some people off oral sex. IUDs and diaphragms must fit properly and spermicides must be used with the latter. Lubricants can be used with any barrier method of contraception (condoms, diaphragms, etc.) but should not contain petroleum (as Vaseline and some hair oils do) since this attacks rubber and latex. Breaking off from sexual arousal to roll on a condom or insert a diaphragm is not particularly romantic, although some couples apply such devices as part of sex play. Men in particular complain about the loss of sensitivity when wearing a condom. All of these factors make attitudes towards contraceptive precautions less than enthusiastic. There is also the strongly held belief, particularly among the young, that coitus and sexual play are somehow spoiled by thoughts of devices and chemicals; they would rather think of hearts,

Condom earrings. Political statement or fashion statement?

and flowers, moon and June....

Such considerations aside, certainly for the majority of men and women contraceptives remove the anxiety of unwanted pregnancy, and with methods like the IUD, the pill, and sterilization — so-called coitus-independent methods — one can 'set it and forget it'. Sex play and contraception are separated in time and thought, so sex can be spontaneous. There are of course those who rather like the element of spice and risk connected with less reliable methods of contraception, especially if a child is wanted 'some time' in the future. On the other hand, there are women who say that if contraception is too reliable they can no longer use fear of pregnancy as an excuse for saying no to sex. Some women simply dislike the idea of anything chemical or physical inside their body for fear of side effects, an attitude which is in tune with environmentalism and the green movement.

Attitudes towards contraceptives mirror attitudes towards sex in general. Those who feel at ease with sex, who are 'erotophilic' rather than 'erotophobic', to use the terms coined by social psychologist Donn Byrne, usually feel at ease with contraception and choose the more effective, longer-acting methods, and enjoy sex more as a result. Statistically, with millions upon millions of people using contraceptives, it is inevitable that some will get pregnant, suffer distressing side effects, and fall ill. But for the overwhelming majority, contraceptives enhance sexual enjoyment and life fulfilment.

Interception and RU-486

This is analogous to blocking the stable door after the horse has bolted, since it involves halting the reproductive process after conception rather than before it. But neither human beings nor contraceptives are perfect, and accidents happen. Women coming up to the menopause and assuming they no longer need contraception can be 'surprised', oral contraceptives are often forgotten, a cap or diaphragm can be dislodged, a condom slip off or split, the heat and pace of arousal overcome the best of intentions. 'Morning after' methods are needed and appreciated.

The 'morning after pill' is a actually a series of high-dose oestrogen and progesterone pills taken for three to seven days following coitus; these make the hormonal environment of the female reproductive tract inhospitable to the fertilized egg. The method is highly effective, if started within 48 hours of coitus, although it makes some women nauseous and often disturbs the following menstrual period. It is not intended for regular or repeated use. Post-coital insertion of a copper-active IUD has also been shown to prevent implantation and therefore intercept pregnancy.

RU-486, manufactured by the French company Roussel Uclaf, is the hottest new item in the family planning armamentarium, and very controversial. It is an interceptive and was developed by Etienne-Emile Baulieu and his team in 1980. Also known as the 'French abortion pill', RU-486 blocks the ability of progesterone to nourish the uterus and therefore reduces the uterus' ability to support a fertilized egg. Typically it is used in conjunction with prostaglandins (see below) which induce uterine contractions. Taken at any time during the first seven weeks of pregnancy, RU-486 causes the products of conception to be expelled. It is remarkably safe and effective, and has also shown promise in the treatment of breast and brain cancers, osteoporosis, endometriosis, and AIDS. I see this drug as a modern-day equivalent of penicillin. For his development of RU-486 Baulieu received the Lasker Award, the most prestigious award for medical research given in the United States. He is certainly a candidate for a Nobel Prize.

Prostaglandins are naturally occurring substances that can be used to induce menstruation or miscarriage early in pregnancy, but unwanted effects such as uterine cramps, vomiting, and diarrhoea have restricted their use. Inserted as vaginal suppositories, they cause contractions of the uterus and expulsion of the products of pregnancy. Prostaglandins are now being used to complement progesterone blockers such as RU-486, and with further development may become available for home use.

However the anti-abortion lobby disapproves of these drugs. Initially the use of RU-486 was blocked even in France until the then Minister of Health Claude Evin gave it government approval, declaring that RU-486 was 'the moral property of women'. The drug is now available in Britain, Sweden, and the Netherlands, and China has developed its own counterpart formula. In other countries, including America, its introduction is still being delayed. In the United States the manufacturer has been threatened with a commercial boycott of all its products (worth more than $6 billion per year in sales) and the Republican administration, which has made an anti-abortion stance part of its political platform, threatened with election defeat. However, those who believe that women should have the right to safe and convenient abortion, the large majority of the American public in fact, are mustering their forces to overturn the ban. The American Medical Association has given the drug its unanimous support, and so have the American Association for the Advancement of Science, the American Psychological Association, the National Alliance of Breast Cancer Organizations, and dozens of other health care and scientific organizations. The ban will probably be lifted within a few years. To quote Mark Green, Commissioner of the New York City Department of Consumer Affairs: 'It's one thing for RU-486 opponents to say they are "pro-life" and quite another to be pro-cancer.' Until it is legally available, RU-486 will be bought on the black market.

The significance of a drug like RU-486 is truly staggering. It has the potential to save literally hundreds of thousands of women's lives — this is the number of women who die every year around the world as a result of primitive, unsanitary, non-medical abortions — and an even greater number of women are psychologically traumatized and physically injured by botched abortions. Millions of women who suffer from breast cancer and endometriosis (which now affect 1 in 10 women worldwide), not to mention osteoporosis and AIDS, could also benefit from RU-486. There are too many human lives at stake for a drug like RU-486 to remain hostage to blatant commercial and political interests.

Abortion

A late period worries most women, especially if they are sexually active and do not want to get pregnant. 'Can you help me bring on my period' is a common euphemism for 'I think I may be pregnant. Can you do anything about it?' In many countries it is perfectly legal, whether or not pregnancy is suspected, for a trained practitioner to insert a flexible straw-thin tube into the uterus through the vagina and remove the uterine lining by gentle suction. Menstrual extraction, or menstrual aspiration, as it is called, is becoming an increasingly common procedure around the world. It is relatively simple, safe, and inexpensive, and can be done by a trained health care worker. Against the advice of physicians, some women's groups in the United States have been advocating menstrual extraction as a routine procedure (even done by one woman to another) to shorten menstrual bleeding time and obviate the need for contraceptives. The Federation of Feminist Women's Health Centers has clinics in several states, including California, which perform such extractions. President of the Federation, Dido Hasper, says that between 1989, when the U.S. Supreme Court first gave states the right to impose restrictions on abortion, and 1992 she received hundreds of requests to teach women's groups around the United States how to do home abortions in case legal abortion suddenly became illegal.

Up until four to six weeks of pregnancy (and in some hands eight weeks) menstrual extraction is easy and untraumatic if done in proper conditions by a trained person. It takes just a few minutes. Normal activities can be resumed after a brief rest, but the usual advice is to abstain from coitus for at least a week. If the woman is not pregnant, all that happens is that a period is induced. If she is pregnant, the process is, in effect, a very early abortion.

Abortion, certainly the most common method of interception, is now legal for more than 90 per cent of the world's population. In Belgium, Ireland, Spain, and many Muslim and Latin American countries abortion is still a crime. But illegality does not mean that abortion is not available, from trained or untrained practitioners, if one has the money and the contacts. Abortion can be an ugly and risky procedure if performed by a backstreet operator. Even done properly in clinical conditions it is not an altogether pleasant experience, although it is certainly less risky than giving birth.

Until the twelfth week of pregnancy the abortion method most commonly used is similar to menstrual extraction. In most clinics this procedure has replaced the older D & C (dilatation and curettage) technique, which involved scraping away the uterine lining, and any embryo or foetus attached to it, with an instrument called a curette. But after the

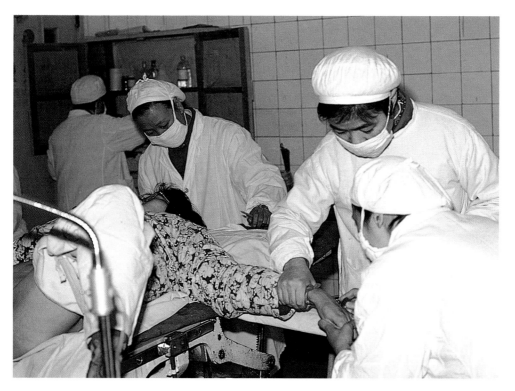

Abortion under acupuncture in a hospital in Xian province, China. In some parts of China heavy 'persuasion' is brought to bear on mothers pregnant with their second child. In the West only 1 in 100 abortions is done because of foetal abnormalities. In Britain and the United States abortion is only legal up to 28 weeks; after week 20 it cannot be done unless resuscitation equipment is available.

twelfth week the foetus is too big to be simply sucked or scraped from the uterus. Thereafter the preferred method is to place prostaglandins directly into the uterus or vagina or inject a salt solution into the fluids surrounding the foetus. This brings on contractions and within hours the foetus is expelled. After a day or two of rest, most women resume their normal routine, although some physicians advise women to refrain from intercourse for at least a week.

Although there is a greater or lesser degree of psychological pain involved, almost all women who abort feel they are making the best decision in the circumstances. Follow-up studies have consistently shown 'no regrets' to be the predominant response, regardless of religious persuasion, mental state, or nationality. Where abortion is regretted, who is to know whether having a child would have been an even greater cause for regret? Where women have been denied abortions for governmental or medical reasons, research has shown that their offspring are more likely to suffer social and medical problems than their wanted peers.

In 1992 a particularly poignant case brought many of these issues to world attention. A 14-year-old Irish girl who had been raped by her best friend's father attempted to cross to England to have an abortion, as more than 4,000 Irish women do each year because abortion is illegal under the Irish constitution. The Irish authorities found out and placed a travel ban on her and her family. She threatened suicide and her parents made her plight known in an attempt to have the government's ruling reversed. After examining her a psychologist said: 'The damage to her mental health would be devastating' if she bore an unwanted child. After a week or two of stormy national and international debate the Irish Supreme Court overturned the travel ban. Political leaders welcomed the decision, as did pro-choice groups and even the Catholic Church, which wanted off the hot seat. Moves are now afoot to change the Republic's constitution. Ireland is sensitive to the opinions of fellow members of the European Community, which in this case were overwhelmingly negative, not least because no member state can deny free travel within the Community. In most countries of the world women have a legal right to abortion, provided certain criteria are met.

In 1979 and again in 1989 approximately 14 out of every 1,000 French and Italian women between the ages of 15 and 49 had abortions. The figures for non-Catholic countries such as Canada, England, Wales, Finland, Denmark, and Norway were not very different. These are all countries where contraceptives are well used, so abortion is a method of last resort. It is a different story in countries where contraception is not available. In Bulgaria, for example, recent reports are that about 65 women per 1,000 have abortions in any one year, in Romania about 90, and in the former Soviet Union about 112, but the true figures may be even higher (for propaganda purposes they are kept 'low'). In Russia the typical woman may face eight or more abortions during her lifetime. In Western Europe as a whole between 20 and 30 per cent of all pregnancies are aborted, and in Japan, Romania, and the Soviet Union as many as 70 per cent. In areas of the China the percentage may be even higher.

When contraceptives are readily available abortion is not usually regarded as a substitute for them; rather it is resorted to when contraceptive methods fail. Single and young women who get pregnant and have abortions are more likely to revise their ideas about birth control or seek a more reliable method rather than have repeated pregnancies and abortions. Despite its prevalence and legality, abortion is seldom talked about openly, except in general political terms. Pregnancy and birth are greeted with social support and general rejoicing, but abortion is done without fanfare or advertisement. Even close friends may be unaware of the event; if they are told later it is a mark of special intimacy. There is the underlying feeling of personal failure — as an adult, as a parent, as someone who ought to have been contraceptively aware and responsible but somehow wasn't. Women in particular, but sometimes their partners and families too, undergo in private an experience that might be better borne with social support. In China it is the 'done thing' to empathize with a women who has had an abortion; friends and co-workers praise her for demonstrating her commitment to the government's one-child policy.

A recent *Time* magazine article titled 'When Abortions Save Lives' highlighted the fact that the products of abortion may be medically useful. Foetuses need not be wasted. There have been attempts to use foetal cells to combat movement disorders such as Parkinson's disease and Huntington's chorea, Alzheimer's disease, and some types of diabetes. Whether these attempts are eventually successful or not, the possibility of their being so has dramatically shifted the grounds of the ethical debate for and against abortion. Many opponents of abortion have broken ranks over the issue. If a woman is considering abortion, the possibility that her foetus may help another human being may tilt the balance or at least reduce her anguish.

As yet there is no safe way for a woman, privately and by herself, to abort a pregnancy, but the option is already on the

A birth control/AIDS festival in an American university. College-sponsored and peer-led events like this are well accepted and very positive in their effect. Contraceptive choice and responsibility are openly discussed.

horizon. RU-486 and prostaglandins, or refined and enhanced drugs like them, will soon be available and will give women the option of terminating early pregnancies themselves in their own homes. I have little doubt that such an option will bring about a major change in social attitudes to reproduction and sexual activity. It will surpass even the changes associated with the pill. The pill was the first simple way women had to control their reproductive lives — the decision to prevent pregnancy was literally put into their hands on a day-to-day basis and became more associated with brushing teeth or taking morning coffee than with love-making. Without sterilization, of course, there is always the tiny possibility of becoming pregnant. But with RU-486 and similar drugs, millions of women who have neither the knowledge nor the wish to think daily about such things as contraception will be able to control this most intimate and important part of their lives without medical intervention. This new generation of interceptive drugs will alter the basic social contract.

For any sexually active and fertile couple conception is a probability that cannot be dodged. It is no good hoping that it won't happen; hope is not a contraceptive method. There is now such a wide array of family planning methods, especially in the West, that most couples and individuals should be able to find at least one that meets their needs. If one method is tried and found unsuitable, there are always others. With continued research, the development of safer and more reliable techniques, and better means of educating people about them, unplanned and unwelcome births should become rarer and rarer. With the world in a true overpopulation crisis even the United States will fall into line and cease its pronatalist stance. This cannot happen too soon. Every 24 hours another 250,000 new souls come into this world, to be fed, clothed, housed, and educated.

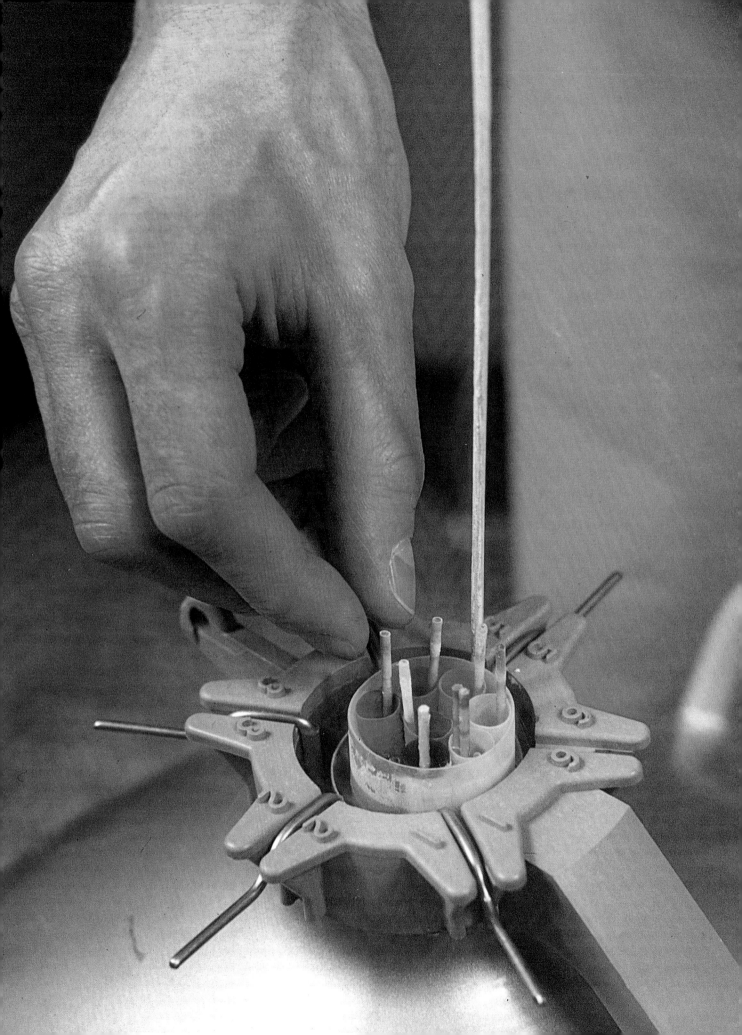

Chapter 13

Sex as work

Couples who cannot, for various reasons, have a baby of their own making suffer a particular kind of heartbreak. For them, headlines about 'miracle' fertility drugs and 'test tube' babies offer hope but also rub salt into the wound.

Infertility is more common than is realized. It affects about 1 in 7 to 10 couples in the West and in countries where health care and general health are poor the figure is much higher. And for reasons poorly understood, and no doubt connected with reproductive tract infections and general environmental pollution, infertility is becoming more common.

Generally speaking, if conception does not occur within one or two years, one or both partners may be infertile. However, infertility is defined differently by different clinicians and researchers, so it is relative, not absolute. Without any special effort about 25 per cent of women conceive during the first cycle in which coitus occurs, about 65 per cent conceive within six months of regular coitus, about 85 per cent within a year, and about 90 per cent within 18 months. The remainder may never get pregnant even with professional help.

Surveys have repeatedly found that more than 90 per cent of newlyweds plan to have children. Whether the reasons are psychological or biological, self-worth is often seen in terms of children. Children are wanted for many reasons — to satisfy family and friends and society at large, to achieve personal growth and fulfilment, to graduate from being a child of parents to being the parent of children, to conform to religious, political, or cultural teachings, to swell the population of a group or tribe. Children are also a means of legitimizing sexual activities, a demonstration of sexual potency ('they have five children so they must be very sexy'), an affirmation of masculinity or femininity. That said, many couples want children simply because they feel they have a lot of love to give and because they anticipate receiving great pleasure and joy from parenthood.

The search of the childless for children can become acute and obsessional. One infertile husband admitted: 'There is nothing that hits into the very essence of what I am more than this.' One woman in Australia threatened suicide if her request for in vitro ('test tube') fertilization was turned down. Judy Carr, the first woman in the United States to benefit from this procedure, strongly criticized medical insurance companies for classifying it as 'elective' rather than necessary: 'They're saying this is an option. But for me it was not an option.'

For infertile couples sexual activities can become work rather than play, dictated by the thermometer and the calendar rather than by passion and interest. Schedules for sex may become as rigid as train timetables. To increase the likelihood of pregnancy, coitus must happen as close to ovulation as possible (the exact opposite of the rhythm method of contraception), regardless of when that occurs; and if sperm are in short supply, coitus should not take place except during ovulation. Strictures like these make every demand for erection or lubrication a test of self-worth and commitment. Reproduction, not satisfaction, becomes the goal. Sex as the expression of love takes second place to sex as a means to an end. Efforts to 'soften' the coital atmosphere with flowers, candles, and other romantic images meet with varying degrees of success, for when reproduction becomes the only goal of sex, spontaneity and love are almost sure to be lost.

Although infertility is *prima facie* a physical or physiological problem, it can quite

Opposite: Human sperm, in straw-like containers, being removed from a canister of liquid nitrogen. Eggs can also be frozen and stored in this way, and then used for artificial insemination (AI) or in vitro fertilization (IVF).

A Chinese almanac and a charm to prevent miscarriage. Almanacs like this, which still sell briskly among traditional Chinese, contain advice on how to get pregnant, how to avoid pregnancy, how to abort pregnancy, how to court and woo a loved one, how to know if someone lusts after you...and much other sex-related information.

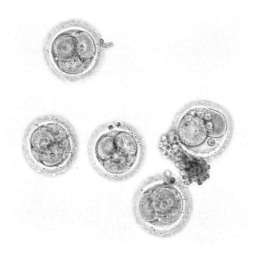

quickly become a psychological one. Since it often comes up early in a marriage, it can severely strain and test a couple's ability to communicate about sexual needs and pleasures, about reproductive goals, about the future they see for their marriage, about their overall agenda in life. Biologically it may be 'his' or 'her' problem, or occasionally 'their' problem, but unless the couple sees is as 'our' problem the marriage will irreparably suffer.

There is also the inescapable fact that even the best fertility clinics fail more often than they succeed. In both Britain and the United States only about 10 per cent of treated couples carry a baby to term, and treatment can take years and be both physically and emotionally painful. In the United States even the best clinics consider themselves fortunate if they achieve a 'baby take home rate' of 1 in 3 or 1 in 4; the majority of pregnancies are lost. A great deal depends on how infertility is defined, how early it is 'diagnosed', how soon treatment is initiated, how 'heroic' the couple and the clinicians are prepared to be, how many attempts are made over how many years, and how much money is spent.

A cohort of human embryos developed from eggs 'harvested' by laparoscopy and fertilized in vitro.

Causes of infertility

There are three main tiers, or levels, of problems that lead to infertility. One level consists of problems that can be resolved relatively simply, by counselling, injection, or surgery, for example. Problems on the second level are more difficult to solve, and fall into three categories: blocked tubes from ovaries to uterus in women or from testes to urethra in men, or ovaries that are occasionally or fully anovulatory; abnormal eggs or sperm, or sperm of poor quality or in insufficient quantity; and testicular or uterine problems. The other cause of intertility, not yet well understood, is stress and anxiety. According to Ronald Burke, director of the Fertility and Women's Health Care Center in Springfield, Massachusetts, 71 per cent of couples who joined an infertility support group later conceived compared with

Human sperm being checked for viability under a light microscope linked to television monitors. Sperm for AI or IVF may be used fresh or thawed from storage.

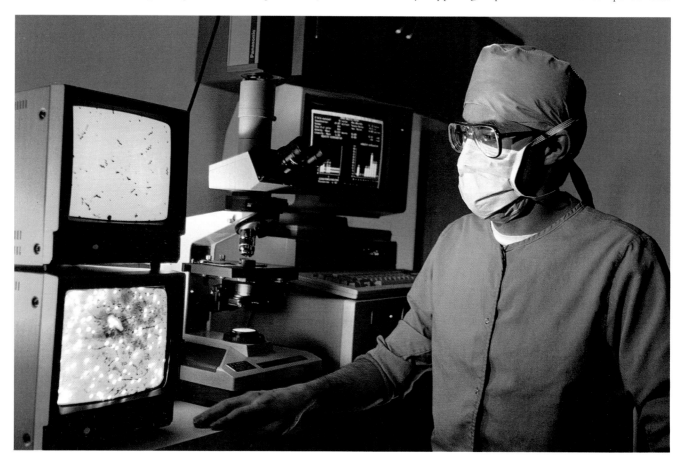

only 25 per cent of couples who did not join the support group.

Obstruction of the tubes, frequently the result of low-grade but persistent and undetected infections or venereal disease, is an increasingly common cause of infertility. Untreated occult infection produces scar tissue which blocks the passage of eggs and sperm. Obstructions can be removed by a technique know as insufflation, which involves forcing gas through the oviducts or vasa deferentia, or by microsurgery, now often with lasers (microsurgery is also used to repair or bypass the results of sterilization). But these techniques are not always successful. If they fail or are not feasible and the woman is in good health otherwise, *in vitro* fertilization (IVF), or fertilizing an egg outside the women's body and then implanting it in the womb, may be the last resort. Until recently men whose tubes could not be repaired did not have a similar option. Now microsurgical aspiration techniques allow sperm to be removed from the epididymides, matured, and used for IVF. However, the results of such manipulation — as with all IVF techniques — are often disappointing.

When not enough sperm or eggs are produced because the hormones that stimulate their production are in short supply, one possible solution is to take extra hormones, natural or synthetic. One or two weeks of hormone treatment is often successful in helping women to ovulate, but because so-called fertility drugs can induce more than one egg to develop at a time, they are often responsible for multiple births. Men are less likely to be helped by hormone treatments, partly because sperm production takes much longer (between 60 and 72 days) and is a less understood and apparently more complicated process.

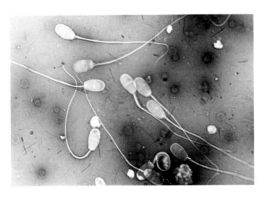

Female infertility is also linked to endometriosis. For reasons not properly understood, the endometrium, the tissue that lines the inside of the uterus, overruns its normal boundaries and seeds itself elsewhere in the female reproductive tract and in the pelvic cavity, preventing conception. Rough estimates are that 1 in 10 women in the United States has endometriosis. In men, abnormally growing varicose veins, or varicoceles, in the testes or ducts are also linked with infertility. One theory is that varicoceles hamper sperm development by raising the temperature of the testes. Successful treatment of endometriosis or varicocele is often followed by pregnancy.

Several healthily swimming sperm can be seen in this stained semen sample. It takes many sperm to fertilize a single egg because a single sperm does not contain enough enzymes to break down the membrane around the egg. Many sperm must release their acrosomal enzymes so that one can penetrate and fertilize the egg.

In a few instances coitus occurs so infrequently that fertilization is a statistical improbability. Also, if a couple is sexually and biologically naive, ejaculation may never occur inside the vagina. There are even reports that in some men the regular wearing of tight underpants or the nightly taking of long hot baths is associated with infertility (because they raise the temperature of the scrotum). In such cases the remedies are simple.

It is also the case that after the age of 35 a women is half as fertile (half as likely to conceive) as she was at 25. All the eggs that a woman has are 'ready' before she is even born. They age as she ages, so the eggs her ovaries mature and release in her late 30s are 'older' than those produced in her 20s. Many women who put off child-bearing until they have fulfilled career and other aspirations find their 'biological clock' running out on them. Sperm, on the other hand, are produced fresh every day, so a man can remain fertile until well into his 60s or 70s or beyond.

New routes to fertilization

Infertile couples now have two main options if they cannot or do not wish to adopt children or if fertility drugs are not the solution: artificial insemination (AI) or *in vitro* fertilization (IVF). The first method involves collecting sperm from the husband or from a donor and introducing it into the uterus at a time when the chances of conceiving are greatest. The sperm sample, usually obtained by masturbation, may be fresh or it may have been frozen for several months. If the husband has a low sperm count it may be necessary for him to produce several ejaculates. Or his donations may be supplemented by those of a donor. If his sperm are defective, the sample used for insemination will come from a donor alone.

The alternative procedure, IVF, is used when the woman's oviducts are irrevocably blocked. With painstaking care an egg is removed from or from near the ovary, mixed with sperm and, after a period of development in a glass laboratory dish (nothing like the 'test tube' of media mythology), introduced into the uterus to await implantation. The first baby born as a result of IVF was Louise Brown in 1978. Her birth focused worldwide attention on the British medical team responsible, headed by Robert Edwards and Patrick Steptoe. Since then many other 'test tube' babies have been born, including twins and triplets.

Another technique, with the wonderful acronym GIFT (gamete intrafallopian transfer), involves obtaining eggs and sperm as in IVF but allows fertilization and initial development to occur within the oviduct. ZIFT (zygote intrafallopian transfer) is a new variant in which the fertilized egg, or zygote, is allowed to develop *in vitro* into an embryo before being transferred to the oviduct. Techniques have now been perfected, amidst a flurry of controversy, to allow women to give birth from frozen embryos. This involves 'harvesting' a batch of eggs, fertilizing them *in vitro*, freezing them, then transferring some of them to the uterus at the appropriate time. The advantage of using frozen embryos is that it gives a couple a second chance if a first attempt to achieve implantation fails. Since the late 1980s fertility clinics have also made more use of egg donors. After hormone priming, the donor's eggs can be retrieved through the vagina in a 10-minute procedure using an ultrasound probe; they are then fertilized with sperm and transferred to the uterus. In all of these procedures several eggs are utilized at a time to enhance the probability of at least one surviving. Often none do. But, on the other hand, multiple pregnancies and births are not uncommon.

Success for a couple who persued the IVF route when it became known that the mother's oviducts were blocked. Their son began life as one of several frozen embryos. These were transplanted into the womb six months after in vitro *fertilization. In this case only one embryo implanted and developed. Before eggs are 'harvested' for IVF, drugs are given which cause the ovaries to ovulate more eggs than normal.*

Attempts to make IVF more widely suitable and available are continuing in many countries, but the techniques are arduous and at present the chances of successful implantation are less than 50:50. Naturally the pleasure or disappointment of would-be parents is made even more intense by the effort and emotional investment that IVF involves. As many as 30 per cent of effortlessly normal pregnancies end in early miscarriage, but the risks of losing an IVF pregnancy are much higher. Each menstrual period becomes, as one woman expressed it, 'like a little death'.

Artifical insemination and *in vitro* fertilization have been condemned by various church leaders as 'immoral', 'illicit', or contrary to a proper 'reverence for life'. As in other matters the clergy may preach one way but their parishioners go another. Surveys in the United States, Britain, Australia, and the Netherlands, those nations in the forefront of IVF research, have all shown that the majority of those questioned approve of 'test tube' help for infertile couples. Some clinicians, in an attempt to defuse religious objections, recommend that couples have coitus soon after IVF or AI so that the link between love, sex, and reproduction is affirmed. Other clinicians say this jeopardizes the chances of successful pregnancy (semen characteristics may be poor or there may be undue movement of the uterus and oviducts during intercourse).

Adoption

In many cultures throughout history childless couples have simply been given children by friends or relations. Among the Hawaiians and other Polynesian peoples this custom is known as *hanai*. To be a *hanai* child is an honour, a mark of great desire and great love; *hanai* children are given to couples with or without children of their own. But in industrialized societies adoption is usually less simple. Although informal and private adoptions do occur, legal adoption· is hedged about with obstacles. In the West it is no honour to be adopted, because the motives for putting a child up for adoption usually spring from poverty, inadequacy, or unhappy circumstances; usually the mother is forced to give up her child through circumstances beyond her control. Many adopted children feel this stigma, even though they receive all the love their adoptive parents are capable of. The adopters also bear part of this stigma, as if the stigma of infertility were not enough. Actually adopted children should feel pride at having been 'chosen' and adoptive parents should take pride in the fact that they have opened their hearts and homes.

Up until the 1960s much of the demand for children by infertile couples in Western countries was met by legal placement. Today better contraception, legal abortion, and slow improvements in social support systems for single mothers are reducing the number of children available for adoption in the West, so illegal and private adoptions have increased. Private transactions motivated by good will still persist, although they are frowned on by legal and religious authorities. Most adoptions involve healthy infants, but children with handicaps are also taken. Couples wishing to adopt are now turning to countries outside Europe and North America. With the fall of Eastern Bloc communism, there was a rush for Russian, Polish, and Rumanian children (former Rumanian dictator Nikolai Ceaucescu was accused of masterminding commercial baby-selling projects and using Rumanian women as breeding machines). Now children are being sought from Latin America and Asia, where poverty and lack of family planning facilities make unwanted births a problem.

Nations and cultures differ greatly in their attitudes towards adoption. In Japan adoption is illegal; all births are registered and records kept of family trees. In North Korea families are supposed to remain 'pure', so adoption is not part of the culture, although it is not illegal. South Korea has a record of 'exporting' orphaned children. Other countries consider it acceptable for their children to be adopted at home, but shameful if they are adopted abroad.

Worldwide, there is no shortage of children for adoption. But adopting parents usually want children that will perpetuate certain aspects of themselves, which is why cross-race or handicapped children are less often chosen. Even if parents are not fussy or opt for children of other racial groups, there are sometimes obstacles. For example, white parents wishing to adopt a black baby may find themselves prevented from doing so by black political and social work organizations. Similarly, religious organizations may intervene to prevent the adoption of a child by parents of different beliefs. Gay couples and single people who want to adopt also meet with daunting resistance. This is unfortunate since the larger picture seems to be that there are more children needing love and protection than there are homes to go around. Everyone agrees that the best instition is no match for a good home, but there is less agreement as to what 'a good home' is.

Mixed emotions as Rumanian orphans meet their adoptive parents. Television audiences all over Europe were appalled by the plight of Rumania's 'forgotten children', children vegetating and dying in filthy orphanages. Many opened their hearts and homes to them.

There is now an international convention on cross-border adoption, signed by more than 50 nations. The work of The Hague Conference on Private International Law, it encourages every effort to be made for local adoption before a child is offered to a foreign family; it also calls for efforts to prevent the abduction or sale of children, and trafficking in children.

Surrogate parenting

This highly controversial practice — one woman bearing a baby on behalf of another — is now becoming more common, but it is not new. In *Genesis* we read: 'And Sarai said unto Abram, Behold now, the Lord hath restrained me from bearing. I pray thee, go unto my maid; it may be that I may obtain children by her. And Abram harkened to the voice of Sarai.' Quite recently the newspapers had a field day when two mothers, one in South Africa and one in America, gave birth to triplets and twins on behalf on their own daughters.

Governments and religious bodies generally disapprove of commercial surrogating, and so do many ordinary people. Ellen Goodman, writing for *The Boston Globe*, spoke for a large unaffiliated lobby when she wrote that surrogating for a fee 'encourages people to regard parents as customers rather than caretakers.... We've learned to be wary of people who regard babies as just another product for an eager and vulnerable market.'

In some countries, notably in the United States, paid surrogate parenting is now becoming an institution. Married and single women are offering themselves for hire to conceive and bear children for others, and organizations such as Surrogate Parenting Associates Inc. have been formed to put them in touch with hopeful parents. Dr. Richard Levin of Kentucky claims to be the first physician to have established a surrogate-couple screening and matching system. Even so, laws regarding surrogate parenting vary from state to state. In Britain, surrogate parenting is against the law if a fee is involved. In other words, it is illegal to charge for bearing a baby for someone else. Nevertheless it does happen and cases are known where the surrogate mother has changed her mind and wanted to keep the baby. Other countries have their own laws, but most do not legally permit or forbid surrogating, tacitly allowing what has been going on, without fanfare, since Biblical times.

In themselves the technical advances and administrative procedures that have made it possible to match sperm donors with hopeful mothers, and 'wombs for rent' with hopeful fathers, are commendable. But with these New Age benefits have come some very hoary controversies — religious, moral, social, and sexual. In the past it was not unusual, although not widely announced, for infertile couples, husband and wife together or separately, to arrange for natural insemination. The wish to have a baby overrode the usual taboos about coitus outside marriage. A relative, friend, or willing 'other' either bore the baby or acted as impregnator. One woman I interviewed described her feelings about surrogate fathering like this: 'I was past the age of 30 and didn't see marriage in my future. Yet I very dearly wanted to have a baby and to be a mother, more than I wanted marriage in fact. I also knew who I wanted to be the father. He was married but someone I admired and respected and thought would be ideal. I asked him and he said yes. The insemination was natural.'

There are certainly many men and women willing to offer surrogate services, free or for a price. Surrogate mother Carol Pavek, a midwife with a husband and son, spoke for many women who would like to bear babies for others when she said: 'It would be wonderful to keep having babies without the responsibility of raising them.' Many of the men who donate sperm are medical students, simply because they form the bulk of the healthy male population within easy reach of donor centres.

Should we concern ourselves with the intelligence, morality, and emotional involvement of sperm donors and surrogate mothers, or should we limit our interest to medically significant genetic factors? A student of mine who was a regular donor used to fantasize: 'My progeny are improving the general calibre of the population.' *Folie de grandeur* indeed! He was never the slightest bit concerned about the destiny of his sperm, an attitude common among other donors. However, some donors I have interviewed say they do occasionally think of their 'children', but most of them are not sufficiently uncomfortable with the idea to stop donating. Most admit they would masturbate anyway.

The emotional investment of the surrogate mother, who surrenders the baby she has been carrying for nine months, is easier to empathize with. Elizabeth Kane (a *nom de maternité* used by the first acknowledged surrogate mother in the United States) thinks more attention should be paid to the emotional needs of women like herself: 'We need support groups both during the pregnancy and after we give up our babies' she says. 'The first time I saw the adoptive mother hold the baby it was thrilling. But I also went through depression.... I cried for weeks every Sunday because he was born on a Sunday.'

Psychiatrist Philip J. Parker, who made a study of 125 women before, during, and after their surrogate experience, claims that there is 'no evidence to support the notion that surrogate motherhood with or without a fee leads to serious psychological consequences'.

Since these women embark on pregnancy knowing that they will give up the baby and that, in the meantime, their womb is 'for hire', they consider it 'the couple's baby' rather than their own and so reduce their emotional investment. During pregnancy a surrogate mother may refer to 'their baby' rather than to 'my baby'.

How do surrogate mothers themselves say they feel? One woman, who has two children of her own from a dissolved marriage, put her feelings like this: 'It's a business endeavour that satisfied monetary needs and emotional needs.... I have very easy pregnancies and enjoy the idea of being able to provide for a couple that can't have a child by themselves. It's almost as if I'm being paid to be who I am and I can't thing of anything more ideal.'

Currently, in the United States, surrogate mothers can claim up to $20,000 (about £15,000) plus expenses for their nine-month assignment. In Britain, where surrogate mothering is illegal, charges vary considerably and so a figure cannot be put on what 'undercover' surrogate mothers charge. But it is not illegal for British surrogates to give birth outside the United Kingdom and give up the baby there, or for them to be paid for a diary or medical record kept during their pregnancy (rather than for the pregnancy *per se*).

To couples who hire surrogate mothers the cost, including the surrogate's fees and expenses, and the fees of the physicians and lawyers involved, is high, sometimes nearly double what the surrogate mother receives. The expense involved in IVF or AI is also high. Should the possibility of having a child by either of these methods or through surrogating go to the highest bidder, or to those likely to be the best parents? Should governments be persuaded to foot the bill? Should the children born by means of such arrangements be permitted to know the identity of their biological father or their surrogate mother? 'I see no reason for anonymity', says Dr. S.J. Behrman, writing for the prestigious *New England Journal of Medicine*. 'It's really only to protect the husband's vanity.' However, not everyone believes it is quite so simple.

The bond between partners

The marriage bed cannot for long, or happily, accommodate two lovers and a doctor who monitors their performance. If the partners see their acts of affection and play as acts of work, their relationship is almost bound to suffer. If they see their attempts to reproduce as opportunities to express their desire for each other, as expressions of love, they may achieve their goal without emotional damage and even find that the bond between them has been strengthened. Some couples who have tried for children and failed also say that the effort involved has brought them closer together. For those who are successful the effort almost always seems worthwhile in retrospect.

There are many legal and ethical problems attached to all the methods — AI, IVF, surrogate parenting — I have been talking about, and a lot more could be said about them. But to infertile couples who feel that full pleasure and satisfaction cannot be gained from marriage unless it includes children, they are secondary. For many people children are a unique and irreplaceable means of affirming manhood and womanhood.

A mother and son visit a fertility shrine in Northern Honshu, Japan. Fertility shrines are common all over the Far East. There is even one in the garden of the Hilton Hotel in Bangkok.

Chapter 14

Watch out

Much of the time sex is pleasurable and rewarding, but everyone knows that it has a darker side. Various diseases, some causing severe physical and mental distress and even death, are closely related to sexual behaviour. Many people react to this hard fact by refusing to think about the possibility of disease until they are personally infected or affected — a typical human trait perhaps, but one which aggravates the problem. Prevention rather than cure is in everyone's best interest. Not all sex-related diseases can yet be cured, but most can be controlled.

Sexually transmitted diseases (STDs) are those diseases that are passed directly from one person to another through sexual contact. They include those ailments traditionally called venereal diseases (VD) as well as many others. Usually it is possible to trace these diseases back to a specific sexual contact or time, but sexual activity is not the only way of acquiring them — I am thinking here of babies infected by mothers during delivery or nursing, haemophiliacs and others who receive tainted blood, and drug users who share needles.

There are also diseases which, though not contagious as far as we know or specifically related to sexual behaviour, affect the sexual organs or parts of the body directly involved in sexual play — breast, uterine, and testicular cancers, for example. Early diagnosis and treatment give the greatest chance of cure. Sexual ability and desire can also be undermined by chronic illnesses such as diabetes, heart disease, and arthritis, or by fatigue, pain, and lack of energy, whatever their cause.

Opposite: AIDS quilts on display in Hawaii. Similar quilts, with panels stitched by the families or friends of people who have died of AIDS, are being made all over the world. By the end of this century few families will not have been touched by AIDS. Syphilis was similarly prevalent from the early 16th century right up until the 1950s.

Sexually transmitted diseases

Venereal diseases are not new. Both syphilis and gonorrhea are mentioned in writings from Ancient Egypt and China and also in the Bible. In medieval times syphilis was known as the 'great pox', to distinguish it from smallpox, which was considered a minor problem by comparison. At different times syphilis became known as the French, German, and Italian disease and was routinely treated, usually ineffectively, with preparations containing mercury. Caused by a microorganism called *Treponema pallidum* which enters the body through a mucous membrane or a break in the skin, it causes skin sores and rashes. In the long term it attacks the brain and spinal cord, causing brain damage and paralysis. Until the widespread use of penicillin in the 1950s more people were committed to mental institutions because of the ravages of syphilis than from any other cause. Penicillin and other antibiotics have now brought the disease under control.

Gonorrhea, caused by a bacterium (*Neisseria gonorrhoeae*) that invades the mucous membranes, has also yielded to antibiotics. Though not as devastating or potentially lethal as syphilis, untreated gonorrhea can lead to infertility, arthritis, and stricture of the urethra, making urination painful or impossible. At one time it was the most common cause of congenital blindness: the bacterium entered the

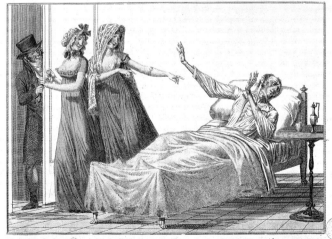

Suite Effrayante des Fréquentations du Sérail

Se Vend à Paris chez Martinet Rue du Coq St Honoré

In this early 18th-century cartoon a patient in the advanced stages of syphilis swears off all future contact with the fair sex.

mucous membranes of the eyes as the baby passed through the birth canal, causing blindness soon after. For this reason babies' eyes are usually prophylactically treated with antibiotics at birth. Delivery by Caesarean section prevents infection.

Recent medical advances have checked some of the worst effects of sexually transmissible diseases, but the contemporary picture is far from rosy. According to the British Medical Association there are about 0.5 million new cases of venereal disease in Britain every year — a new patient applies for treatment every two minutes. In the United States, with its much larger population, there are 10 million new STD cases a year, and this figure has stayed more or less the same for the last decade despite the higher media profile of STDs. In 1992 the World Health Organization estimated that there are some 250 million new STD cases a year worldwide. In the United States there are something like 2 million cases of gonorrhea annually, and another 2 million of gonorrhea-like disease, mainly among 15- to 30-year-olds. Elsewhere in the world venereal disease may not affect such a high proportion of teenagers and young adults, but it is on the increase. A particular problem at present is the prevalence of several strains of gonorrhea that can be treated but not cured. These strains have developed resistance to the present array of antibiotics. Also worrying are the climbing statistics for chlamydia (*Chlamydia trachomatis*) infections, venereal warts (*Condyloma acuminatum*), and hepatitis B. Chlamydia infects between 3 and 4 million Americans every year, venereal warts about 1 million, and hepatitis B about 300,000. Overshadowing all of these are AIDS and herpes. In short, in the last decade STDs have been thrust into personal lives and consciousness as never before.

A late 1940s VD poster. Unfortunately gonorrhea and syphilis are still with us despite effective and readily available medical treatment.

In men the first symptoms of gonorrhea and chlamydia, among the most common STDs, are pain or itching during urination and a discharge of pus from the penis, or pain and swelling in the testicles. These occur within three to ten days of infection. Most women who are infected with gonorrhea or chlamydia have no noticeable symptoms; only a minority experience abnormal vaginal discharges, burning pain on urination, lower abdominal pain, bleeding between menstrual periods, or low-grade fever. Symptomatic or symptomless, however, both types of infection can lead to pelvic inflammatory disease (PID), which silently causes sterility by scarring and closing the oviducts. Between 10 and 15 per cent of men with gonorrhea or chlamydia have no obvious symptoms either, although the results can be equally serious. Both diseases can be passed on, knowingly or not, to new sexual partners. Three out of ten respondents to *Playboy*'s 1982 survey admitted to having had intercourse knowing they had an infection but without telling their partners. Non-disclosure of HIV infection may be at a similar level. A 1992 study of men infected with HIV (Human Immunodeficiency Virus, the virus that causes AIDS) investigated at a public clinic in Los Angeles found that 20 per cent had not used condoms or told their partners about their illness.

Although relatively rare in the past, chlamydia has spread rapidly in recent times. Estimates are that between 10 and 15 per cent of Americans between the ages of 15 and 30 contract the disease every year. These figures are duplicated in both developing and developed countries. The People's Republic of China, for example, unofficially acknowledges a 10 per cent rate of infection. Ten years ago chlamydia was considered unusual and difficult to detect, a 'rogue' type of urethritis. Now tests which identify chlamydial infection are readily available, simple, and not painful. The same applies to gonorrhea. Treatment for both diseases is also simple.

Herpes is a viral disease that periodically produces painful crops of genital blisters. Not being a bacterium, it is not treatable with penicillin and other antibiotics. Between 20 and 30 million people in the United States today (between 1 in 7 and 1 in 12 people), have the disease, which appears to be spreading at the rate of 500,000 new cases a year. These numbers, like many others in this chapter, are approximate because few governments require such diseases to be reported to a central statistics bureau. Syphilis, gonorrhea, and AIDS, however, *are* notifiable. Unfortunately, not all physicians comply with reporting requirements.

Sexually transmitted hepatitis is particularly prevalent among the homosexual community. One in two gay males tested in various clinics in the United States was found to have hepatitis. Greater use of anal intercourse also means that, as a group, gays are at greater risk of diseases which attack the digestive system than of those which attack the genitals. In the West the incidence of AIDS, though not confined to gays, has been higher among male homosexuals than among any other affected group.

HIV and AIDS

'Epidemic — the mysterious and deadly disease called AIDS may be the public health threat of the century. How did it start? Can it be stopped?' This was the headline on the cover of the April 18, 1983, issue of *Newsweek* magazine. In February 1983, in the gay newspaper *New York Native*, lead writer Larry Kramer warned, in an article prefaced with equally large headlines: 'If this article doesn't scare the shit out of you we're in real trouble. If this article doesn't rouse you to anger, fury, rage and action, gay men have no future on this earth. Our continued existence depends on how angry you can get.' Headlines in the 1990s are no less alarming: 'World Health Organization predicts 40 million AIDS cases by the end of the century', 'AIDS is wiping out South African workers'....

In 1981, with the help of Dr. James Curran, who now heads the United States government's effort to combat AIDS, I published a chapter on sexually transmitted diseases in an American Medical Association handbook on sexuality. I said not a word about AIDS, which was not reported upon by Michael Gottlieb and colleagues at UCLA until the summer of that year. At that time it was still a disease without a name. It soon became obvious that AIDS, like syphilis in the days before antibiotics, would be the new 'great pox'. In 1985 I founded the Hawaii AIDS Task Group which attempts to originate and coordinate ways of dealing with the social, psychological, and medical issues surrounding the disease. Its scope now extends to all public and private agencies dealing with AIDS in Hawaii.

AIDS (Acquired Immunodeficiency Syndrome) is the end stage of HIV (Human Immunodeficiency Virus) disease. HIV-1 is the most common virus involved, but there are others (e.g. HIV-2). The interval between being infected with HIV and developing the first symptoms of HIV disease may be 10 years or more, and AIDS may not develop for years after that. Usually health authorities record only cases of full-blown AIDS, but these are only the visible part of the iceberg. For every individual above the waterline, as it were, there are probably five to ten HIV-positive individuals below it. These individuals will get AIDS sooner or later.

AIDS became the label used for a group of symptoms seen in a number of men who first came under observation in 1979. In just over 10 years, from 1981 to 1991, AIDS attacked more than 200,000 people, mostly male, in the United States alone. Between 1981 and 1985–86 the number of victims in the United States, Canada, and Europe more or less doubled every year, then began to taper off to a much lower rate of increase. There were 33,000 new cases of AIDS in the United States in 1991. The United Kingdom reported 510 cases in 1986 and 833 in 1989. France reported 2,004 cases in 1987 and 2,828 in 1989, partly a reflection of the high level of contact between France and Africa. Actually it is the *rate* of increase which is more telling than the actual numbers. In Europe the countries with the highest AIDS rates to date are Switzerland, France, and Spain, but this may be a reflection of willingness and ability to report rather than a sign of greater incidence. The number of AIDS cases is also a function of testing. No testing means no AIDS cases to report. Until the late 1980s even the African nations most impacted by the disease denied its prevalence.

The doubling progression of AIDS initially seen in America and Europe has continued longer in Central Africa, where the disease first attacted worldwide attention. Did the disease originate in Africa? There is a theory that it passed to humans from green monkeys eaten for food. Equally unprovable is the gossip that it was developed as a biological warfare weapon by American or Soviet scientists (take your pick!) or as a vaccine for animals or humans which somehow went wrong. As with most other infectious diseases, no one knows. No one wants to accept the honour.

In Africa, as elsewhere in the less medically developed world, accurate figures for AIDS are difficult to obtain; they are seen as a public embarrassment and as a hindrance to

LE GRAND MAITRE FRANCO
INTERPELLE LA SOCIETE
DANS
"ATTENTION NA SIDA"

'Attention na SIDA' (Watch out for AIDS), a record by Zairean pop star Franco. So far, governments excepted, the music and entertainment communities have made the greatest contribution to AIDS awareness worldwide.

tourism and foreign investment. Nevertheless some data are available. One study of outpatients and 'healthy' adults at a rural clinic in Uganda found that the percentage of those infected with HIV rose from 1 to 14 per cent between 1984 and 1986. In Zaire a study among employees in a hospital in Kinshasa showed a rise from 6 to 9 per cent over the same period. According to a newspaper article by Leon Delport, a South African government health expert, unless dramatic action is taken 'all Africans will have the disease by 1995 and half will be dead by 2003'. Some of the gloomiest predictions for the continent have come from South African economist Keith Edelston, author of *AIDS: Countdown to Doomsday.* Why the rapid spread in Africa? Multiple wives and mistresses are common among all religious groups in Africa — in Ghana, for example, polygamy is practised by 27 per cent of Roman Catholics, 29 per cent of other Christians, 45 per cent of Muslims, and 45 percent of traditional religionists. Add to this the widespread prevalence of genital sores and ulcers, poor hygiene, prostitution, reuse of injection needles, and lack of sterile conditions even in hospitals, and opportunities and routes for viral infection are very numerous indeed.

In Asia and parts of Latin America, where it has a firm hold, AIDS also seems to have a doubling progression. Not surprisingly the numbers for China and India are in keeping with their huge populations; Bombay hospitals now refuse to admit any more AIDS patients. In a slum prenatal clinic in Haiti in 1988 it was found that 15 per cent of women were infected. In the same year about 30 per cent of homosexual men in Guadalajara, Mexico, were found to be infected. In the absence of widespread education programs, sterile medical procedures, and rigorous testing of blood supplies the poorest countries in Asia and Latin America will be devastated by AIDs within the next two decades.

In the United States, Britain, and Northern Europe AIDS has been primarily transmitted via homosexual and bisexual activities (mostly through being the 'receiver' during anal sex). In Southern Europe, Africa, and Asia heterosexual and bisexual activities (vaginal, oral, and anal sex) mainly acount for its spread. As with most other STDs, the female is more vulnerable than the male because she receives the ejaculate which contains the virus. One can acquire the virus from vaginal secretions during oral sex, but this is less likely. It is now obvious that AIDS does not distinguish between homosexual and heterosexual. It is an individual's behaviour, not his or her sexual preference, that determines risk.

Injected drug use and contaminated blood have also been potent vectors of AIDS. In the former Soviet Union and in Rumania unsterilized medical equipment spread AIDS among hundreds of hospitalized infants. HIV-contaminated needles used for injecting illegal drugs are even more noted for transmitting the disease. More than 70 per cent of intravenous (IV) drug users in Milan, Italy, almost 60 per cent in New York City, and between 40 and

50 per cent in Bangkok were HIV-positive in surveys done between 1986 and 1989. In Brazil the number of infected IV drug users rose from 3 to 13 per cent in just one year, 1988-89. HIV-infected drug users often infect non-drug using and unsuspecting partners. This is now the most common way for babies to get HIV; their mothers are drug users or the partners of drug users. Also, among the drug-using community sex is often traded for crack and other drugs, putting another multiplier into the HIV transmission equation. It is a vicious and deadly cycle. In an attempt to break it some authorities now offer to exchange dirty needles for clean ones. In fact Hawaii was the first American state to introduce an exchange program, which has successfully put the brakes on the rise of infection among IV drug users.

Blood supplies were not monitored for HIV until 1985, when accurate and sensitive tests first became available (actually these tests are for antibodies to the virus, not for the virus itself). By then haemophiliacs and others all over the world had received untested and untreated blood; between 30 and 70 per cent of them now have AIDS. In many parts of the world blood screening is still seen as a luxury, but until blood for surgery and other uses is monitored and properly treated HIV will continue to spread by this route. The innocent recipient of a transfusion may be infected and spread the infection to others for more than a decade before he or she suspects anything. Even when testing is available, many people who suspect that they or their loved ones have the virus would rather not know ('What can I do anyway? There's no cure for it, is there?', 'I couldn't live with the knowledge', 'Someone's bound to find out and then everyone will know').

Youngsters infected from received blood have special problems. Often their parents, even if they know, shy away from telling them because it means explaining 'the facts of life', what AIDS is and how it is spread, and talking about the possibility of early death. All of this cuts deeply into the energy and optimism which a teenager needs to make the step from child to adult. Secrecy also endangers the youngster's future partners.

Given the numbers of people affected and the nature of sexual epidemiology, it was inevitable that AIDS should spread into the heterosexual community in the West. A person who has AIDS loses his or her natural ability to fight invading organisms. Bacteria which would normally be disposed of by the immune system go unchallenged. Various types of pneumonia and cancer (such as Kaposi's syndrome), and other rare or highly serious conditions, easily take hold. While the adult herpes sufferer, in spite of painful and occasionally disfiguring rashes and ulcers, can be fairly sure that he or she will survive, the outlook for AIDS sufferers is unrelievedly bleak at present.

The symptoms of AIDS are not very specific. They include recurrent fever, fatigue, unexplained and rapid weight loss, swollen lymph glands, recurrent headaches, chills, and general aches and pains. Since these symptoms can accompany many other conditions, from flu to cancer, the best policy is 'When in doubt, check it out.' The HIV antibody test is a simple procedure which requires a small blood sample for analysis. Saliva tests are also being developed. If you intend to get pregnant and have the slightest grounds for suspicion, have a test. About one in three babies of HIV-infected women also have the virus.

The standard (ELISA) HIV test will show 'positive' or 'negative'. HIV-positive means that your body had produced antibodies to the virus, so the virus is probably present in your blood; I say 'probably' because sometimes the test is wrong. HIV-negative means that you have not developed antibodies so probably have not been infected; here too the test may be wrong, particularly if the infection is at a very early stage. As with any other test, errors in testing technique can give misleading results. If there is any doubt about the results of a standard HIV test, it should be retaken a few weeks later. There is another test, the Western blot test, which is more precise and can be used to confirm or disprove the standard test. Many people, whether they are positive or negative, like to take a repeat test for peace of mind. HIV tests are private and confidential and can be done by physicians or clinics, and all good test sites also offer counselling. Testing is free in most clinics in the United States and Britain, but it can be very expensive if done by private clinics and practitioners.

If you have been taking risks, a negative test is a huge relief. That you came through OK

The number of children with AIDS is increasing. About 1 in 3 children born to HIV-positive mothers contracts the disease.

I HAVE AiDS
PLease hug me

I can't make you sick

J.Keeler

AIDS HOT LINE FOR KIDS
CENTER FOR ATTITUDINAL HEALING
19 MAIN ST, TIBURON, CA 94920, (415) 435-5022

Fans say farewell to Queen lead singer and AIDS victim Freddie Mercury at a memorial concert in the spring of 1992.

does not mean that you are immune, merely that you were lucky. Use that sense of relief to modify your sexual behaviour before HIV modifies it for you.

A positive test means that you are infected, not that life is over. Many good years of life remain to be lived even without treatment. The immediate difference is that you are now capable of infecting others. All previous partners should be notified and advised that they should be tested. Present and future partners must also be told so that appropriate precautions can be taken. Condoms or dental dams (thin plastic wrap or latex squares to cover the vulva during oral sex) should be used in any encounter where there is a potential transfer of semen or vaginal secretions.

As far as we know at present, all individuals who test HIV-positive will eventually develop AIDS. Cases of spontaneous cure have been reported, but have not been substantiated. But AIDS may not show itself until 10 or more years after the infection has been acquired, or after a positive test. When the disease was first being studied, it was conceptualized as a regular progression from asymptomatic HIV infection to AIDS illness, AIDS Related Complex (ARC), and finally 'full blown' AIDS. Such distinctions now seem less helpful; it is now obvious that HIV disease can take many paths towards AIDS, whose definition has been changing. The United States Centers for Disease Control (CDC) now define AIDS as an infectious disease caused by the Human Immunodeficiency Virus which reduces the CD-4 T series of 'helper' cells of the immune system to concentrations below $200/mm^3$. The virus actually targets and destroys these cells, which help the body to fight off infection. For many reasons, this definition is not universally accepted. The World Health Organization and the European Centre for the Epidemiological Monitoring of AIDS, for instance, have their own definitions. But however it is defined, life does not end with a diagnosis of AIDS. With good health care and virus-fighting drugs like AZT (zidovudine), people with AIDS can live for years. In medically advanced countries HIV disease is no longer seen as an acute illness, but as a chronic condition requiring long-term management.

People with HIV or AIDS suffer from great depression and anxiety. Like people with cancer and other life-threatening conditions, they are especially vulnerable to quacks ready to sell false remedies and false hope. In many towns and cities there are PWA (Persons/People With AIDS) groups who provide emotional and informational support. As one person notified of being HIV-positive said to me: 'The counselling I received was crucial. I learned how to live, rather than looking forward to how to die.' Also crucial is a knowledgeable and sympathetic physician. Unfortunately there are still too many health workers who are frightened of and ill-informed about the disease.

The fear factor

Does fear of venereal disease prevent or change sexual activity? Yes and no. Herpes and gonorrhea were both known to the Ancient Greeks. The Roman emperor Tiberius, in an attempt to stem herpes (probably the non-genital kind, better known as cold sores), outlawed kissing in public. He suspected kissing had something to do with the spread of the disease. But prohibition and the possibility of infection are only deterrents for some people. Fear may be a factor in the incidence of AIDS levelling off, and much research does shows that, for a majority, fear and awareness of AIDS and other STDs are causing them to be more cautious, but fear itself is often not enough. In the opinion of AIDS educator Jo Kenny, humour/ridicule is also a very effective weapon in the fight against AIDS. Whatever it takes to make people change their behaviour is valid.

As with cigarettes and car seat belts, there will always be a minority of people willing to gamble with their lives. When it comes to STDs, a crucial factor seems to be how fastidious one is about health in general and how one weighs instant gratification against long-term risk. The flesh is notoriously weak. The diaries of James Boswell, biographer of the great Dr. Johnson, tell us that he suffered from gonorrhea at least a dozen times. He desperately tried to be selective about his partners, choosing 'perfect, sure people'. He also tried using condoms. But there was no cure for gonorrhea in the eighteenth century and the malady kept recurring. I remember that when I was in the army one soldier in my unit repeatedly got gonorrhea from the same woman. With penicillin an ever-ready cure, he thought it no more serious than catching a cold. Indeed familiarity is part of the problem. Gonorrhea is somehow neutralized and made acceptable by referring to it as 'drip', 'gleet', or 'clap'. Syphilis becomes less alarming when vaguely referred to as 'syph' or VD. Yet both are much worse and much more serious than a cold.

Herpes and AIDS are more difficult to sanitize and trivialize in this way. In fact they seem to be changing attitudes towards STDs in general. The motivation for this change is almost certainly fear or, more correctly in the case of AIDS, terror. People are becoming more cautious, taking longer between meeting and bedding. Baths where gay sex was common have closed and cruising is being done more warily. Word is spreading from those who are afflicted that sexually transmitted

Preparations containing mercury (calomel, for example) were once used to treat many ailments, including syphilis. Mercury certainly poisons disease organisms in the body, but it also does fatal damage to the brain, nervous system, and kidneys. It is five times more toxic than lead.

AIDS · SIDA

**SIK IA AIDS I KILIM MAN.
I NO GAT MERESIN.
SIK IA I PAS LONG TAEM WE
MAN I SLIP WETEM WOMAN.
LUKAOT !**

BLOKEM SIK IA AIDS

1. Stap kwaet wetem woman o man blong yu nomo.
2. Sipos yu no save gud laef blong wan fren, man i mas putum kondom (o plastik) fastaem.

• Helt Edukesen, Vanuatu.

AIDS has reached the island communities of Melanesia in the Western Pacific. This poster, in pidgin, appeared in Vanuatu. Roughly translated, it says: 'AIDS can kill you. There is no medicine for it...look out. Stay with your own man or woman...wear a condom.' AIDS is configured into a shark, a threat all islanders know well.

diseases can be debilitating, painful, and even lethal.

It is not my wish to encourage a negative attitude towards sex but to demonstrate that sex has certain risks attached to it. There are simple methods of minimizing these risks, generally referred to as 'safer sex' practices, and various steps that can be taken if a problem already exists.

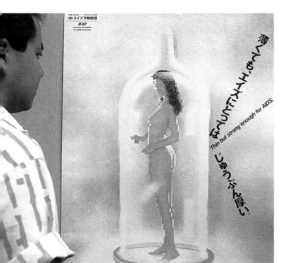

Women's groups in Japan objected to this AIDS prevention poster. Beyond the overt 'wear a condom' message, they detected the implication that condoms protect men from women. Might they not also protect women from men?

Taking precautions

While most people who are sexually active worry about getting AIDS and take preventive measures, the probability of acquiring some other sexually transmitted infection is much higher. Fortunately, the measures that protect against AIDS also protect against most other STDs. An ounce of prevention is worth a pound of cure.

Obviously sexual partners should be chosen with care. If you have reason or need to be suspicious, try to discuss the subject. Be open about your own anxieties and encourage the other person to be open as well. After all, if you are prepared to share your body, why not share your concern about its health? To broach the subject you might say, for example, 'I had a complete check-up last week and was glad to find I didn't have VD or AIDS. Have you ever been checked?' or 'I had VD several years ago and had to give up sex until they cured it. I wouldn't want anyone to pass it on to me again.' Or with a half smile you might ask: 'Do you have anything I can catch?' The actual words are less important than the message.

Check that your intended partner has no obvious signs of infection — unusual rashes, blisters, ulcers, discharges, odours. The best place to do this, and the most fun, is in the bath or shower. Urinate and wash your genitals after coitus. Although soap and water are not wholly effective against disease, they can do no harm and may do some good. If your suspicions persist, postpone genital contact — have a diplomatic headache, think of a reason why you have to be somewhere else right away, or simply say no. This may nip a new relationship in the bud, but you won't end up with gonorrhea, herpes, or AIDS.

If you decide to go ahead, protect yourself. Male or female condoms used with vaginal foams or jellies with nonoxynol are not 100 per cent effective, but nearly so, and should be used with every new partner. In such instances their purpose is protection from disease, so they must be in place whether other contraceptive methods are used or not. Unless you know that you and your partner are disease-free, anal sex should be avoided.

There is no doubt that being wary and taking precautions interferes with spontaneity, passion, and fantasy, but contracting an unwelcome disease is a much worse interference. Be careful with any new partner, especially if you know he or she has had a lot of short-lived or anonymous relationships. Usually those whose sexual style puts them most at risk of disease are those least likely to take precautions. To be concerned about the possibility of disease hardly fits the 'cool' approach to sex that teenagers, macho males, swingers, and promiscuous homosexuals like to project. The risk of disease is accepted as the price of sexual 'freedom'. And the popular belief that male and female prostitutes

Prostitute 'cages' in Bombay, India. The bars are to keep men out rather than women in. Note the openness and the children wandering about. Many men in India, especially those who leave their families at home in order to find work in the cities, visit prostitutes. Prostitution and drug use are major vectors of AIDS in India.

have regular check-ups and treatment for STDs is rarely true. The nature of their work and, in the Third World, their lack of education make them highly likely to be reservoirs of disease. In the West prostitutes usually insist upon condoms for their customers (but not for their regular partners). Even with regular check-ups, anyone who has sex with many partners can become infected between check-ups and infect others. The odds are against anyone who promiscuously rides the sexual merry-go-round.

Too many people are fatalists when it comes to STDs. There is, for example, a proven hepatitis B vaccine which is offered free or inexpensively in the United States and recommended by the CDC for all sexually active people with more than one partner. Fewer than 1 per cent of those at risk have taken advantage of this offer. If and when an AIDS vaccine is perfected, what will the take-up rate be? And many studies have shown that condom use is inconsistent even among those who know about and recognize the risks of STDs and AIDS. Don't be one of them. The strongest incentive to use safer-sex practices is knowing someone who has died of AIDS. Don't wait for that.

Treatment and help

First of all, not all genital rashes and odours or vaginal discharges are venereal in nature. Most of them readily respond to soap and water. If they don't, consult your physician; prescribed medication will usually solve the problem.

If you suspect you might have been infected, go and see your doctor right away. Don't wait for visible symptoms to appear, and do refrain from intercourse until you know you are in the clear. Your partner deserves the care and respect you would apply to yourself. Tests for STDs are painless, at most requiring a blood sample. Medical staff are not there to make judgements. In the long run you will save a lot of time and anguish if you act early on well founded suspicions. If you have a reasonably active sex life, especially if it involves frequent changes of partner, make sure that any regular health checks include tests for STDs, including HIV. Such tests are not done routinely. Indeed in many countries they must be asked for specifically. In the United States, for example, it is *illegal* (for reasons of confidentiality) to test for STDs or HIV without specific permission. Generally these tests, and treatment if needed, are available from public and private clinics. In the United Kingdom, which still adheres to the Venereal Disease Act of 1917, it is illegal for anyone, including private STD clinics, to advertise these services.

How do you tell a current or prospective partner that you have something he or she could catch? Naturally much depends on the nature of the relationship and the level of intimacy and communication between you. As one herpes sufferer remarked to me: 'It's a funny topic to bring up early in a relationship. But if anything is going to come out of it — and I only go to bed with people who have that potential — I think, well, better safe than sorry and better early than late. So I tell them, usually before we get close to the bedroom. I would feel terribly guilty otherwise. So far two guys have said no thanks and bowed out, and two have said it's OK. So far neither has caught herpes from me, but we always use condoms and we never make love when the disease is active.'

In some countries there are contact groups where those with specific diseases can meet socially and sexually. This is particularly the case with herpes and HIV infection, since both are lifelong conditions. In stark contrast, there are places, such as the former Soviet Union, Cuba, and some states in America, where sexual activity between a PWA and someone uninfected is illegal and subject to imprisonment. In Cuba, HIV testing of all adults is mandatory and anyone found to be infected is put into quarantine, where he or she is separated from family and friends as well as the general public.

There is no doubt that disease can act as a brake on casual or impromptu sex. An STD introduced into an established relationship will certainly put it to the test, but it may deepen intimacy and lead to alternative expressions of sexual love.

STDs are often accompanied by fear, guilt, and frustration, not only as reactions to the disease itself but because infection means making changes in social and sexual behaviour. Psychological help can be just as essential to coping and recovery as medical help. Individual conselling is one option. Self-help groups (such as the herpes sufferers' group HELP in the United States, or PWA groups) are another. At group sessions participants can express their real feelings, get information, learn how others cope, and gradually regain their self-esteem and sexual confidence. For many individuals, STDs severely curtail sexual activity, whether with a regular partner or not, and depression and bottled-up aggression are common.

Ethics on trial

STDs still carry a stigma. Though intended to be more 'neutral' than the older acronym VD, STDs still attract moral judgements, spoken or implied. AIDS is often used as a metaphor for everything that moralists consider bad. PWAs are seen not as people who happen to have AIDS but as walking examples of disease. AIDS and STDs in general have infused sex with worrying thoughts about the past and future (the sexual past of one's partner, the possibility of death in the future) rather than enjoyment in the here and now.

Embarrassment, guilt, and secrecy hamper open discussion of STDs. For centuries the preferred method of control has been disapproval and public moralizing against any sexual activity outside marriage. With the increase in non-monogamous relationships and prostitution during and after World War I, the emphasis veered towards acceptance of a wider range of sexual behaviours and trying to prevent disease. Condoms were advertised 'for the prevention of disease' (there was no mention of their possible use as contraceptives) and people were warned to be choosy about their sexual partners. There were public health drives against prostitutes as 'reservoirs of venereal disease'. Then, as antibiotics came into use, the emphasis changed again, from prevention to treatment. Many people now see the central problem not as an ethical one but as one of encouraging those at risk to come forward for diagnosis, treatment, and advice on how to prevent the spread of STDs.

Of all the issues I've considered in sexology in years of study — rape, pornography, sexual harassment, EMS, abortion — none are so beset with thickets of ethical controversy as STDs and AIDS. Here are just a few of them.

Should people be tested for HIV without their knowledge or permission? Many health care workers want to test everyone admitted to hospital, for example. Not everyone can deal with the knowledge that they are HIV-positive, so there would have to be more extensive counselling services. Also, what forms of discrimination are likely to follow from compulsory testing?

Kimberly Bergalis, seen here on American television, contracted HIV from her dentist and died of AIDS at the age of 23. She was the first person known to have been infected in this way. Various consumer groups have lobbied Congress to make HIV testing of health workers mandatory, but in statistical terms health workers are more likely to be infected by patients than vice versa.

Should health care workers regularly or occasionally exposed to patients with STDs/AIDS be required to take periodic tests? Health care workers say no, but their fearful patients say yes. The cost would be great and the benefits probably small. The money might be better spent on education, research, or treatment programs.

Should health care workers — whether they are physicians, dentists, nurses, or social workers — have the right to choose *not* to work with STD/AIDS patients? And what about janitorial staff? Shouldn't they have the same right?

Should sexual partners be warned that their partner is infected? If doctor/patient confidentiality is breached, fewer people will go for tests and check-ups. Confidentiality is fundamental in any doctor/patient relationship and, except in clearly defined circumstances, cannot be broken. Yet if the patient will not tell his or her partner, who will? Must everyone continually use safer sex, even within a 'monogamous' relationship? How do you tell a regular partner that you want to use a condom when that is not your usual method of contraception?

Should people with HIV disease be isolated or quarantined? They are in Cuba. Where should the quarantine facilities be, how big should they be, and who should pay for them? Is quarantine the best way of controlling the spread of HIV infection?

Should we make a distinction between 'innocent' and 'guilty' victims? The Japanese don't include haemophiliacs with HIV disease in their AIDS statistics. Babies infected at birth or hospital patients receiving transfusions do not knowingly put themselves at risk, but neither do many sexually active people (the typical American woman with AIDS has had fewer than three partners). Does it matter whether HIV infection is acquired through heterosexual or homosexual sex? Surely everyone who is ill, no matter how they became ill, should be treated with the same compassion?

How much of a nation's resources should be directed toward research and treatment?

Should STDs and AIDS have the same priority as heart disease, cancer, and diabetes? These diseases are stable in terms of number of people affected, but STDs and AIDS are increasing yearly (in the United States the number of AIDS deaths used to be compared with the number of bike accidents; now the comparison is with the number of deaths from car accidents). Should insurance companies have a say in how such resources are spent?

Should prostitution be legalized in the interests of public health? Should prostitutes be licensed, inspected, and have compulsory check-ups? (Between 1864 and 1886 prostitution in 18 military and naval towns in England and Wales was controlled by the government under the Contagious Diseases Act. Italy had government-regulated brothels until 1958; by 1960 the syphilis infection rate was double what it was before prostitution was made illegal.)

Lastly, why do people persist in believing that AIDS can be transmitted by insects, touch, dirty clothes, contaminated food, casual contact, swimming pools, or by *donating* blood? None of this is true.

These are questions that are being asked in almost every country in the world. Answers to them must come from the best minds in government, medicine, science, ethics, the humanities, and religion.

Immediately, in my view, the wisest social response to the rising incidence of STDs would be a better level of public education. Until something better comes along, education is our vaccine. The coverage that television, radio, and newspapers give to other public health issues such as smoking and drinking should also be given to STDs, and their prevention, detection, and treatment. I would advocate the slogan 'Cool to care, risky to dare, sexy to be aware'. Individual responsibility should be strongly stressed — the individual may succeed where the forces of religion, law, and public health have failed. At the same time more funds should be made available for research and treatment.

Cancer and sex

There are a number of cancers which affect the sexual organs, but as far as we know they cannot be passed from person to person by sexual or non-sexual contact. Nor is it possible to predict which individuals are most at risk. Only cervical cancer in women has been related to any particular type or frequency of sexual behaviour. There is a correlation with frequent coitus with many different partners from an early age, and also evidence that the herpes or wart (papilloma) virus harboured in the foreskin smegma of uncircumcised men may trigger carcinogenic change. Careful hygiene and the use of condoms are sensible preventives.

Worldwide, about 1 in every 10 women now develops breast cancer (about 1 in 9 in Britain and the United States). This rate has risen dramatically in the last decade, but we do not know why. Some researchers believe pollutants or high-fat diets are to blame. Whatever the cause, a condition that affects so many women, and increasing numbers of them, demands urgent action. Women and their supporters must encourage governments to make breast cancer research and treatment a priority. Options for women with detected breast cancer are limited. Surgery is the solution most frequently recommended. Thousands of women, fearful that the cancer will spread, still opt for mastectomy, which removes the entire breast, rather than the less radical, breast-saving 'lumpectomy' which removes just the tumour and surrounding tissue. In this they are often encouraged by physicians and surgeons. There is a need for more information and more thorough discussion in this whole area. After surgery the anti-oestrogen drug tamoxifen (also helpful in heart disease and osteoporosis) is usually given; this significantly reduces the chances of cancer spreading to the unaffected breast or to other sites. RU-486 may also have a role to play here.

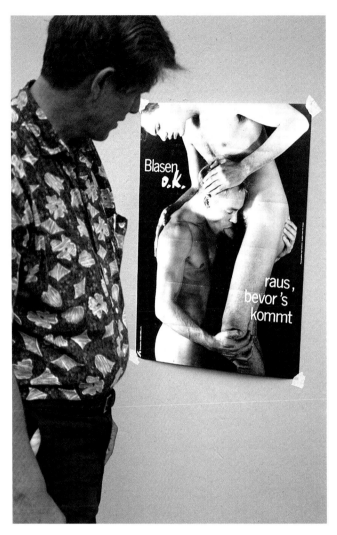

This German AIDS prevention poster aimed at the gay community was strongly criticized for being too blatant and for giving misleading information. The slogan says: 'It's OK to suck, but pull out before you come.' While the rate of transmission of HIV infection from oral sex is low, it is still possible.

219

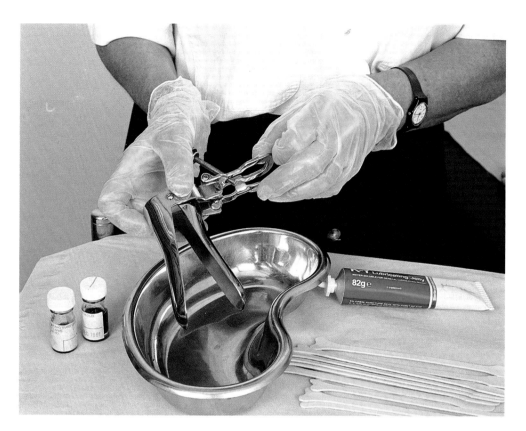

Apparatus used to take a cervical sample or smear. Many different types of speculum are used to hold the walls of the vagina apart so that the cervix can be visualized. This is a duck bill or Cusco speculum. Warmed and coated with lubricating jelly, it is inserted into the vagina in the closed position. A smear (mucus containing a few cells) is then taken from the vagina or cervix with a cotton swab or spatula, and examined under a microscope.

Coming to terms with the mutilation that mastectomy involves is difficult, for women themselves and for their partners. Reconstructive surgery and implants, which can help to restore self-esteem and self-confidence, are not widely available except in the United States. In some parts of Britain, for example, a woman may have to fight very hard for plastic surgery or an implant unless she has private medical insurance. In the United States silicone implants have been sufficiently implicated in autoimmune reactions and infections — they have also been known to leak, harden, and shift their position, causing pain and disfigurement — for the goverment to curtail their use for routine cosmetic surgery. Silicone implants may continue to be used after mastectomy. Saline implants are an alternative. Another technique, known as TRAM-flap (transverse rectus abdominis myocutaneous flap), involves transplanting a flap of abdominal muscle to the breast immediately after the diseased breast is removed; after about six weeks a nipple and areola are constructed and tatooed to match the intact breast. But such solutions are not simple. Some critics believe that many women would be better advised to have psychotherapy than cosmetic surgery. As television host Jenny Jones said, after six breast operations in 11 years: 'I'd sell everything I own to have back the body I gave up.' She opted for silicone breast augmentation just to improve her figure, and thought that would be the end of it. Then the problems started.

Uterine, vulval, and vaginal cancers are less common than breast cancer. In men cancer can affect the testicles and penis and, in some cases, the breasts, but these types of cancer are much less frequent than those that specifically affect women. Self-examination maximizes the chances of detecting cancer early. Any change in the colour, shape, size, or texture of the breasts or genitals should be noted, not ignored. Compare one side of the body with the other, the left breast or testicle with the right, any swelling or tenderness on one side of the body with the corresponding area on the other. Often a lump or noticeable change is not malignant, but it is worth investigating for peace of mind. If it is cancer, the earlier it is diagnosed the more successful treatment will be.

Women should examine their breasts once a month, and once a year they should have a smear (Pap) test for cervical cancer; in fact some clinics recommend a twice-yearly smear test for women over 35. Men over 40 should have an annual check for cancer of the rectum, a common site of cancer in men. They should also be checked for enlargement or cancer of the prostate. New drugs are being developed to treat these problems. One, proscar, can shrink an enlarged prostate over several months, obviating the need for surgery. Woman over 40 should have a mammogram biannually and annually after the age of 50. About 80 per cent of all breast cancers occur in women over 50, but 90 per cent of these can be successfully treated if caught early.

Cancers of the sexual organs affect the most private and personal aspects of self-image and behaviour. As with STDs, greater public knowledge about the detection and treatment of cancer would mean earlier diagnosis and much less pain and anguish. Those parts of the body we seldom discuss are often the focus of our deepest anxieties and insecurities. How do you tell your partner that you have breast or genital cancer? How do you cope with his or her fear and anxiety as well as your own? How do you both feel about the changes that the disease or the treatment may make to your lifestyle and sexual activity? There are a number of self-help organizations that offer precious advice and support to cancer patients and their partners, and some specifically aim to help with sexual problems. Accepting that cancer is not contagious, not something that can be passed on during sexual contact, is a positive first step. Where treatment involves surgery, pre- and post-operative counselling is especially important. Dealing with a partner's changed appearance can be very difficult. Discussing the treatment options together can be constructive; so can looking at the scars together while they are healing.

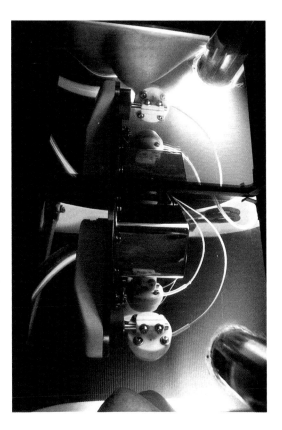

Waterpath ultrasonography is a more comfortable way of screening for breast cancer than mammography, which involves compressing the breasts between two glass plates and taking X-rays. For waterpath ultrasonography the patient lies face down on a special table with the breasts immersed in warm water. Ultrasound waves from a transducer at the bottom of the water tank enter the breasts in cross sections, and reflected waves are analysed by computer and displayed on a video screen.

This chapter has mentioned only the most obvious and life-threatening diseases related to sexual behaviour and the reproductive organs. But any medical or physical handicap — a heart problem, a stroke, arthritis, blindness, deafness, disfigurement, amputation — can profoundly influence sexual practices and attitudes. Individuals who have to live with such conditions deserve as much love, sex, and affection as the hale and hearty. Tender loving care has a wonderfully revitalizing effect on all of us.

Despite the arguments of some religious fundamentalists, sex-related illnesses are not scourges sent to afflict unrepentant sinners. Like tuberculosis or dysentery, they are communicable diseases which spread most easily among individuals in frequent or close contact, often among those we love most. The future will undoubtedly bring cures. We can only pray it will be sooner rather than later.

Chapter 15

Contemporary issues

Thus far it has been my intent to alert sexwatchers to those aspects of sex which surround us in ways less emphasized by the media but nevertheless pervasive and important. In this chapter I am going to focus on a cross-section of sexual topics — rape, sexual harassment, pornography, prostitution, sex discrimination, the media's coverage of sex — that reflect changing attitudes towards sex in the West today. I'll also comment about changes occurring elsewhere.

An infinite variety of sexual expression occurs behind closed doors and glimpses of that variety are occasionally seen in public. But social rules about the kind of sexual behaviour that is acceptable and unacceptable in public evolve because groups of people come to a consensus. But many laws and conventions, whether based on moral, economic, or demographic principles, conflict with actual sexual behaviour and with fashions in sexual behaviour. Laws and the consensus principle on which they are based change much more slowly than fashion.

A great deal of technically illegal behaviour goes unremarked and unprosecuted unless it is waved in the face of authority. Where oral and anal sex are banned, for example, straights as well as gays regularly have to break the law to satisfy their sexual needs. But if enough people actively oppose a law or cease publicly to uphold it, the law may get changed. An example of this is recent legislation against sexual harassment and sex discrimination, and laws decriminalizing same-sex activities. Even so, legislation takes a very long time to change intolerance and prejudice. Even if there is a radical change in the law, the hearts and minds of the majority may take a long time to change.

Religion and custom, while they do not have the force of law, are also powerful moderators of sexual behaviour. Roman Catholic and Muslim teachings, for example, are powerfully conservative. More subtle is the inertia of custom and use. In Thailand, for example, it is traditional for the younger daughter and her husband to live with her parents to support them in their old age; when they die, the couple takes over the parental home. In China and Japan the eldest son and his wife are expected to do this, but they live in and take over the home of the son's parents. In the West arrangements like this are less formal, but lean economic times are forcing more and more couples to live with in-laws. Inevitably this affects sexual intimacy in the home. In Cuba, Japan, the Philippines, and many other countries where privacy is at a premium, couples often resort to renting hotel rooms by the hour. This is made difficult in China where, to discourage unmarried couples, hotels require identity cards to be shown.

Sexual assault

One category of sexual behaviour commonly legislated against is that which contains a large element of intrusion or assault. Rape is assault, but rigorous proof is needed to make a rape charge stick. There are many legal loopholes and ambiguous standards that allow accused rapists to escape conviction, not the least being interpretation of the word 'consent'. Do rape

Early evening in the Shyinjuku 'kabuki-cho' district of Tokyo. The multicoloured neon signs advertise just about every form of sexual entertainment — old and new — that one can think of.

victims 'consent' if they are too terrified or exhausted to struggle? Does rape have to leave physical evidence of assault?

Combining as it does current Western fascinations with sex and violence and the acting out of a very common sexual fantasy, rape makes good media copy. In fantasy the victim remains in control of the rapist and of the level of violence, but in real life the victim is not in control. Reading the newspapers one might be excused for thinking that rape is on the increase, but it is hard to be sure. Certainly it is more frequently reported, because women's attitudes towards their sexual rights are changing, and because society now expects rape victims to speak up rather than suffer in silence.

Traditionally rape has been thought of as a crime by males against females. This is true in the majority of cases, but lately there have been more reports of men raping men and a few of women raping men. The incidence of reported rapes in the United States as a whole increased markedly in the late 1960s and early 1970s. Recent U.S. Department of Justice data, however, indicate that between the mid-1970s and the late 1980s attempted rapes declined by almost half. Completed rapes declined by almost 20 per cent during the 1980s compared with the 1970s. Greater appreciation of women's concerns and heightened awareness of what constitutes rape may be responsible for this change. Higher reporting rates among victims would tend to increase rather than decrease such statistics, so the trend is definitely positive.

In my own state of Hawaii, as elsewhere in the United States, the rate of rape of males by males is hard to determine since statistics are rarely kept. About 3 per cent of the rape victims attending the Hawaii Sexual Abuse Center are men who have been assaulted by other men. No reliable figures exist for men raped by women, probably because the men concerned are ashamed to admit to such an experience or do not expect to be believed. Shame and disbelief are potent deterrents for female rape victims too.

Why is it so difficult to prove a charge of rape? Police and prosecutors tread warily if the evidence is not absolutely sound. False accusations are infrequent, but they do occur. More at issue is the question of whether or not the victim somehow provoked the incident. Most often the people involved are known to each other, as acquaintances, friends, live-in partners, or present or past spouses. Did something in the victim's behaviour express willingness to have sex? The old cliché that women say no when they mean yes has a lot to answer for. Rape victims often suffer a sense of self-blame, or feel that society is pressuring them into accepting responsibility for having been raped. As one woman remarked bitterly: 'My father always said that whatever a man did to a woman, she provoked it.' Wearing flamboyant clothes, having a drink too many, entering a bar alone, walking in the street at night...all of these things can be construed, and often are construed, as 'asking for it'. The fear of being assaulted, sexually or otherwise, makes a significant difference to the way many women live their lives. Some women refuse to enter an elevator alone with a man; others cross the street rather than walk past bushes or doorways where someone might be hiding; others simply do not go out alone after dark. Many would agree with former Israeli prime minister Golda Meir who said, in reply to a male colleague who proposed that women should be kept off the streets after dark to protect them from rape: 'No! Keep the MEN off the streets after dark!'

The term 'rape' covers many types of situations. For example, there is stranger rape and acquaintance rape, and in both categories there may be power rape ('I'll show you who's boss!'), opportunistic rape ('I was there and she was there'), psychotic rape ('She was wearing my sign of the zodiac and it was Friday the 13th'), and sexual rape ('I felt horny'). Any one of these may have been planned or spontaneous.

Methods of investigating rape charges and conducting rape trials have been a special target of the women's movement. They represent, say the campaigners for reform, a closing of male ranks to protect men and red tape excuses for male violence against women. Defending counsel usually cannot resist casting doubt on the morals of a female victim; if it can be proved that she has had 'sexual experience', the jury will be asked to believe that she 'led the man on' or at least, that she did not object. Faced with this line of reasoning, what chance would a prostitute have of proving rape? Male gays, transvestites, drag queens, and male prostitutes who are raped are also likely to be met with the comment 'What did you expect?'

Two recent rape trials in the United States made world headlines. The first involved socialite William Kennedy Smith, a scion of the Kennedy clan, and his accuser Patricia Bowman. The second involved world heavyweight boxing champion Mike Tyson and his

In March 1992 world champion heavyweight boxer Mike Tyson, seen here in police custody, was sentenced to six years in prison for raping Miss Black America Beauty Pageant contestant Desirée Washington in an Indianapolis hotel. The trial made 'date rape' (Washington agreed to go to Tyson's hotel room) a talking point for many months.

Was the William Kennedy Smith rape trial, seen here on television, a media 'circus' that turned justice into pornography? Many commentators thought so. The alleged victim abandoned her anonymity in a television interview after the 'not guilty' verdict, claiming that millions of Americans believed her story, not William Kennedy Smith's. The defendant claimed he was picked up by Ms. Bowman, not the other way around.

accuser Desirée Washington. The identity of the accused added extra piquancy to both cases. Under American law, rape and child abuse trials are the only instances in which the identity of the 'victim' may be kept secret. The Smith and Tyson cases set people thinking about whether it is better or worse not to disclose the identity of rape victims. Is secrecy another form of assault? Does disclosure aggravate the injury suffered? What about the rights of the accused? In the Smith and Tyson cases money was not the issue; all sides spent millions of dollars in legal fees. Neither Smith nor Tyson denied that intercourse had occurred, but both claimed it was consensual. In neither case was there evidence of force. Smith was acquitted and Tyson was convicted.

Evidence of considerable physical violence does not always help in obtaining a conviction for rape. In fact most victims of rape delay reporting it, either through shock or fear. Often they rush to cleanse their bodies, even if they cannot purge their minds. Insisting that a competent medical authority examine them and record the event and the damage is often the last thing they think of doing. But, for legal reasons, that is precisely one of the first things they should do. Victims are faced with a nasty choice, to fight their assailant and risk even worse violence, or not to fight and perhaps be accused of having consented. Actually, most rape counsellors believe it is best to yell for help and attempt resistance. But the decision is still the victim's. A lot depends on the rapist and the situation in which the rape attempt takes place.

Some victims of rape appear better equipped to deal with its aftermath than others. Sociologist Libby Ruch and colleagues, interviewing rape victims immediately after the assault, found that the dominant feelings were anger against the assailant (not against the police or the 'system'), worry about how to disclose the incident to others, and some degree of self-blame ('Did I somehow contribute to what happened?'). Not surprisingly, fear of contracting an STD, especially HIV, was high on the list. Another interesting finding was that rape crisis centre staff, though trained to deal with rape situations, did not evaluate the trauma of the incident as the victims did. Ruch concluded: 'It is misleading to accept the stereotype of sexual assault victims as visibly traumatized...assessments of global trauma may indicate that cognitive trauma is more difficult to observe.'

From my own clinical experience, and from the reports of other professionals, I would say that a positive view of sex is a powerful aid to recovery. Although the person may have experienced physical fear and gross bodily insult, she (or he) is not usually as traumatized as a person who has a generally negative view of sex. The psychological damage that can occur in the case of the latter is yet another reason why I feel it is important to erase the guilt, fear, and secrecy that still tend to colour individual and social attitudes to sex in the West.

Rape within marriage is a concept that has been filtering into public consciousness on both sides of the Atlantic for at least a decade now. The idea that a wife or husband who does not consent to coitus can be violated by his or her spouse directly confronts the traditional view of sex as one of the duties of marriage, and the associated idea that married partners are each other's sexual property. However, as of the early 1990s, marital rape laws are on the statute book in only two American states. In the United Kingdom, rape within marriage became an indictable offence in 1991.

There are many different motives for rape. Should rape be classed as a sexual crime at all? Shouldn't it be regarded as physical assault? Evidence suggests that where assailants and victims are complete strangers, the assailant is more concerned with aggression than with sex. The act is a power play, a way of dominating and degrading another human being; gratification is achieved by thoroughly violating the emotional and physical privacy of the other person. Rape perpetrated by a spouse, lover, or friend is more complex; what it represents is power play plus an extreme failure of communication.

The majority of men sincerely decry rape, but that does not and will not stop them from seeing women, in fantasy and in real life, as objects of flirtation and lust. Women see men that way too. It is not hypocrisy to decry rape and continue to lust. In fact a great deal of lust is deflected by humour — jokes, banter, *double entendres* — by pornography, and by rape fantasies.

But if one looks outside Western culture, rape takes on a rather different perspective. Rape was almost unheard of among the Mbuti of East Africa, and in traditional Hawaii and other Oceanian cultures. In these societies sex was not a restricted commodity. On those rare occasions when an individual forced himself sexually on another, it was viewed as an instance of extreme arousal; the sought-after individual was more likely to be flattered than offended, and the 'punishment' for the perpetrator, if any, was ridicule for not having found a willing partner. By contrast, the Gusii of Kenya routinely practise what we in the West would regard as rape — normal sexual coupling involves overcoming resistance and inflicting a degree of pain. Among the traditional Arunta of Australia, 14-year-old girls are gang-raped to mark their transition to marriageable status. Despite such examples, anthropologist Peggy Reeves Sanday observes that 'in societies where nature is held sacred, rape occurs only rarely'. The implication here is that rape is an 'unnatural' act and most likely to occur in societies (such as our own highly industrialized model) that have lost touch with nature. I also think that in most 'modern' societies conflict and aggression, rather than mediation and empathy, are regularly presented — particular on television and in films — as ways of solving problems.

Sexual harassment

Though less dramatic than rape, sexual harassment is another form of power play that has become increasingly recognized by women in America, in the West generally, and even in Japan. It is even more difficult to define than rape, but includes unwelcome sexual advances, requests for sexual favours, and physical and verbal behaviour that cause embarrassment. All of these things might be merely annoying if they did not occur in situations where the 'victim' is somehow 'trapped', where her or his or job, or pay rise, or bonus, or promotion may be the cost of non-compliance. In 1991 Justice Clarence Thomas was nominated for the U.S. Supreme Court, only to have his nomination challenged by charges of sexual harrassment from a former aide, law professor Anita Hill, who claimed that he had repeatedly made suggestive advances to her which made her working situation difficult and repressive. Two-thirds of those who heard and saw the charges discussed on television, women as well as men, believed him rather than her. In the end, as so often in rape cases, it was again one person's word against another. Clarence Thomas made it to the Supreme Court. Nevertheless the hearings sensitized millions of people to sexual harassment as an issue in the workplace and elsewhere. If a sexual harrassment claim can be made to stick, the plaintiff can claim civil damages.

Legislation in this area is still evolving, but there are many difficulties. When is a friendly overture too friendly? What happens when a comment to Sally is taken in good part but considered offensive by Betty? As everyone knows, many marriages and lifelong relationships begin with flirting at college, university, or in the workplace. Probably more 'eyes meet' over desks in offices and classrooms than on the dance floor.

President Bush's choice of black lawyer Clarence Thomas as a Justice of the U.S. Supreme Court was predictably a test of racial views among the liberal establishment in the United States. What it also brought to light was the intense issue of sexual harassment. The benefit of the doubt was given to Judge Thomas, here being sworn in at the White House in the presence of George and Barbara Bush.

Very relevant here is a ruling made in the United States in 1986 in the case of 'Meritor Savings Bank v. Vinson'. This established that a 'sexually hostile environment' may constitute sexual harassment. Since 1986 women in America have brought suit to have pin-ups removed from shops and stores, bikini-clad women removed from company advertisements, and lectures using sexist language or slides cancelled. Even in male-oriented Japan a small publishing company was recently found guilty of abusing one of their employees sufficiently to make her resign. Further, for the first time in American courts, a decision in a sexual harassment case may rest on what the average *woman* thinks rather than the average man. Should behaviours and environments that women are comfortable with prevail over those that men are comfortable with, or vice versa? Were officials at Pennsylvania State University right to remove a copy of Goya's famous *Nude Maja* from a classroom after a female faculty member claimed that it created an atmosphere of sexual harassment?

Pornography

Pornographic books, films, videos, and telephone chat lines are often accused of encouraging sex crimes. Whether they actually do is another matter — there is no good evidence that they do. But for the moment let us concern ourselves with the perennial and thorny question: What is pornography?

To some people a picture of a nursing woman with one breast exposed is pornographic; to others, scenes of oral and group sex are no big deal. A film or painting may be highly arousing for some, a powerful focus for sexual feelings; for others it may have no resonance at all, or be seen as squalid, depressing, or offensive. The legal problem is to arrive at a definition that reflects a majority standard of decency or offensiveness without infringing the rights of minorities. Actually, as society changes, so do ideas of what is acceptable or not, obscene or not, pornographic or not. In the United States, in the middle of this century, contraceptives were seen as pornographic; one could be arrested for sending condoms through the mail. Now they are distributed in high schools. Not so very long ago D.H. Lawrence's *Lady Chatterley's Lover* and James Joyce's *Ulysses* were banned as pornography; now no university graduate is considered literate if he or she had not read them. Until recently, the definition of pornography in the United States included the words 'utterly without redeeming social value'. This has now changed. Now erotica should have 'serious literary, artistic, political or scientific value' to pass muster and must not offend comtemporary community standards. In England the courts struggled for years to decide if various publications were obscene on the basis of the definition that obscene material 'tends to deprave and corrupt'. In 1992 the Canadian Supreme Court ruled that material which 'subordinates or degrades women' was pornographic. How this will be interpreted remains to be seen. Is material that subordinates and degrades men not pornographic? The confusion resulting from all these definitions was well summed up in a remark made by U.S. Supreme Court Justice Stephens in 1977: 'A nuisance may merely be a right thing in the wrong place — like a pig in the parlor instead of in the barnyard. Whether a pig or a picture is offensive is a question that cannot be answered in the abstract.'

Pornography is an outward sign of the large fantasy component in human sexuality. That is why there is no universally true definition of the word. Material intended to arouse is as varied as the people it arouses. Is it not extremely peculiar that critics of pornography always claim not to be aroused by pornographic material but are concerned that others might be? Many of the readers of this book may be less than tempted by an evening of *Lady Chatterley in Tokyo*, *Lost in the Swamps*, or even the all-time bestsellers *Deep Throat* and *Fanny Hill*, but those attitudes contribute to denying or condoning another person's pleasure. Objecting or not objecting to erotica influences its availability.

On many occasions states, counties, and cities across the United States have conducted surveys and taken votes and polls on whether pornography should be available to their citizens. Invariably the consensus has been that adults should have the right to view, read, or own sexually explicit material, providing it does not involve children. If a line has to be drawn somewhere, it is between minors and adults. The majority accept adult material for adults, although the voice of a minority against erotica is often more loudly heard.

Does pornography encourage sex crimes? Probably not. Most researchers have found that sex offenders typically have sexually repressive, often overly religious backgrounds, and rigidly conservative attitudes to sexuality. As adolescents and adults they are no more obsessed by erotic or pornographic material than any other group of invividuals. The work of Danish criminologist Berl Kutchinsky is most revealing in this respect. Comparing rape statistics for the years 1964–1984 in Denmark, Sweden, and West Germany (pornography was legalized in these countries in 1969, 1970, and 1973 respectively), he found that 'rape increased less than non-sexual assault...and in West Germany rape did not increase at all.' During the same period the amount of pornography available increased markedly. A preliminary study in Japan done by Ayako Uchiyama of the Japanese Institute of Police Science and myself shows a similar picture; although the market for pornography has steadily increased over the last 20 years, the incidence of rape has decreased. Most serious researchers consider that rape mirrors the overall level of violence in a society rather than the quantity of pornography available. Pornography seems to act as a displacement for frustration rather than as a stimulus to overt behaviour. Those concerned with the relationship of pornography to antisocial behaviour might more profitably direct their attention to the role played by organized crime in its production and distribution, or to the amount of police time that would be freed for worthier tasks if pornography laws were relaxed.

There is absolutely no doubt that pornography is a substitute for sex for people who don't have or don't want a real sexual partner or who see it as more pleasurable and less bother than other options. But it can also be a welcome aphrodisiac, a means of arousing oneself or a partner. It can be as diverting and as fascinating as a detective movie, a romantic novel, a science fiction story, or a painting by a great master — many artists have turned their pens and brushes to erotic art. One need look no further than Walt Whitman and Picasso. Nor is all pornography laced with ropes, whips, and knives; a lot of it takes place in elaborate, fairytale settings. Some even constitutes useful sex education. An assessment of pornographic material illegally taken into Japan in 1982 showed that 48 per cent of offenders were returning honeymoon couples, not depraved or deprived flashers or rapists.

Pressure to ban pornography comes mainly from two groups, from right-wing, self-

Surveys have shown that the majority of VCR owners in the United States use them to watch blue movies. However the genre is losing some of its appeal because product quality — plot, script, acting, direction — is generally tacky.

appointed guardians of public morals, and from radical socialist and feminist organizations — somewhat strange bedfellows. Members of the first group simply take a strict line on sex in general and view pornography as one of its more depraved manifestations. Members of the second object to it as an instrument of male oppression, as a symptom of broader social forces that undermine the status of women. Ostensibly to pacify the women's movement, and to give 'liberated' women 'what they want', publishers and movie makers have created pornography aimed at women, much of it produced by women themselves. But is yet more 'sexploitation' what women want? Porn for women has not taken hold in the same way as porn for men, but the market has been increasing both among heterosexual men and women and lesbians. Interestingly, some lesbian and all-gay male groups defend homosexual pornography, even of the S & M (sadomasochistic) kind, on the grounds that it portrays them as sex objects, which they applaud.

A public advertisement for a pornographic film in Athens. Pornography is legal and popular in Greece, despite the strong influence of the Greek Orthodox Church. It is also legal and popular in Muslim Turkey on the other side of the Aegean.

Japanese manga (comics) show just about every type of sexual activity imaginable. This one caters to necrophiliacs. There is no age restriction on readership.

Regardless of whose sensibilities it offends, pornography flourishes because there is a huge market for it. People vote for it with their wallets and purses. But in every locale, standards of display vary. Page three of one of Britain's popular daily newspapers regularly shows female nudity and the front page of Hong Kong's main newspaper often carries prominent advertisments for bedroom wear which include scantily clad women. In the United States, however, even in major cities, the covers of magazines such as *Playboy*, *Penthouse*, and *Hustler* are usually covered on display racks, although much more salacious offerings may be available under the counter. Society bows to certain sensitivities while accommodating others.

The oldest profession

In the public mind pornography and prostitution are closely linked, and with good reason. Pornography is a word derived from two Greeks words, *porne* and *graphos*, meaning 'writings of harlots', and so-called red light districts usually contain or are contained within areas where pornography is freely available. Prostitution and pornography are sometimes part of the same business empire. Also, in many countries, prostitution and pornography have the same half-accepted status. People's feelings about pornography and prostitution usually go hand in hand: those who find sex *per se* distasteful disapprove and those who see sex positively either approve or don't much care.

Prostitution is illegal in all but one of America's 50 states, but is rarely severely punished. In England, Germany, the Netherlands, Holland, Korea, and Sweden it is legal. In many others it is illegal but the authorities do not pay much attention to it, or police and other officials extract 'fees' for looking the other way. Only in a few societies is prostitution an honour, not a disgrace. Punishment is harshest in Islamic and communist countries, where it conflicts sharply with the prevailing ideology. That does not mean that it does not exist. In 1990 it was estimated that there were approximately 8,000 prostitutes in Shanghai, and 'hotel girls' were well known in Moscow before the break-up of the Soviet Union. Prostitutes were among the first migrants from East to West when the Berlin Wall came down (drugs and porn from the West moved East). There are also occasional news reports of executions (sometimes by stoning) of individuals engaged in prostitution in Iran, Pakistan, and other fundamentalist countries.

Fifty years ago, according to Kinsey and his colleagues, the majority of men in the

Callgirl cards in a Japanese telephone booth. Go into a telephone booth in the centre of any large city in the West and a smorgasbord of erotic experience is just a phone call away.

United States had their first experience of sex with a prostitute. This is no longer true, but it remains true in Latin America, although even here things are changing and for the same reason that they changed in the United States: the 'girl next door' is now more available.

Prostitutes in the West today are usually partner substitutes, hired to provide more sex than is usually available or sex of a kind not available from a regular partner. The number of male prostitutes, mostly servicing other males, seems to be increasing. Male prostitution is not new of course, but it is more openly acknowledged today than it used to be. In Japan, which is a highly sex-segregated society, there are male prostitutes who cater to women; during the day affluent women can easily find the time and freedom to pay for sex without their husbands' knowledge. A new institution that has developed in Japan over the last 10 years is the 'mistress bank', supplying female companions for rich men on a regular but part-time basis; many of these 'mistresses' are housewives or students earning extra income and some have the approval of their husbands or regular partners. Call girls are also popular. Phone booths in the tourist areas of major Japanese cities are plastered with advertisments for female companions. Call girls or escorts, male and female, are part of the scene in most major cities in the United States, Britain, and Europe, although their methods of advertising differ.

Around the world mistresses and call girls occupy a rather different social niche from street prostitutes or 'house girls'. They are usually less visible and better paid, and may even live quite well. The clever ones may even enjoy a certain amount of power, notoriety, and status, although most lead a shadowy existence. Street prostitutes, as opposed to independent call girls or house prostitutes who depend on 'madams', are still largely dependent on pimps to protect their interests and are more or less exploited in the process. Theirs is a hard life. Many street prostitutes 'trick' several times a night, every night, seven days a week. When officialdom decides to clamp down, it is usually the whore or the hustler who pays the penalty, not the client, although this is changing in some places. This may be a victory for equality, but it is seen as 'bad for business'.

Motives for becoming a prostitute are many and varied. Studies show that most prostitutes enjoy sex and feel they are filling a needed role in society. The money is attractive, especially for those with little education or opportunity to earn money in other occupations. High-class escorts can earn more than schoolteachers. There is also a thrill and glamour which appeals. On the other hand, there is also danger,

Street prostitutes in Bombay, India. This brother and sister are hardly more than slaves to the pimps they work for. Of low caste, their options were extremely limited; prostitution seemed to be the best of them.

degradation, the likelihood of unwanted pregnancy, and the even greater likelihood of disease. Many runaways reluctantly turn to street prostitution since it is one of the few ways in which they can support themselves.

The economic aspect of prostitution has become an international issue. In many Asian countries, in the Philippines, Thailand, and South Korea, for example, sexual services provide a large part of income from tourism. Japanese businessmen can fly on one-night *kisaeng* (sex) tours to South Korea. Between 200,000 and 300,000 women work in Bangkok's massage parlours, tea houses, nightclubs, brothels, and disco-restaurants. Thousands of military and civilian personnel arrive every day in Angeles City and Olongapo in the Philippines for 'R-and-R'. The girls and women who cater to sexual tourists are divided. How else, they ask, can they earn in an evening more than their parents make in a month? The World Ecumenical Coalition comments: 'Within the wealthy nations, from which the men come who visit the towns and regions of the Third World...the protests of women's and human rights groups are dismissed and slandered as "moralizing", "feminist", etc. Stalwart economic interests — of the tourist industry, the "pleasure business", and other connected circles — stand just as much in the way of introducing effective control measures as do the old established, racist, and chauvinist prejudices.' It is one thing for sexual services to be bought and sold by choice, another when they are fueled by poverty and overpopulation. Indeed, in many countries prostitution is a form of slavery.

A client enters a brothel in Bombay. Prostitution exists because of simple supply and demand. Almost everywhere in the world sex without complications is a scarce commodity for which men are willing to pay.

In the United States, Britain, France, and elsewhere prostitutes are forming pressure groups, collectives, even trades unions, to provide mutual support and secure greater rights and protection. One such organization in the United States goes under the acronym COYOTE (Call Off Your Old Time Ethics). Comparable groups are the Organization for the Rights of Prostitutes in Canada and EMPOWER in Thailand. Periodicals like *PONY Xpress* exist specifically for prostitutes; *Whorezine* has a wider readership (erotic dancers, fantasy phone talkers, and others providing sexual services).

The legacy of feminism

The introduction of sexual harassment laws and the unionization of prostitutes are symptoms of the assertiveness of various groups — mainly of women — in search of what they see as their sexual and civil rights. Often such groups are in direct conflict with each other. There are groups pro-life and pro-abortion, groups pro-prostitution and anti-prostitution. Markist thinkers like Eugene Genovese and Elizabeth Fox-Genovese would say that such groups are merely manifestations of 'bourgeois individualism', a by-product of the evil empire of capitalism. Whether one regards choice as a civil liberty or as a sign of decadence, the fact that sexual harassment, rape, pornography, and prostitution are now public issues, widely discussed, and the subject of new social and legal initiatives, is due in large measure to the strong pressures unleashed by the women's movement in the 1960s and 1970s. The media have certainly sensationalized these issues, but their presence on the social and political agenda today marks a fundamental shift in consciousness. Feminism grew from an awareness that women were discriminated against when it came to jobs, pay, political rights, and social arrangements, and under its banner men and women have fought long and hard to gain equity for women.

The battle has been difficult and tiring and relatively little ground has been gained. Most women are still sharply aware that what they see and what they experience are not what 'should be'. Greater awareness of inequality is not the same as abolishing inequality. Women's pay has improved, but in 1990 in the United States it was still only 71 per cent of men's (59 per cent in 1980). Women are still performing their traditional roles and still exploited as cheap labour. With unemployment increasing, they are often first to be be made redundant, leaving the workplace open to men. Men still control the centres of power — governments, banks, industry, the armed forces. The popularity and longevity of Margaret Thatcher, Britain's first woman Prime Minister, might have been expected to sweep more women into government and parliament, but it did not. The Reagan and Bush administrations have been notably hostile to women's rights, using the 'family values' plea to defend their policies. There are more female than male voters in the United States, yet by and large they do not vote women into power.

Modern contraceptives and fertility drugs, among the most important advances in modern medicine, have theoretically given women the freedom to become pregnant if and when they want to; I say 'theoretically' because even in technologically and medically advanced countries many pregnancies are unplanned and many couples remain unhappily childless. Reproductive freedom has certainly given women access to sexual liberties previously available only to men, liberties within and outside marriage. Data on EMS and other sexual activities support the view that more women have begun to take advantage of their reproductive freedom. But the majority of women have not made reproductive freedom an excuse for promiscuity or felt pressured into promiscuity because of it. Rather they have treated it as an extension of existing options.

Yet with this imperfect freedom have come increased social and economic pressures. For nearly 30 years now women have been oppressed by the Superwoman image — top marks at school, rapid progress up the career ladder, spotless home, spotless children, and a husband who is mad about her because she is terrific in bed. The pressures on men are a little more recent; men now feel that as well as being providers they have to be more sensitive, more caring, more willing to share responsibilities in the home, and more willing to please their women sexually. Fax machines, computers, and robots have made certain aspects of men's work easier, but the workplace is still very competitive. New technology in the home has certainly changed the character of women's traditional work, but it has not reduced demands on their time or essentially changed their domestic responsibilities. All the options are there, for both men and women, but few of us seem capable of taking advantage of them.

There are sensitive, successful men and high-flying women, but the majority of men and women remain slaves to convention, whether one ragards such conventions as man-made (literally) or nature-given. More women have economic independence than in the past, but there are now so many more people vying for the finite resources of the planet that women are not, in overall terms, much better off. The role of women in the Third World is changing, but how far will the changes go and in what direction? It is still too soon to say.

Feminism is not a spent force, although its progeny are sometimes difficult to recognize. A 1991 poll showed that less than one third of American women consider themselves feminists and less than half think that feminism reflects the views of most women. Pulitzer prize-winning author Susan Faludi has identified a backlash against feminism. She thinks that the reason why most women do not identify themselves with the movement is that conservatives, the courts, and above all the mass media have waged an insidious campaign against it. The 1980s saw a lot of changes in favour of women, who now have greater educational, social, and job opportunities than ever before — since the 1950s the number of women working outside the home has roughly doubled — but these opportunities have had their downside. Certainly not all women are happier. Most of them do not work from choice, but from economic necessity. In a 1985 poll 51 per cent of American women said they would prefer to have a job rather than stay at home and look after the family. In 1991, with 7 out of 10 women working, the numbers reversed: 53 per cent said they would rather stay at home. Does this mean they are tired, disillusioned, realistic, or expressing an opinion that comes from choice? The same question is never asked of men; they are rarely given a choice, the assumption being that they must work outside the home. Calls for men to assert and explore their 'other selves' have never met with wide acceptance among men themselves or generally. But I agree with Betty Friedan, the mother of modern feminism, who has been quoted as saying that we now need to 'transcend sexual politics and anger...to express a new vision of family and community...to mobilize the new power of women and men for a larger political agenda on the priorities of life.' What we have been seeing in the last two decades are efforts on the part of men and women, separately and together, to reassess their social and professional lives.

Titillation versus information

In the West today most adults of both sexes take the view that sexuality is an important part of their personal identity, an important tool of self-realization, an important motivating force in their own lives and the lives of others. More is expected and demanded of sex than in the past. Sex excites more interest for its own sake than it did in the past. Magazines such as *Playboy*, *Hustler*, *Ms*, *Cosmopolitan*, and *New Woman* deliver sexual information, fantasy, humour, and other notabilia month in, month out. Sexual curiosity can be satisfied by reading sex manuals, sending away for sex aids, or attending sex workshops — you can spend a weekend trying to locate your G spot and finding out what to do with it, or learning how to make an orgasm last half an hour or more, or how to be multiply orgasmic. Or how about a swinger weekend or a swinger convention, or a week-long cruise for gays only? Also on offer are an increasing variety of sex therapies — counselling, drugs, massage, nudity, groups — and problems can even be aired and discussed on television and radio with professional counsellors.

Even though the intent behind much of the comment that gushes forth from newspapers, magazines, books, television, radio, movies, and audio and video cassettes is to shock and titillate rather than sensibly inform, I see increased willingness to talk about sex unashamedly and look for ways to 'make it better' as an encouraging trend. One of the positive effects of AIDS has been a greater need and willingness to talk candidly about sex in personal and global terms. Men and women are learning to understand and appreciate their bodies better; they are learning to identify and ask for what they want in sexual relationships. As this knowledge becomes less esoteric and more sophisticated I hope that fewer people will glibly assume that sexual problems can be solved simply by pushing the right physical button. Sexual problems are more often psychological than physical. In fact

A male stripper performs before a female audience. Many women, once they develop a taste for it, enjoy 'a night out with the girls'.

there is still lively debate among counsellors and therapists, and indeed among the public at large, as to what constitutes a 'sexual problem' and what constitutes a 'solution' or 'cure'. Is learning to achieve orgasms the 'solution' to not being able to achieve orgasms? Or is it learning to find greater pleasure in other phases of the response cycle? Or not giving a damn because the rest of the relationship is good? Or finding a partner specifically to provide orgasms, much as one might find someone to play tennis with? Dilemmas like this are very much part of the contemporary sexual scene.

An interesting concept that has gained currency in the last few years is that of 'sexual addiction'. Alcohol and drug addiction counsellor Patrick Carnes has described sexual addiction as sexual behaviour that is unstoppable despite serious potential or actual consequences; these may be physical (self-mutilation, violence, disease, unwanted pregnancy), or occupational (absenteeism, job loss, financial loss), or affect family and other relationships. Instead of reaching for drugs or booze, the sexual addict reaches for some kind of sexual activity when he or she is feeling stressed, frustrated, and low. Like drugs and alcohol, this provides only temporary solace, and so the cycle continues. Carnes recommends a 12-step program (similar to that used to treat alcoholism) to combat 'sexual addiction'.

But when does a particular sexual activity become an addiction? Who is to decide what is a 'normal' frequency for such activity? Who is qualified to treat sexual addicts? What treatment works best, if any? Family therapist and author Marty Klein is probably the most articulate opponent of the idea of sexual addiction, arguing that it is culturally naive, dangerous because it tempts people to self-diagnose themselves or their partners, and rooted in a sex-negative attitude which sees sex outside 'committed, monogamous, loving, heterosexual relationships' as wrong. What is wrong, he asks, with using sex to feel better about yourself or to escape from other problems? Most people do.

New media sex

The sudden explosion of the home video market has made X-rated movies available to all. Video stores almost everywhere carry a good stock of 'adult' movies. Though not always on open display, they are there for the asking. Actually, in most countries, after several years of great popularity, their share of the video market is declining. The novelty has worn off, particularly in Denmark, Sweden, the Netherlands, and Germany where other forms of pornography are freely available. Also many sexploitation movies, despite the aspirations of some of their makers, lack the quality and originality that viewers have come to expect from films on general release. Nevertheless the bill of fare is wide, limited only by local preferences, ordinances, and law enforcement. In Japan, pornographic videos and magazines are available from automatic outdoor vending machines; in Hong Kong, India, and rural areas in Asia they are sold openly from street stalls.

Among the more bizarre developments in the United States are pay and cable television quiz games that offer viewers the chance to pick up a date, strip, or act out sexual fantasies on screen; other shows are 'no holds barred' counselling sessions in which couples thrash out their most private and intimate problems in full view of millions of people 'just like themselves'. In the United States, Europe, Japan, and elsewhere there are telephone chat lines that provide live and very sexy conversation or play sex tapes. There are also serious telephone information lines that offer instruction on everything

A porn vending machine on a residential street in Kyoto, Japan. Machines like this light up after dark, displaying porn books and videos. One-way glass prevents children from seeing their wares during the day.

from protection against AIDS and improving your sex life to pleasing a sexual partner and knowing if you are in love. The demand for sexual entertainment and information is enormous, probably because there are a lot of sexually frustrated and lonely people out there and also because the topic has inherent interest and value. Videos, magazines, and fantasy calls are a way of circumventing sexual repression and censorship.

Rock music has punched a huge hole in traditional tight-lipped moralism too. In the early 1970s even the most obliquely suggestive songs were banned on radio or television. Now they come across the airwaves hot and strong, often with explicit sexual references and loudly uttered obscenities. Daytime talk shows interview swingers and threesomes, transsexuals and transvestites, and individuals of just about every other sexual stripe, the

more exotic the better (pregnant nuns into S & M with underage animals would be mindblowing). Characters in afternoon television soaps play 'musical beds', *sans* the actual sex, often to very young audiences. Nudity and simulated sex quite frequently appear on stage, although even in the early 1980s British morality choked on a simulated homosexual rape scene at London's Royal National Theatre. Art galleries have always broken the bounds of 'decency' in the name of art, but sexual come-ons are now explicit in the graphics visible in any main street.

Even more explicit are some offerings available on computer. On-line computer networks that allow one to call up news, weather forecasts, and travel information also allow for the exchange of sexy gossip, erotic fantasies, and pornographic images that leave nothing to the imagination. These can be spontaneous creations or the commercial output of otherwise respectable companies, with program names like Sexxcapades, MacPlaymate, The Fuller Brush Man, Tillie Earns Her Keep, Leisure Suit Harry.... When virtual reality disks become available, I confidently predict that X-rated features will be among the first offerings.

A female stripper in a Honolulu nightclub where patrons are invited to take photographs. Some come equipped as if they are about to do a gynaecological examination.

Censorship

Not surprisingly, all of these new developments have been met with vigorous opposition from parents and teachers concerned about the corruptibility of the young, evangelists concerned about people's immortal souls ('sex rots your soul quicker than candies rot your teeth'), and the Moral Majority concerned that the media message seems to be that sex is as easy and as pleasurable as having a good meal (and, I might add, less expensive).

Governments too are concerned. The Bush administration signalled as much when National Endowment for the Arts (NEA) director John Frohnmayer was fired after a public outcry against the homoerotic photographs of Robert Mapplethorpe and André Serrano's 'Piss Christ', a depiction of a crucifix submerged in urine. The U.S. Senate put a one-year curb on the NEA, forbidding it to support artists whose productions 'may be considered obscene, including but not limited to depictions of sadomasochism, homoeroticism, the sexual exploitation of children, or individuals engaged in sex acts and which, when taken as a whole, do not have serious literary, artistic, political, or scientific value.' The U.S. Public Broadcasting System now self-censors programs for their sexual content. In the United Kingdom similar concerns led to the setting up of the British Broadcasting Council, which monitors sex and violence on television and radio.

The controversy over what is art or not, and what is acceptable or not, continues and is far from esoteric, for it determines official support and censorship. Now arguments for less permissive public standards are coming from a new quarter, from left-wing academics among whom the idea of 'political correctness' (PC) once applied to more overtly political issues such as race and the environment is now being applied to sexual matters. Sexually graphic depictions and stereotypes of female beauty and gender differences are not PC. As I have remarked before, sexual issues sometimes make strange bedfellows.

But there is light on the horizon. Lord Rees-Mogg, head of the British Broadcasting Council, indicated that he was more concerned with violence than sex, and in the United States the majority of the arts community and the general public, as well as the courts, supported Mapplethorpe, Serrano, and others. And an easing-off seems to be occurring elsewhere in the world. Despite the objections of Muslim clerics, Pakistan's Minister of Cultural Affairs invited Michael Jackson to join Madonna in a charity entertainment extravaganza to be be shown on national television, and promised to be less restrictive on imported sitcoms and news. For some years now Brazil has allowed 'adult' movies to be shown on television after midnight; Thailand recently followed suit. In 1992 Mexico's most controversial statue, a voluptuous larger-than-life nude sculpture of Diana the Huntress by Juan Olguibel Rosenzweig, as popular as Copenhagen's water maid, was rescued from an obscure location and re-erected in the middle of a traffic island in the Reforma in Mexico City. In Japan, where 21 prefectural governments decided that the burgeoning of sexually orientated publications was harmful to youth (sales increased by 13 per cent in 1990 alone), publishers and distributors have been allowed to regulate themselves; publications are sealed and bookstores put all sealed material on sale in 'adult' areas. In 1989, for the first time, the Indonesian government allowed the production and screening of a film with openly gay characters in it, and even saw it nominated for several national film awards. Even in the Chinese People's Republic sex research is now tolerated and written about in magazines and newspapers intended for general circulation; recently it was reported that 3 out of 4 Chinese approve of sex before marriage and 7 out of 10 condone extramarital affairs. Public displays of affection are becoming more commonplace too. All of this would have been unthinkable less than 10 years ago.

Perhaps the most dramatic changes have occurred in Eastern Europe. In Czechoslovakia, Hungary, Poland, and many of the newly independent republics of the Soviet Union, artists, writers, and others are enjoying a new freedom of expression. Budapest has established itself as the sexual Mecca of Central Europe; all kinds of pornography and erotic services are openly available there. Warsaw and Bratislava are no longer sexually isolated and neuter. What was once East Germany now hosts an exhibition of erotic photography. And, wonder of wonders, according to a report in the Soviet youth daily *Komsomolskaya Pravda* a striptease school has opened in the Siberian city of Omsk; it is training artistes for jobs at home and abroad. Will the novelties of sexual *glasnost* quickly shake down and become 'normal'? While past levels of censorship are probably gone for good, the new freedoms are tenuous and must continue to be fought for.

It is mainly through the media that we gauge how typical we are in our own preferences

Revellers on the Berlin Wall in November 1989 celebrate the end of Eastern Europe's isolation from the West. A whole sexual underworld has emerged into the light since the official demise of Communism.

and practices. In general the centralized media, as opposed to fringe or specialist TV channels or publications, cater for a relatively conservative slice of the population, supposedly the majority. It is in their interests to make an accurate assessment of public taste. To be too conservative is to risk boring consumers; to be too sensational or radical is to risk alienating them. Though some editors and producers take the occasional risk for the sake of highlighting a particular issue or making a quick killing in sales or audience ratings, most media items are carefully pitched at, or only slightly ahead of, an average level of public acceptance. There is very rapid, and ferocious, feedback if they go too far. We, the consumers, have great influence. Whatever we want will become or continue to be available if we make our wishes known. We can vote with our ballots and with our money.

Chapter 16

Future tense

The year 2000 draws near. The date has a certain resonance. We cannot know what its historic significance will be, but it invites speculation. If there is one prediction that can be made with certainty it is that most predictions will turn out to be wrong! In 1939 psychologist Lewis Terman predicted that by the 1960s no American woman would be a virgin on her wedding day. At least 50 per cent of brides in the 1960s proved him wrong. The 1960s saw the so-called sexual revolution: cohabitation became more open, contraceptive techniques improved, homosexuality came out of the closet, swinging couples became less coy about their activities, and communal lifestyles were experimented with. Jeremiahs by the score foresaw an end to 'civilized' moral codes. Now, in the 1990s, we can look back and say that the sexual revolution was not really a revolution at all. At most it was an evolution. Most of the behaviour trumpeted as 'new' in the 1960s was not really new at all and those behaviours which caused most stir — premarital and extramarital sex, swinging, homosexuality, divorce — have in fact levelled off and come to be accepted, or at least better understood. Most people still see in themselves and others the reality that tomorrow's behaviours will be much like today's. We have not, it turns out, descended into sexual anarchy or risen to sexual heaven.

Nevertheless, since World War II, choice in sexual matters has broadened enormously. That does not mean that everyone takes advantage of the possibilities open to them — the possibility of sleeping around, protected by the pill, condoms, and antibiotics, does not make every adult promiscuous, nor does the legality of same-sex sex mean that more people are homosexually active. Broader choice in sexual matters is a trend that can be expected to continue. And when choice is available, consumers generally become more discriminating, more demanding, and surer of what they want.

Living with insecurity

Will we reach the year 2000? Ten years ago this was a real question. The cold war, with its potential for nuclear catastrophe, cast a shadow over everyone's lives. Rogue governments like those in Iraq and Iran, Libya and Syria, supported terrorists whose activities were not bound by common standards of reason or humanity. With the easing of tension between the superpowers, the prospect of Armageddon has receded, but the future is still uncertain. How will the nations of the world deal with overpopulation, environmental pollution, global warming, unemployment, and the spreading scourge of HIV disease? These are problems which touch us all. They are very relevant to personal planning, whether that planning concerns marriage, family, career, or retirement. Fear of pollution-led extinction or vitiation of our species, and of many other species, is something that many people feel even if they do not openly articulate it.

The best-selling author of the 1970s was not Shere Hite, Jackie Collins, or any other chronicler of our sexual mores. By a gigantic margin — 15 million copies worldwide — the spokesman of that era was Hal Lindsay with his book *The Late Great Planet Earth*, a prophecy of final, apocalyptic conflict. Today our anxieties are less focused. Removal of the nuclear threat has, if anything, made us more aware of the depth and breadth and complexity of the world's ills. Resources are finite, but every day there are more people who need food, shelter, and employment. And in addition to chronic poverty and famine and disease (malaria and dysentery still kill millions of people every year), there is a new plague

Pollution control and population control must go hand in hand if large portions of the human race are to have any quality of life in the 21st century. Pollution can be seen as a form of earth-rape — immediate gratification without regard for others or the future.

to be fought: HIV disease and AIDS.

Reaction to threat can take many forms, with hedonism at one extreme and total withdrawal at the other. In sexual terms these extremes might translate into unbridled sexual activity regardless of the consequences, disabling guilt and neuroticism about sexual activity, or celibacy. The in-between reaction, the reaction typical of most of us, is to carry on more or less as normal, more or less afflicted by anxiety, unable to absorb or deflect the perceived threat. Anxiety inhibits all kinds of pleasure, especially sexual, and has a direct bearing on important decisions such as whether to marry, divorce, or bring children into the world.

Advances and checks in medical science

In the last few decades the social consequences of coitus have been greatly modified by medical science. That modification is not reversible. In fact the methods we use to control reproduction are likely to become even more efficient. We have safe and easy-to-use contraceptives, although the main burden of responsibility for using them will, I believe, continue to rest with women. Abortion and sterilization are simpler than ever before. Already we have home pregnancy testing kits and home abortion drugs are just around the corner. Infertility has been challenged but not conquered; however it is no longer the barrier to parenthood that it once was. Almost daily there appear new diagnostic and therapeutic procedures that ensure safer pregnancy and earlier detection of foetal abnormalities.

The speed with which medical research can tackle herpes and AIDS, the one incurable and the other almost inevitably fatal, will be a decisive factor in future attitudes to sexually transmitted diseases and to sexual encounters in general. New awareness of the prevalence of chlamydia infection will also colour our attitudes towards sex. In the 1970s we got used to living rather carelessly, relying on antibiotics and other medical miracles to get us out of trouble. Now large groups of people are having to modify their sexual behaviour and lifestyles. Although there will always be hard-core sexual game-players and others who take chances, among homosexual and heterosexual populations AIDS has brought about a return to old-fashioned dating behaviour; people want to get to know each other better before they jump into bed. HIV disease is now a significant concern for almost everyone who is sexually active with more than one partner. Unless a medical breakthrough occurs soon — and from now until the end of the century is not long in terms of medical research — AIDS will taint many more sexual relationships. Anyone who intends to be chaste until marriage or until a relationship is established, and to be monogamous thereafter with a monogamous partner, will not have to worry. But statistics show that such lifestyles are becoming increasingly rare. I predict that HIV disease and AIDS will spare few families, touching an aunt or a cousin here, a brother or a friend there.

The DIY abortion pill, RU-486 or a derivative, will be as far-reaching in its effects as the Pill has been in the last 30 years. Will it become universally available? Vested commercial, medical, and religious interests are trying to restrict its use in many countries.

Women, work, and power

Superwoman and Superman are no longer models that women or men feel comfortable with, if they ever did. They demand too much. It also seems that the super-macho male, in North America and Europe at least, has had his day. Economic recession and new technology are obliging both sexes to re-evaluate their social status and roles. However, I do not see the male/female balance, or rather imbalance, of power changing much, unless men suddenly become more willing to take on more tasks in the home and allow women more leadership roles and advancement opportunities outside it. If and how this comes about will differ from country to country, and not always in predictable ways. There will probably be advances in Europe, but elsewhere progress will be patchy. In 1980 a United Nations Convention on the Elimination of All Forms of Discrimination Against Women (CEDAW) drafted a treaty which has still not been ratified by all the industrialized nations; the United States and South Africa have not yet signed, nor have many Third World countries seen fit to do so. And even if they did, I doubt that the treaty would be enforced to any degree. Many governments pledged to abolish slavery under the League of Nations' Slavery Convention of 1926 and the 1948 Universal Declaration of Human Rights made the abolition of slavery one of its cornerstones, but slavery, particularly of women and children, still exists and is growing; only its forms have changed. Forced marriage, debt servitude, and forced prostitution are *de facto* slavery. Britain's Anti-Slavery International organization claimed that in 1992 there were more than 100 million slaves worldwide. Mauretania, Mozambique, Bangladesh,

Pakistan, Kuwait, India, Haiti, and the Dominican Republic are among the most blatant offenders.

It is often said that new technology advantages women rather than men — certainly physical strength becomes academic as soon as machines and microchips take over. But present-generation computers still require keyboard skills, precisely the skills possessed by more women than men. The computer, the fax machine, and the telephone switchboard have propelled very few women, as a proportion of the total female workforce, into positions of power. I see no reason to expect computer skills or technology *per se* to radically alter this state of affairs.

Sophisticated computing and telecommunications equipment will, it is often said, eventually lead to a dispersal of office work; more work will be done via terminals in the home. This will be welcomed by a minority of men. Though some women may also welcome the opportunity of combining their work with looking after babies and children, in a sense the combination is retrograde, a reversal of freedoms that many women have fought hard for since World War II. Now that full-time, well-paid jobs are becoming increasingly scarce, many women are being forced back into part-time, low-paid work, precisely the workstyle they have been fighting to change.

But, overall, the world of 2000 and beyond is a world that men may find more difficult to adjust to than women. Overall I see an era of male readjustment rather than female conquest, an era in which the battle for survival will be more important than the battle of the sexes. We must train our children for an economic and social world rather different from the one we ourselves occupy, and the most realistic target we can aim for is to make the fullest possible range of choice available to everyone. No one should be barred from any work, paid or unpaid, part-time or full-time, in the home or out of the home, on the grounds that not many members of his or her sex do that work. Nor should they be barred from any lifestyle just because it is novel.

President Bush about to be burned in effigy. The addition of a penis is meant to add insult to the political message. Sex itself is political.

Sex ratios

In a previous chapter I discussed the gender imbalance in various Asian countries; there it is females who are missing. In the West, however, females outnumber males. Inevitably this will affect sexual mores. In the West the ratio of adult males to females has been falling since the 1940s. At birth, the ratio between the sexes is about equal, or slightly weighted in favour of males (about 105 males to every 100 females), but as time goes on the situation changes. More men than women die young, in their 20s and 30s, from accidents and injuries. Female deaths from pregnancy and childbirth are now rare in the West. In their middle years men are more vulnerable than women to life-threatening diseases, especially cardiovascular disease. Women also live longer.

By the year 2000 women in their late 20s and early 30s will find a shortage of men for sexual relationships, at least for the long-term sexual relationships that most people, straight and gay, aspire to. But there is no reason to assume that marriage will be knocked off its pedestal. For a percentage of women, however, marriage and long-term partnerships will not be options in the strictly statistical sense. The odds against a woman remarrying after divorce or the death of her husband will be even greater than they are today.

It is unlikely that bigamy or polygamy will suddenly become socially acceptable. But for emotional, economic, erotic, and reproductive reasons many women will be obliged to consider, and society will tacitly accept, mate-sharing. This is a pattern already seen among various black communities in the United States. Sharing may take the form of a man openly having both a wife and a mistress, as is traditional in China and Japan, where such triangular arrangements are not necessarily furtive or frowned upon. Or it might take the form of a man and two women sharing a home and openly acknowledging the sexual component of both relationships. Alternatively, women may have to get used to short-term sexual relationships with men but satisfy their emotional needs through other relationships; multiple friendships would take the place of marriage. Some women might seek sexual satisfaction in lesbian relationships — coitus with a man is no longer a precondition for pregnancy if artificial insemination is available. My own feeling is that few women will choose the lesbian option since sexual orientation is not a matter of convenience and personal and social taboos against homosexual behaviour are still strong. Another mechanism of adjustment might be that more marriages will take place across the divides of generation, race, and religion. The convention of looking for a partner of roughly the same age and social group will simply become less and less practical.

Disparities in sex ratios will have other effects too. In Asian societies, where most marriages are arranged, marriageable females from the upper classes will be at a premium; among the lower classes prostitution will increase, and more females will be bought, hired, or married to serve males as domestics. This is already happening. In the West it is predicted that women will become increasingly competitive with each other, and in ways designed to appeal to men — in looks and willingness to please — precisely the directions that women have been trying to move away from since the 1960s.

The world's population is set to rise from its present 5.4 billion to 8.5 billion by 2025, and 90 per cent of that growth will occur in Third World cities. This is Dhaka, the capital of Bangladesh, which will have a population in excess of 10 million by the year 2000.

People, people, people

I have little doubt that by the year 2000 many of the dire predictions about overpopulation in the Third World will have come to pass. Technological and medical advances available to those of us in industrialized and modern societies will not be available to all. Many countries will react to overpopulation pressures with unprecedentedly stringent attempts to control reproduction and sexual activities. Moves to force sterilization on the populations of India and China were only a first sign of this. China's one-child family policy has made perennial famines a thing of the past. Other countries are considering similar policies. Cuba and Indonesia (the world's fourth most populous country after China, India, and the United States) have set national goals of two children per family by the year 2010. More laws controlling sexual relations — marriage not allowed until after the age of 25, for instance — will be another sign. Contraception and abortion will increasingly be seen as socially beneficial and responsible. In environmentally sensitive countries the emphasis will change from ZPG (Zero Population Growth) to NPG (Negative Population Growth).

As many observers have pointed out, HIV disease and AIDS may actually foster NPG. Without AIDS, Thailand's population is expected to increase to 65 million by the year 2015, but if AIDS continues to spread at its present rate the population in 2015 could be 57 million. Such projections have given the Thai government pause for thought. Resources devoted to

AIDS education programs will save lives and contribute to population growth; resources devoted to family planning will slow down population growth. There is a dilemma here. When resources are limited, as they are in most countries, which has priority, population control or disease control? AIDS has already had a profound impact on the countries of Central Africa and the nations of Asia will be next.

Sexual privacy will be, and has been, one of the first casualties of overcrowding and concern about HIV infection. All forms of sexual behaviour are being subjected to more rather than less public scrutiny. New technology has made snooping easier. Electronic eavesdropping and computer paper trails, phone taps, and video cameras assist vigilant eyes and ears. Anticipating more and more violations of personal privacy, the European Community is working towards introducing uniform privacy laws in the mid-1990s.

Every year 14 million children in the Third World die from malnutrition. This mother and her children, living in a resettlement camp in Mali, lost everything in the 1985 Sahel drought. She smiles for a gift of food for her children.

On the other hand, the press of numbers will offer increased sexual opportunities; the more people you meet the more likely you are to find a sexually compatible and willing partner. Also, for increasing numbers of people, the primary goal of sex will not be reproduction, but recreation and the reduction of stress.

Divorce and marriage

Far from representing a crumbling of the institutions of marriage and the family, the high divorce rates we are seeing today mirror the high hopes, perhaps unrealistically high, that most people have of marriage. Those who bewail the fact that so many marriages in the United States and Britain end in divorce would do well to reflect that an even greater number of marriages manage to survive the pressures of late twentieth-century life. In any case, high divorce rates are not universal. In Japan only 1 in 15 marriages end in divorce; in Italy only 1 in 50 couples divorce. Divorce rates in the United States and Britain have already begun to level off and for economic reasons alone, as times get harder, the rate is likely to drop. Marriage and family will continue to provide the areas of greatest satisfaction in most people's lives.

Alternative lifestyles

In 1992 the European Court of Human Rights ordered the Republic of Ireland to rescind its anti-homosexual laws (anal sex is punishable by life imprisonment), which are in violation of the European Convention on Human Rights. As of January 1993 homosexuality ceased to be classified as a disease by the World Health Organization. As the millennium approaches, discrimination on the basis of sexual orientation will diminish markedly in the West and in modern societies elsewhere. Nudists, transsexuals, transvestites, fetishists, and other

minorities will benefit from this and find fewer obstacles to marriage, adoption, and other social privileges placed in their way.

At the Barcelona Olympics in 1992 chromosome testing of female athletes was dropped. Any individual who lives as a woman should be entitled to compete as a woman and not be confronted with chromosomal anomalies that make a nonsense of years of effort. Eventually, it is hoped, the British legal system will accept that transsexuals are indeed who they say they are, and not defined solely by their chromosomes.

'Sex offender' is a label that will be used with more discrimination. As we saw with prostitution, pornography, EMS, incest, rape, and abortion, different cultures take different views of similar behaviour. Within the next decade, many of the laws that criminalize such practices will have to be reviewed. Flashing and peeping, for example, could become misdemeanours rather than felonies, or decriminalized completely.

Sex teaching

A change I would very much like to predict is better sex education in schools and homes. Many Western societies pretend that childhood sexuality does not exist and keep children damagingly ignorant of their own bodies, and of their physical development and sexual potential. Prodded by HIV disease, most communities now realize that ostrich-like behaviour may not only result in pregnancy and heartache but in death as well. More and better sex education, and more open and matter-of-fact attitudes to sex, would help to prevent unwanted pregnancies and high divorce rates among those who marry young. The teaching of sex techniques in the classroom is still a long way off, although there is a good deal of straightforward biological and social information that could be more effectively presented within present educational frameworks.

Ideal sex education should teach individuals how to make personally relevant decisions rather than copy desirable models, but sexual decision-making is not a skill that is easily taught or a freedom that is easily granted. Also, knowledge must go hand in hand with resources. It is no good knowing about contraceptive methods and safer-sex practices if the necessary devices and drugs are not readily available.

In 1992 sex education became compulsory in Japanese secondary schools; unfortunately, any girl who gets pregnant is automatically barred from school on the grounds that she is a 'poor example'. In the United States and Britain some schools provide special classes for pregnant pupils to teach them how to be good mothers and productive members of society.

Therapy and tolerance

Therapies and counselling services for sexual problems are becoming more numerous and more widely used, and I see no reason why this trend should not continue. It represents not only a liberalizing of attitudes toward sex but also higher personal expectations of sex. Unfortunately, therapy is largely a prerogative of the rich and will remain so until more private and national health administrators realize its value, and I predict they will. Sexual balance is important to health.

Nevertheless, as I have said before, greater tolerance does not automatically translate into changes in sexual practice. Telecommunications, global travel, and contacts with immigrant groups are giving us new perspectives on our own sexual behaviour and helping to dissolve rigid customs and conventions. The direction of this tide of change — from less to more liberal — will not easily be reversed. Of course there will always be exceptions. In Iran, for example, liberal influences were extinguished in a matter of months by a return to Islamic fundamentalism. About-turns are not unusual in countries where democracy is weak or non-existent. But, lest we be too complacent, it is worth noting that, as of the early

1990s, several of the most powerful democracies in the West have governments of a conservative hue; a succession of conservative governments might conceivably redirect the tide of change, but if they did it would not be with the mandate of their electorates.

We should also be wary, in this post-Freudian age, of replacing one collection of inhibitions with another. Many authors have pointed out how we in the West have exchanged concepts like 'sin' and 'shame' in sexual matters for 'neurosis' and 'immaturity'. We are still liable to make judgements about ourselves and each other that may unnecessarily inhibit sexual behaviour, but this tendency is decreasing.

In many Third World countries peasant communities are in conflict with big business. This family in the Dominican Republic, was evicted from subsistence farming land. Many such families crave birth control methods to help their plight.

Conflict

Many of the changes that will come about in the next decade will be won by conflict and confrontation rather than negotiation and mediation. The battle lines will be drawn not only between different religious beliefs and different ideas of morality and the greater good, but between different socioeconomic groups, betweeen cultures (East versus West, North versus South), and between men and women. These divisions have already made themselves felt over issues such as abortion. Gays and AIDS campaigners will escalate their political activities. Proponents and opponents of sex education will plead their causes with equal gusto. Many groups will be playing to the media, but driving them on will be a deep feeling of being correct and an earnest effort to do good. Whatever the issue, all sides will lay claim to the moral high ground, and there will be good points on all sides. We will see more coded battle cries, such as 'right to life', 'freedom of choice', 'erotica not pornography', 'silence equals death', and so on. The conflict will be furious, but the sexwatching will be exciting, and frustrating. Let us hope that the contestants will lob good research data and not just emotional hunches into the fray.

Final words

In terms of personal sexuality the outlook is bright, provided the pitfalls of infection and unwanted pregnancy are avoided. Many options exist and appear to be expanding. We have tacitly accepted the needs of the unmarried adult, and we are learning to recognize the sexual needs and potential of the sick, the handicapped, and the old, even if fashion and advertising continue to be targeted at the young and able-bodied. We accept that many people prefer partners of their own sex, or that others want two and some do not want any and have other ways of satisfying their needs. Instead of having one standard of sexual behaviour for all, we are increasingly tolerant of a flexible array with a great deal of choice.

The disadvantaged and handicapped have as much right to sexual fulfilment as anyone else. In the coming years they too will enjoy a climate of greater tolerance. This couple is helping to lead the way.

What all this means is that fewer people are prepared to put up with second best, with situations that are frustrating, disappointing, or unwanted. Though romance will never be totally abandoned, nor should it be, I think we will become better at tailoring our expectations to the relationships on offer, better at distinguishing between erotic excitement and the pleasures of companionship, and better at looking for reflections of the different facets of ourselves in different people, because all of these things will relieve us of the search for unreachable ideals, and of the burden of unreasonable expectation we place on ourselves and our partners. A world perspective rather than a view of our own backyard is immensely helpful in this respect. If these things come to pass, we will indeed have a more joyous world in which to live, love, and sexwatch.

Chapter 1 *What is sexwatching?*

ABERLE, S. and CORNER, G. *Twenty-five Years of Sex Research*, 1953, Saunders, Philadelphia, Pa.

BARNES, H.J. introduction to Calverton, V.C. *Sex Expression in Literature*, 1926, Boni & Liveright, New York

BLOCH, I. *The Sexual Life of Our Time*, 1912, Allied Book Co., New York

BOSWELL, J. *Christianity, Social Tolerance and Homosexuality*, 1980, University of Chicago Press, Chicago

BULLOUGH, V. and BULLOUGH, B. 'Why the hostility of sex?' in *Sin, Sickness, and Sanity: a history of sexual attitudes*, 10–23, 1977, Meridian Books, New York

DAVIS, J.A. and SMITH, T.W. NORC *General Social Surveys, 1972–1990: Cumulative Codebook*, 1990, National Opinion Research Center, Chicago

ELLIS, H. *Studies in the Psychology of Sex*, 1942, Random House, New York

EPSTEIN, L.M. *Sex Laws and Customs in Judaism*, 1948, KTAV Publishing House, New York

EXNER, M.J. *Problems and Principles of Sex Education: a study of 948 college men*, 1915, Association Press, New York

FAY, R.E., TURNER, C.F., KLASSEN, A.D. and GAGNON, J.H. 'Prevalence and patterns of same-gender sexual contact among men', *Science*, 20 January 1989, *243* : 343–48

FOUCAULT, M. *The History of Sexuality: An Introduction*, Vol. 1, 1980, Viking, New York

FREUD, S. *Three Essays on the Theory of Sexuality*, 1905 (J. Strachey trans.), 1969, Avon, New York

HAEBERLE, E.J. 'The Jewish contribution to the development of sexology', *J. Sex Res.*, 1982, *18* (4): 305–23

HITE, S. *The Hite Report: a nationwide study on female sexuality*, 1976, Macmillan, New York

HITE, S. *The Hite Report on Male Sexuality*, 1981, Alfred A. Knopf, New York

KINSEY, A.C., POMEROY, W.B. AND MARTIN, C.E. *Sexual Behavior in the Human Male*, 1948, Saunders, Philadelphia, Pa.

KINSEY, A.C., POMEROY, W.B., MARTIN, C.E. and GEBHARD, P.H. *Sexual Behavior in the Human Female*, 1953, Saunders, Philadelphia, Pa.

MANTEGAZZA, P. *The Sexual Relations of Mankind* (Samuel Putnam trans.), 1935, Eugenics Publishing, New York

MASTERS, W.H. and JOHNSON, V.E. *Human Sexual Response*, 1966, Little, Brown & Co., Boston, Mass.

MASTERS, W.H. and JOHNSON, V.E. *Human Sexual Inadequacy*, 1970, Little, Brown & Co., Boston, Mass.

MOLL, A. *Die Konträre Sexualempfindung*, 1891, H. Kornfeld, Berlin

MOLL, A. *Untersuchungen über die Libido Sexualis*, 43–44, 1897, Fischers Medizinische Buchhandlung, Berlin

MOLL, A. *The Sexual Life of the Child*, 1890 (trans. 1912), Macmillan, New York

NISSO, *Sexual Practices in the Netherlands*, 1990, Nederlands Instituut voor Sociaal Sexualogisch Onderzoek

Playboy Readers' Sex Survey, 1983, Part One (Jan): 108, 241–2, 244, 246, 250; Part Two (Mar): 90, 92, 178, 180, 182, 184; Part Three (May): 126, 128, 136, 210, 212, 215, 216, 219, 220; Part Four (Jul): 130, 132, 192, 193, 196–8, 200, 203; Part Five (Sep): 92, 94, 96, 182, 184, 185, 186, 187, 188

RUBIN, G. 'Thinking sex: notes for a radical theory of the politics of sexuality', *Pleasure and Danger*, 1984,

Routledge & Kegan Paul, Boston, Mass.

TAVRIS, C. and SADD, S. *The Redbook Report on Female Sexuality*, 1979, Dell Books, New York

TIEFER, L. 'Historical, scientific, clinical and feminist criticisms of "The Human Sexual Response Cycle" model, *Ann. Rev. Sex Res.*, 1991, 2 : 1–23

WELLINGS, K., FIELD, J., WADSWORTH, A.M., JOHNSON, A.M., ANDERSON, R.M. and BRADSHAW, S.A. 'Sexual Lifestyles under scrutiny', *Nature*, 22 November 1990, *348* : 276–78

WOLFE, L. *The Cosmo Report: women and sex in the 80s*, 1982, Bantam Books, New York

Chapter 2 *Excitement and arousal*

ASSOCIATION, A.P. *Diagnostic and Statistical Manual of Mental Disorders*, 1987, American Psychiatric Association, Washington DC

BAILEY, R.C., CHOROSEVIC, T., WHITE, D. and WHITE, H. 'Physiological arousal and perceptions of a member of the opposite sex', *J. Soc. Psychol.*, 1981, *115* : 271–276

BANCROFT, J. *Human Sexuality and its Problems*, 1983, Churchill Livingstone, Edinburgh

BANCROFT, J. 'The relationship between hormones and sexual behavior in humans', in Hutchison, J.B. (ed.) *Biological Determinants of Sexual Behavior*, 1978, Wiley, New York

BECK, J.G., BOZMAN, A.W. and QUALTROUGH, T. 'The experience of sexual desire: psychological correlates in a college sample, *J. Sex Res.*, 1991, *28* (3): 443–456

CLARK, R.D. and HATFIELD, E. 'Gender differences in receptivity to sexual offers', *J. Psychol. & Hum. Sex.*, 1989, 2 (1): 39–55

DAVENPORT, W.H. 'Sex in cross-cultural perspective', in Beach, F.A. (ed.) *Human Sexuality in Four Perspectives*, 115–163, 1876, Johns Hopkins University Press, Baltimore, Md.

DEKKER, J. and EVERARD, W. 'A study suggesting two kinds of information processing of the sexual response', *Arch. Sex. Behav.*, 1989, *18* (5): 435–438

DION, K.K. 'Physical attractiveness, sex roles and heterosexual attraction', in Cook, M. (ed.) *The Basis of Human Sexual Attraction*, 3–22, 1981, Academic Press, London

DOTY, R.L. 'Olfactory communication in humans', *Chemical Senses*, 1981, 6 (4): 351–376

DUTTON, D.G. and ARON, A.P. 'Some evidence for heightened sexual attraction under conditions of high anxiety', *J. Pers. & Soc. Psychol.*, 1974, *30* (4): 510–517

HATFIELD, E. and SPRECHER, S. *Mirror, Mirror: the importance of looks in everyday life*, 1986, SUNY Press, Albany NY

EIMAN, J.R. 'Women's sexual arousal', *Psychol. Today*, April 1975: 91–94

GOLDBERG, R.L. and WISE, T.N. 'The importance of the sense of smell in human sexuality', *J. Sex Ed. & Ther.*, 1990, 16 (4): 236–241

JOY, K. and YOUNG, A. *The Gay Report: lesbians and gay men speak out about sexual experiences and lifestyles*, 1977, Summit Books, New York

KAPLAN, H.S. 'Hypoactive sexual desire', *J. Sex. & Mar. Ther.*, 1977, 3 : 3–9

LEVIN, R.J. and WAGNER, G. 'Orgasm in women in the laboratory: qualitative studies on duration, intensity, latency, and vaginal blood flow', *Arch. Sex. Behav.*, 1985, 14 (5): 439–450

O'CARROLL, R. 'Sexual desire disorders: a review of controlled treatment studies', *J. Sex Res.*, 1991, *28* (4): 607–624

O'DONOHUE, W. and GEER, J.H. 'The habituation of sexual arousal', *Arch. Sex. Behav.*, 1985, *14* (3): 233–246

ROSEN, R.C. and BECK, J.G. *Patterns of sexual*

arousal: psychophysiological processes & clinical applications, Guilford Press, New York

SALMON, U.J. and GEIST, S.H. 'Effect of androgens upon libido in women', *J. Clin. Edocrin.*, 1943, 3 : 235–238

SCHACHTER, S. and SINGER, J.E. 'Cognitive, social and psychological determinants of emotional state', *Psychol. Rev.*, 1962, 69 : 379–399

SCHNARCH, D.M. *Constructing the Sexual Crucible: an integration of sexual and marital therapy*, 1991, W.W. Norton, New York

SPRAGUE, J. and QUADAGNO, D. 'Gender and sexual motivation: an exploration of two assumptions', *J. Psychol. & Hum. Sex.*, 1989, 2 (1): 57–76

STEINMAN, D.L., WINCZE, M.S., SAKHEIM, J.P., BARLOW, D.H. and MAVISSAKALIAN, M. 'A comparison of male and female patterns of sexual arousal', *Arch. Sex. Behav.*, 1981, 10 (6): 529–547

WARNER, P., BANCROFT, J and members of the Edinburgh Human Sexuality Group 'A regional service for sexual problems: a three-year study', *J. Sex. & Mar. Ther.*, 1987, 2 : 115–126

WOLFE, L. *The Cosmo Report: Women and Sex in the 80s*, op. cit. Chapter 1

Chapter 3 *The body you love with*

BAR-TAL, D. and SAXE, L. 'Perceptions of similarly and dissimilarly attractive couples and indivuals', *J. Pers. & Soc. Psychol.*, 1976, *33* : 772–781

BOSTON WOMEN'S HEALTH BOOK COLLECTIVE *Our Bodies, Ourselves: a health book by and for women*, first edition 1973, Simon & Shuster, New York

BURTON, S.W., BURN, S.B., MASON, M. and McKERROW, G. 'AIDS Information' (letter), *Lancet*, 1986, 2 : 1040–1041

COOK, M. (ed.) *The Basis of Human Sexual Attraction*, 1981, Academic Press, London

DICKINSON, R.L. *Human Sex Anatomy*, 1933, Williams & Wilkins, Baltimore, Md.

DION, K., BERSHEID, E. and WALSTER, G.W. 'What is beautiful is good', *J. Pers. & Soc. Psychol.*, 1972, *24* : 285–290

DODSON, B. *Liberating Masturbation: a meditation on self-love*, 1974, Betty Dodson, New York

FRANKFURT, E. 'Vaginal Politics', in Dreifus, C. (ed.) *Seizing Our Bodies: the politics of women's health*, 263–269, 1977, Vintage Books, New York

GARNER, D., GARFINKEL, F. and MOLODOFSKY, H. 'Perceptual experiences in anorexia nervosa and obesity', *Canad. Psychiatric Assoc. J.*, 1978, 23 : 249–263

GRAFENBERG, E. 'The role of the urethra in female orgasm', *Int. J. Sexol.*, 1950, 3 : 145–148

HARTMAN, W.E. and FITHIAN, M.A. *Treatment of Sexual Dysfunction: a bio-psycho-social approach*, 1972, Center for Marital and Sexual Studies, California

HITE, S. *The Hite Report: a nationwide study on female sexuality*, op. cit. Chapter 1

HUNT, M. *Sexual Behavior in the 1970s*, Dell Books, New York

JOY, K. and YOUNG, A. *The Gay Report: lesbian and gay men speak out about sexual experiences and lifestyles*, op. cit. Chapter 2

KINSEY, A.C., POMEROY, W.D. and MARTIN, C.E. *Sexual Behavior in the Human Male*, op. cit. Chapter 1

LADAS, A.K., WHIPPLE, B. and PERRY, J. *The G Spot and Other Recent Discoveries about Human Sexuality*, 1982, Holt, Rinehart & Winston, New York

LANVAL, M. *L'Amour sous le Masque*, 1946,

Le Laurier, Brussels (translated as *An Inquiry into the Intimate Lives of Women*, 1950, Cadillac Publishing, New York)

LOWRY, T.P. (ed.) *The Classic Clitoris: historic contributions to scientific sexuality*, 1978, Nelson-Hall, Chicago

MASTERS, W.H., JOHNSON, V.E. and KOLODNY, R.C. *Masters and Johnson on Sex and Human Loving*, 1986, Little, Brown & Co., Boston, Mass.

MILLER, A. 'Role of physical attractiveness in impression formation', *Psychonom. Science*, 1970, 19 : 241–243

PERRIN, F.A.C. 'Physical attractiveness and repulsiveness', *J. Exper. Psychol.*, 1921, 41 : 203–217

SHEIKH NEFZAOUI, *The Perfumed Garden*, 1964, Lancer Books, New York

SIGAL, H. and LANDY, D. 'Radiating beauty: the effects of having a physically attractive partner on person perception', *J. Pers. & Soc. Psychol.*, 1973, 28 : 218–224

SPADA, J. *The Spada Report: the newest survey of gay male sexuality today*, 1979, New American Library, New York

SPITZ, F. *The First Year of Life*, 1965, International University Press, New York

VOELLER, B. 'Heterosexual anal intercourse: an AIDS risk factor', in *AIDS and Sex*, 1990, Oxford University Press, New York

WALLER, W. 'The rating and dating complex', *Am. Sociol. Rev.*, 1937, 2 : 727–734

WALSTER, E., ARONSON, V., ABRAHAMS, D. and ROTTMAN, L. 'Importance of physical attractiveness in dating behavior', *J. Pers. & Soc. Psychol.*, 1972, 24 : 285–290

WALSTER, E. and WALSTER, G.W. *A New Look at Love*, 1978, Addison Wesley, Boston, Mass.

WEIS, D.L. 'The experience of pain during woman's first sexual intercourse: cultural mythology about female sexual initiation', *Arch. Sex. Behav.*, 1985, 14 (5): 421–438

WHITTEN, P. and WHITESIDE, E.J. 'Can exercise make you sexier?', *Psychol. Today*, April 1989: 42, 44

ZAVIACIC, M. 'Female urethral expulsions evoked by local digital stimulation of the G spot: differences in response patterns', *J. Sex. Res.*, 1988, 24 : 311–318

ZAVIACIC, M., ZAVIACICOVA, A., HOLOMAN, I.K. and MOLCAN, J. 'Concentrations of fructose in female ejaculate and urine: a comparative biochemical study', *J. Sex Res.*, 1988, 24 : 319–325

Chapter 4 *Aphrodisiacs and anaphrodisiacs*

CONDRA, M., MORALES, A., OWEN, J.A., SURRIDGE D.H. and FENEMORE, J. 'Prevalence and significance of tobacco smoking on impotence', *Urology*, 1986, 27 : 495–498

DIAMOND, M. and KAPLAN, A. *Sexual Decisions*, 1980, Little, Brown & Co., Boston

DOUGLAS, N. *Paneros*, 74–75, 1932, Robert McBride, New York

GAWIN, F.H. 'Pharmacologic enhancement of the erotic: implications of an expanded definition of aphrodisiacs', *J. Sex Res.*, 1978, 14 (2): 107–117

KAPLAN, H.S. *The New Sex Therapy: active treatment of sexual dysfunction*, 1974, Brunner/Mazel, New York

KOLODNY, R.C., MASTERS, W.H. and JOHNSON, V.E. *Textbook of Sexual Medicine*, 1979, Little, Brown & Co., Boston, Mass.

LASHET, U. 'Antiandrogens in the treatment of sex offenders', in Zubin, J. and Money, J. (eds.) *Contemporary Sexual Behavior: critical issues in the 70s*, 311–320, 1973, Johns Hopkins University Press, Baltimore, Md.

McILVENNA, R.L. *The Pleasure Quest: the search for aphrodisiacs*, 1988, Specific Press (for the Institute for Advanced Study of Human Sexuality), San Francisco

ROSEN, R.C. 'Alcohol and drug effects on sexual response: human experimental and clinical studies', *Ann. Rev. Sex. Res.*, 1991, 2 : 119–180

SCHIAVI, R.C. 'Chronic alcoholism and male sexual function', *J. Sex & Mar. Ther.*, 1990, 16 : 23–33

SEGRAVES, R.T. 'Pharmacological enhancement of human sexual behavior', *J. Sex Ed. & Ther.*, 1991, 17 (4): 283–289

TABERNER, P.V. *Aphrodisiacs: the science and the myth*, 1985, University of Pennsylvania Press, Philadelphia, Pa.

Chapter 5 *Body language*

BACKMANN, G., LEIBLUM, S.R., KEMMANN, E., COLBURN, D.W., SWARTZMAN, L. and SHELDEN, R. 'Sexual expression and its determinants in the post-menopausal woman', *Maturitas*, 1984, 6 : 12–29

BUSSE, E. 'Sexual attitudes and behavior in the elderly', *Geriat. Focus*, 1973, 12 : 1–7

DAVIDSON, J.M., GRAY, G.D. and SMITH E.R. 'The sexual psychoendocrinology of aging', *Neuroendocrin. Ag.*, 1983, Plenum Press, New York

DIAMOND, M. and KARLEN, A. 'The Sexual Response Cycle', in Lief, H. (ed.) *Sexual Problems in Medical Practice*, 37–51, 1981, American Medical Association, Chicago

HALLSTROM, T. 'Changes in women's sexual desire in middle life: the longitudinal study of women in Gothenberg', *Arch. Sex. Behav.*, 1990, 19 : 259–268

HITE, S. *The Hite Report: a nationwide study on female sexuality*, op. cit. Chapter 1

KAPLAN, H.S. *Sexual Aversion, Sexual Phobias and Panic Disorder*, 1987, Brunner/Mazel, New York

KINSEY, A.C., POMEROY, W.B. and MARTIN, C.E. *Sexual Behavior in the Human Male*, op. cit. Chapter 1

KINSEY, A.C., POMEROY, W.B., MARTIN, C.E. and GEBHARD, P.H. *Sexual Behavior in the Human Female*, op. cit. Chapter 1

MASTERS, W.H. and JOHNSON, V.E. *Human Sexual Response*, op. cit. Chapter 1

PFEIFFER, E., VERWOERDT, A. and WANG, H.-S. 'Sexual behavior in aged men and women: observations on 254 community volunteers', *Arch. Gen. Psychiat.*, 1968, 19 (6): 753–8

SHERWIN, B.B. 'The psychoendocrinology of aging and female sexuality', *Ann. Rev. Sex Res.*, 1991, 2 : 181–198

SINGER, I. *The Goals of Orgasm*, 1973, Schocken, New York

TAVRIS, C. and SADD, S. *The Redbook Report on Female Sexuality*, op. cit. Chapter 1

TIEFER, L. 'Historical, scientific, clinical and feminist criticisms of "The Human Sexual Response Cycle" model', op. cit. Chapter 1

WOLFE, L. *The Cosmo Report: women and sex in the 80s*, op. cit. Chapter 1

Chapter 6 *Growing up*

ALZATE, H. 'Sexual behavior of unmarried Columbian university students: a follow-up', *Arch. Sex. Behav.*, 1989, 18 (3): 239–250

ASSOCIATION, P.H. 'Major study shows change in contraception, fertility', *The Nation's Health*, January 1985:3

BRESLER, F. *Sex and the Law*, 1988, Frederick Muller, London

CALDERONE, M.S. 'Fetal erection and its message', SIECUS Report, May–July 1983: 9–10

CLEMENT, U., SCHMIDT, G. and KRUSE, M. 'Changes in sex differences in sexual behavior: a replication of a study of West German students 1966–1981', *Arch. Sex. Behav.*, 1984, 13 (2): 99–120

DIAMOND, M. 'A critical evaluation of the ontogeny of human sexual behavior', *Quart. Rev. Biology*, 1965, 40 : 147–75 1965

DIAMOND, M. 'Human sexual development: biological foundations for social development', in Beach F.A. (ed.) *Human Sexuality in Four Perspectives*, 1977, Johns Hopkins University Press, Baltimore, Md.

DIAMOND, M. 'Sexual identity and sex roles', *The Humanist*, March–April 1978: 16–19

DIAMOND, M. 'Sexual identity and sex roles', in Bullough, V. (ed.) *The Frontiers of Sex Research*, 39–56, 1979, Prometheus Press, Buffalo, NY

DIAMOND, M. 'Sexual identity, monozygotic twins reared in discordant sex roles, and a BBC follow-up', *Arch. Sex. Behav.*, 1982, 11 (2): 181–185

DIAMOND, M. and DIAMOND, G.H. 'Adolescent sexuality: biological aspects and intervention strategies', *J. Social Work & Hum. Sex.*, 1986, 5 (1): 3–13

DIAMOND, M. 'Selected cross-generational sexual behavior in traditional Hawaii: a sexological ethnography', in Feierman J. (ed.) *Pedophilia: biosocial dimensions* , 422–444, 1990, Springer, New York

FEINLIEB, M.R. Report of the Secretary's Task Force on Youth Suicide, 1989, U.S. Department of Health and Human Services

GAGNON, J.H. 'Attitudes and responses of parents to pre-adolescent masturbation', *Arch. Sex. Behav.*, 1985, 14 (5): 451–466

HATANO, Y. 'Changes in the sexual activities of Japanese youth', *J. Sex Ed. & Ther.*, 1991, 17 (1): 1–14

HELMIUS, G. *Mogen for sex? (mature enough for sex?): the sexually restricting society and adolescent heterosexual joy*, 1990, Graphic Systems, Stockholm

KALLMAN, F.J. *Heredity in Health and Mental Disorder*, 1953, W.W. Norton, New York

KINSEY, A.F., POMEROY, W.B. and MARTIN, C.E. *Sexual Behavior in the Human Male*, op. cit. Chapter 1

KINSEY, A.C., POMEROY, W.B., MARTIN, C.E. and GEBHARD, P.H. *Sexual Behavior in the Human Female*, op. cit. Chapter 1

MARSHALL, D.S. 'Sexual behavior on Mangaia', in Marshall, D.S. and Suggs, R.C. (eds.) *Human Sexual Behavior*, 103–163, 1971, Basic Books, New York

MARSIGLIO, W. and MOTT, F. 'The impact of sex education on sexual activity, contraceptive use and premarital pregnancy among American teenagers', *Fam. Plan. Persp.*, 1986, 18 : 151–162

MARTINSON, F. *Infant and Child Sexuality: a sociological perspective*, 1973, Gustavus Adolphus College Press, St. Peter, Minn.

MESSENGER, J.C. 'Sex and repression in an Irish folk community', in Marshall, D.S. and Suggs, R.C. (eds.), *Human Sexual Behavior*, op. cit. above

MONEY, J. and EHRHARDT, A. *Man and Woman, Boy and Girl*, 1972, Johns Hopkins University Press, Baltimore, Md.

MONEY, J., HAMPSON, J.G. and HAMPSON, J.L. 'Hermaphroditism: recommendations concerning assignment of sex, change of sex and psychological management', *Bull. Johns Hopkins Hospital*, 1955, 97 : 284–300

PHOENIX, C.H., GOY, R.W. and RESKO, J.A. 'Psychosexual differentiation as a function of androgenic stimulation', in Diamond M. (ed.) *Perspectives in Reproduction and Sexual Behavior*, 33–49, 1968, Indiana University Press, Bloomington, Ind.

Population Reports, 1985, *Youth in the 1980s: social and health concerns*

RABOCH, J. and BARTAK, V. 'Changes in the sexual life of Czechoslovak women born between 1911 and 1958', *Arch. Sex. Behav.*, 1980, 9 (6): 477–94

RABOCH, J. and BARTAK, V. 'Coitarche and orgastic capacity', *Arch. Sex. Behav.*, 1983, 12 (5): 409–413

REMAFEDI, G. 'Fundamental issues in the care of homosexual youth', *Med. Clin. North Am.*, 1990, 74 : 1169

REMAFEDI, G., FARROW, J.A. and DEISHER, R.W. 'Risk factors for attempted suicide in gay and bisexual youth', *Pediatrics*, 1991, 87 (6): 869–875

ROSCOE, W. *The Zuni Man-Woman*, 1991, University of New Mexico Press, Albuquerque, N. Mex.

RUBINSON, L. and De RUBERTIS, L. 'Trends in sexual attitudes and behavior of a college population over a 15-year period', *J. Sex Ed. & Ther.*, 1991, 17 (1): 32–41

SCHOFIELD, M. *The Sexual Behaviour of Young Adults*, 1973, Allen Lane, London

SCHOOF-TAMS, K., SCHAEGEL, J. and WALCZAK, L. 'Differentiation of sexual morality between 11 and 16 years', *Arch. Sex. Behav.*, 1976, 5 : 353–370

Sexual Activity of Youth: a survey report on high school and college students in Japan, 1981, Japanese Association for Sex Education, Tokyo

WELLINGS, K., FIELD, J., WADSWORTH, A.M., JOHNSON, A.M., ANDERSON, R.M. and BRADSHAW, S.A. 'Sexual lifestyles under scrutiny', *Nature*, 22 November 1990, 348 : 276–278

WIELAND, H., BOLDSEN, J. and JEUNE, B. 'Age of partners at first intercourse among Danish males and females', *Arch. Sex. Behav.*, 1989, 18 (5): 449–454

WYATT, G.E. 'Re-examining factors predicting Afro-American and white American women's age at first coitus', *Arch. Sex. Behav.*, 1989, 18 (4): 271–298

ZELNICK, M. and KANTNER, J.F. 'Sexual activity, contraceptive use and pregnancy among metropolitan-area teenagers: 1971–1979', *Fam. Plan. Persp.* 1980, 12 (5): 230–7

Chapter 7 *Sexual patterns*

BLUMSTEIN, P. and SCHWARTZ, P. American *Couples: money, work, sex*, 1983, William Morrow Survey, New York; also *Attitudes of Married Men*, 1980, Benton and Bowles Research Surveys, New York

BOUCHARD, T.J., LYKKEN, D.T., McGUE, M., SEGAL, N.L. and TELLEGEN, A. 'Sources of human psychological differences: the Minnesota study of twins reared apart', *Science*, 1990, 250 : 223–228

CLARK, R.D. and HATFIELD, E. 'Gender differences in receptivity to sexual offers', op. cit. Chapter 2

DAHLSTROM, E. and LILJESTROM, R. 'The family and married women at work', in Dahlstrom, E. (ed.) *The Changing Roles of Men and Women*, 19–58, 1971, Beacon Press, Boston, Mass.

DIAMOND, M. 'Sexual identity and sex roles', op. cit. Chapter 6

FREIDL, E. *Women and Men: an anthropologist's view*, 1975, Holt, Rinehart & Winston, New York

GAGNON, J.H. and SIMON, W. *Sexual Conduct: the social origins of human sexuality*, 1973, Aldine, Chicago

GILLIGAN, C. *In a Different Voice: psychological theory and women's development*, 1982, Harvard University Press, Cambridge, Mass.

HITE, S. *Women and Love: a cultural revolution in progress*, 1987, Alfred A. Knopf, New York

KLASSEN, A.D., WILLIAMS, C.J. and LEVITT, E.E. *Sex and morality in the United States: an empirical inquiry under the auspices of the Kinsey Institute*, 1989, Wesleyan Press, Middletown, Conn.

McCRAE, R.R. and COSTA, P.T.J. 'The structure of interpersonal traits: Wiggin's circumplex and the five-factor model', *J. Pers. & Soc. Psychol.*, 1989, 65 (4): 586–595

SCOTT, H. *Does Socialism liberate Women?*, 1974, Beacon Press, Boston, Mass.

SYMONS, D. *The Evolution of Human Sexuality*, 1979, Oxford University Press, Oxford

YOUNG, M.B. (ed.) *Women in China: studies in social change and feminism*, 1973, University of Michigan Press, Ann Arbor, Mich.

Chapter 8 *On being different*

ACKROYD, P. *Dressing up — Transvestism and Drag: the history of an obsession*, 1979, Simon & Schuster, New York

ARMSTRONG, C.N. and WALTON, T. 'Transsexuals and the law', *New Law J.*, 5 October 1990: 1384, 1389–1390

BELL, A.P. and WEINBERG, M.S. *Homosexualities: a study of diversity among men and women*, 1978, Simon & Schuster, New York

BELL, A., WEINBERG, M.S. and Hammersmith, S.K. *Sexual Preference: its development in men and women*, 1981, Indiana University Press, Bloomington, Ind.

BENJAMIN, H. *The Transsexual Phenomenon*, 1966, Julian Press, New York

BOSWELL, J. *Christianity, Social Tolerance and Homosexuality*, 1980, University of Chicago Press, Chicago

COSSEY, C. *My Story*, 1991, Faber & Faber, London

DIAMOND, M. and KARLEN, A. *Sexual Decisions*, op. cit. Chapter 4

DIAMOND, M. 'Selected cross-generational sexual behavior in traditional Hawaii: a sexological ethnography', op. cit. Chapter 6

DIAMOND, M. 'Homosexuality and bisexuality in different populations', *Arch. Sex. Behav.* (in press)

DIAMOND, M. WHITAM, F.L. and DANNEMILLER, J.E. 'Homosexuality in male twins', World Association for Sexology 1987

FADERMAN, L. *Odd Girls and Twilight Lovers: a history of lesbian life in twentieth-century America*, 1991, Columbia University Press, New York

FINKELHOR, D. 'Sex among siblings: a survey on prevalence, variety and effects', *Arch. Sex. Behav.*, 1980, 9 :171–194

FORD, C. and BEACH, F.A. *Patterns of Sexual Behavior*, 1951, Harper & Row, New York

GEBHARD, P.H., GAGNON, J.H., POMEROY, W.B. and CHRISTENSON, C. *Sex Offenders*, 1965, Harper & Row, New York

HERDT, G.H. *Guardians of the Flute: idioms of masculinity*, 1981, McGraw-Hill, New York

HUMPHREYS, L. *Tearoom Trade: impersonal sex in public places*, 1975, Aldine, Chicago

IMPERATO-McGINLEY, J., GUERRERO, L. and GAUTIER, T. 'Steroid 5a-reductase deficiency in man: an inherited form of pseudohermaphroditism', *New England J. Med.*, 1974, 186 : 1213–1215

IMPERATO-McGINLEY, J. and PETERSON, R.E. 'Male pseudohermaphroditism: the complexities of male phenotypic development', *Amer. J. Med.*, 1976, 61 : 251–272

IMPERATO-McGINLEY, J., PETERSON, R.E., GAUTIER, T. and STURLA, E. 'Androgen and evolution of male gender identity among male pseudohermaphrodites with 5a-reductase deficiency', *New Eng. J. Med.*, 1979, 300 : 1233–1237

KARLEN, A. *Sexuality and Homosexuality*, 1971, W.W. Norton, New York

KINSEY, A.C., POMEROY, W.B., MARTIN, C.E. and GEBHARD, P.H. *Sexual Behavior in the Human Female*, op. cit. Chapter 1

MARSHALL, R. 'A blow below the belt', *Newsweek*, 1 July 1991: 39

MORRIS, J. *Conundrum*, 1974, Harcourt Brace Jovanovich, New York

NELSON, J. 'Incest: self-report findings from a non-clinical sample', *J. Sex Res.*, 1986, 22 : 463–477

OVERZIER, C. (ed.) *Intersexuality*, 1963, Academic Press, London

ROSCOE, W. *The Zuni Man-Woman*, op. cit. Chapter 6

SCHIEFENHOVEL, W. 'Ritualized adult male/adolescent-male sexual behavior in Melanesia: an anthropological and ethological perspective', in Feierman, J. (ed.) *Pedophilia: biosocial dimensions*, 1990, Springer, New York

SPONG, J.S. *Rescuing the Bible from Fundamentalism*, 1991, Harper, New York

TRIPP, C.A. *The Homosexual Matrix*, 1975, McGraw-Hill, New York

WALLACE, I., WALLACE, A., WALLECHINSKY, D. and WALLACE, S. *The Intimate Sex Lives of Famous People*, 1982, Dell Books, New York

WHITAM, F.L. 'Childhood indicators of male homosexuality', *Arch. Sex. Behav.*, 1977, 6 : 89–96

WHITAM, F.L. and DIAMOND, M. *The Sexual Orientation of Homosexual Twins*, 1985, International Academy of Sex Research

WHITAM, F.L. and DIAMOND, M. *A Preliminary Report on the Sexual Orientation of Homosexual Twins*, 1986, Society for the Scientific Study of Sex (Western Region)

WHITAM, F.L. and DIAMOND, M. 'Homosexual orientation in twins: a report on 61 pairs and three triplet sets,' *Arch. Sex. Behav.*, 1992 (in press)

WHITAM, F.L., DIAMOND, M. and VACHA, A T. *An Analysis of the Sexual Fantasies of Fraternal and Identical Male Homosexual Twins*, 1988, Society for the Scientific Study of Sex

WHITAM, F.L. and MATHY, R. *Homosexuality in Four Cultures*, 1988, Praeger, New York

Chapter 9 *Loves compared*

BUSCAGLIA, L.F. *Love*, 1972, Charles B. Slack, Thorotare, NJ

CASLER, L. 'Perceptual deprivation in institutional settings', in Newton, G. and Levine, S. (eds.) *Early Experience and Behavior*, 1986, Springer, New York

DE ROUGEMONT, D. *Love in the Western World* (M. Belgion trans.), 1966, Fawcett, New York

ELLIS, A. *The Art and Science of Love*, 1960, Lyle Stuart Books, New York

GOCHROS, H.L., GOCHROS, J.S., and FISCHER, J. (eds.) *Helping the Sexually Oppressed*, 282, 1986, Prentice-Hall, Englewood Cliffs, NJ

GUYON, R. *The Ethics of Sexual Acts* (J.C. and I. Flugel trans.), 1934, Alfred A. Knopf, New York

HARLOW, H.F. *Learning to Love*, 1974, Aronson, New York

JECKER, J. and LANDY, D. 'Liking a person as a function of doing him a favour', *Hum. Relations*, 1969, 22 (4): 371–8

LEE, J.A. *Colours of Love: an exploration of the ways of loving*, 1973, New Press, Toronto

NOVAK, M.A. and HARLOW, H.F. 'Social recovery of monkeys isolated for the first year of life', *Dev. Psychol.*, 1975, 11 : 453–465

PEELE, S. and BRODSKY, A. *Love and Addiction*, 1976, New American Library, New York

PRESCOTT, J.W. 'Alienation of affection', *Psychol. Today*, December 1979: 124

RUBIN, Z. *Liking and Loving*, 1973, Holt, Rinehart &

Winston, New York

SOLOMON, R.C. *Love: emotion, myth and metaphor*, 1981, Anchor Press, New York

SPITZ, R.R. 'Hospitalism: a follow-up report', in Fenichel, D., Greenacre, P. and Freud, A. (eds.) *Psychoanalytic Studies of the Child*, 113–117, 1947, International Universities Press, New York

STERNBERG, R.J. 'A triangular theory of love', *Psychol. Rev.*, 1986, 93 : 119–135

SUOMI, S.J., HARLOW, H.F., and McKINNEY, W.T. 'Monkey psychiatrists', *Am. J. Psych.*, 1971, 128 : 41–46

TENNOV, D. *Love and Limerence: the experience of being in love*, 1979, Stein & Day, New York

WALSTER, E. and WALSTER, W.G. *A New Look at Love*, 1980, Addison-Wesley, Reading, Mass.

Chapter 10 *Relationships*

AVERY, C.S. 'How do you built intimacy in an age of divorce?', *Psychology*, May 1989: 27–31

BARTELL, G.D. *Group Sex*, 1971, New American Library, New York

BLUMSTEIN, P.W. and SCHWARTZ, P. *American Couples*, 1983, William Morrow, New York

BROWDER, S. 'Is living together such a good idea?', *New Woman*, June 1988: 120–124

BUMPASS, L.L. and McLANAHAN, S. 'Unmarried motherhood', *Demography*, 1989, 26 : 279–286

CAPLAN, P.J. *The Myth of Women's Masochism*, 1985, E.P. Dutton, New York

CAREY, J.J. *Presbyterians and Human Sexuality* (203rd General Assembly response to the report of the special committee on human sexuality), 1991, Presbyterian Church, USA

CUPACH, W.R. and COMSTOCK, J. 'Satisfaction with sexual communication in marriage: links to sexual satisfaction and dyadic adjustment', *J. Soc. & Pers. Rel.*, 1990, 7 (2): 179–186

DODDRIDGE, R., SCHUMM, W. and BERGER, M. 'Factors related to decline in preferred frequency of sexual intercourse among young couples', *Psychol. Reports*, 1987, 60 : 391–395

FARREL, W. *Why men are the way they are*, 1986, McGraw-Hill, New York

French Institute of Public Opinion, *Patterns of Sex and Love*, 1961, Panther Books, London

GILMARTIN, B. 'Swinging: who gets involved and how', in Libby, R.W. and Whitehurst, R.N. (eds.) *Marriage and Alternatives*, 161–85, 1977, Scott Foresman, Glenview, Ill.

GORER, G. *Sex and Marriage in England Today*, 1971, Nelson, London

GREELEY, A.M., MICHAEL, R.T. and SMITH, T.W. 'Americans and their sexual partners', *Society*, 1990, 27 (5): 36–42

GUTTENTAG, M. and SECORD, P.F. *Too Many Women: the sex ratio question*, 1983, Sage Publications, Beverly Hills, Ca.

HOFFMAN, S. *Men who are good for you and men who are bad: learning to tell the difference*, 1987, Ten Speed Press, Berkeley, Ca.

HUNT, M. *The Affair: a portrait of extramarital love in contemporary America*, 1969, New American Library, New York

KARLEN, A. *Threesomes: studies in sex, power and intimacy*, 1988, Beech Tree/Morrow, New York

KINSEY, A.C., POMEROY, W.B. and MARTIN, C.E. *Sexual Behavior in the Human Male*, op. cit. Chapter 1

KINSEY, A.C., POMEROY, W.B., MARTIN, C.E. and GEBHARD, P.H. *Sexual Behavior in the Human Female*, 1953 , op. cit. Chapter 1

LAWSON, A. *Adultery: an analysis of love and betrayal*, 1988, Basic Books, New York

MASTERS, W.H. and JOHNSON, V.E. *The Pleasure Bond*, 1975, Little, Brown & Co., Boston, Mass.

McNEIL, L. 'Love among the ruins', *Details*, 1992, 10 (10): 32, 33, 35, 38, 40, 42

McWHIRTER, D. and MATTISON, A. *The Male Couple*, 1983, Prentice-Hall, Englewood Cliffs, NJ

NORTON, A.J. and MOORMAN, J.E. 'Current trends in marriage and divorce among American women', *J. Marriage & Fam.*, 1987, 49 : 3–14

NORWOOD, R. *Women who love too much: when you keep wishing and hoping he'll change*, 1985, St. Martin's Press, New York

PIETROPINTO, A. *Husbands and Wives*, 1979, Time Books, New York

Playboy Readers' Sex Survey, 1983, Part Four (Jul): 130 & passim

REISS, I.L., ANDERSON, R.E. and SPONAUGLE, G.C. 'A multivariate model of the determinants of extramarital sexual permissiveness', *J. Marriage & Fam.*, 1980, 42 : 395–411

SCOTT, J.W. 'From teenage parenthood to polygamy: case studies in black polygamous family formation', *Western J. Black Studies*, 1986, 10 (4): 172–179

SKINNER, B.F. 'Origins of a behaviorist', *Psychol. Today*, September 1983: 22–33

SPANIER, G. and MARGOLIS, R. 'Marital separation and extramarital sexual behavior', *J. Sex Res.*, 1983, 19 (1): 23–48

SPRECHER, S. 'Has the double standard disappeared? An experimental test', *Soc. Psychol. Quart.*, March 1987: 24–31

THAYER, N.S.T. et al. Report of task force on changing patterns of sexuality and family life, 1987, Episcopal Church, Newark, NJ

THOMPSON, A.P. 'Extramarital sex: a review of the research literature', *J. Sex Res.*, 1983, 19 (1): 1–22

WATSON, R. and DeMEO, P. 'Premarital cohabitation vs. traditional courtship and subsequent marital adjustment: a replication and follow-up', *Fam. Relations*, 1987, 36 : 193–197

WEINSTEIN, G.W. 'Major mergers', *Ms*, May 1989: 68, 70–71

Chapter 11 *Reproduction and birthwatching*

BING, E. and COLMAN, L. *Making Love during Pregnancy*, 1977, Bantam Books, New York

CLINTON, J. 'The couvade syndrome', *Med. Asp. Hum. Sex.*, 1987, 22 (1): 115, 132

COALE, A.J. 'Excess female mortality and the balance of the sexes in the population: an estimate of the number of "missing females"', *Pop. & Dev. Rev.*, 1991, 17 (3): 517–523

DICK-READ, G. *Childbirth without Fear*, 1944, Harper & Row, New York

EDWARDS, M. and WALDORF, M. *Reclaiming Birth: history and heroines of American childbirth reform*, 1984, The Crossing Press, New York

EHRENREICH, B. and ENGLISH, D. *Complaints and Disorders: the sexual politics of sickness*, 1973, Feminist Press, New York

FELDMAN, S. *Choices in Childbirth*, 1980, Bantam Books, New York

FORD, C.S. and BEACH, F.A. *Patterns of Sexual Behavior*, 1951, Harper & Row, New York

GRAHAM, H. *Eternal Eve: the mysteries of birth and the customs that surround it*, 1960, Hutchinson, London

KITZINGER, S. *The Experience of Childbirth*, 1962, Victor Gollancz, London

KRISTOF, N. 'The missing 100 million women',

Hong Kong Daily Standard, 10 November 1991: 20–21

LAMAZE, F. *Painless Childbirth: psychoprophylactic method* (L. Celestin trans.), 1970, Regnery, Chicago

LEBOYER, F. *Birth without Violence*, 1975, Alfred A. Knopf, New York

NEWTON, N. 'Interrelationships between sexual responsiveness, birth and breast feeding', in Zubin, J. and Money, J. (eds.) *Contemporary Sexual Behavior: critical issues in the 1970s*, 1973, Johns Hopkins University Press, Baltimore, Md.

NIHELL, E. *A Treatise on the Art of Midwifery, setting forth various abuses therein, especially the practice with instruments*, 1760, London

Population Reports *Issues in World Health — Mothers' Lives Matter: maternal health in the community*, L(7), Johns Hopkins University Population Information Program

RICH, A. *Of Woman Born: motherhood as experience and institution*, 1976, W.W. Norton, New York

SEMMELWEIS, I.P. 'The etiology, the concept and the prophylaxis of childbed fever', *Medical Classics*, 1941, 5 (5): 357–417

Chapter 12 *Sex yes, children no*

APPLEZWEIG, N. 'Will there be enough pills to go around?', *People*, 1975, 2 (1): 10–12

BYRNE, D. and FISHER, W. *Adolescents, Sex and Contraception*, 1983, Erlbaum, Hillsdale, NJ

CARNE, S., DAY, K., ELSTEIN, M., McEWAN, J. and ROBINSON, R. *Handbook of Contraceptive Practice*, 1990, Department of Health, London

FEN, C.C., GRIFFIN, D. and WOOLMAN A. (eds.) *Recent Advances in Fertility Regulation*, 1981, Atar S.A. (Symposium, Beijing 1980), Geneva

GOLDSTEIN, M. 'The future of male birth control', *Planned Parenthood Rev.*, 1986, 6 (3): 11–12

GRAY, M. *Margaret Sanger: a biography of the champion of birth control*, 1979, R. Moreck, New York

GRISWALD vs. Connecticut, 381 U.S. Y79, Y.E.Y. (Physicians & Contraceptives, U.S. Supreme Court Decision)

GUILLEBAUD, J. 'Contraception for women over 35 years of age', in Halbe, H.W. and Rekers, H. (eds.) *Oral Contraception into the 1990s*, 75–83, 1989, Parthenon Publishing Group, Carnforth, Lancs.

HATCHER, R.A. *Contraceptive Technology 1990–1992* (15th edition), 1990, Irvington, NY

PATH (Program for Appropriate Technology in Health) *Private sector local production of contraceptives: current options for A.I.D.*, April 1990, Seattle, Wash.

Population Reports *The use of prostaglandins in human reproduction*, March 1980, G(8)

Population Reports *Periodic Abstinence: how well do new approaches work?*, September 1981, I(3)

Population Reports *Oral Contraceptives in the 1980s*, May–June 1982, A(6)

Population Reports *IUDs: an appropriate contraceptive for many women*, July 1982, B(4)

Population Reports *IUDS: a new look*, 1988, B(5), Johns Hopkins University Population Information Program

Population Reports *Condoms: now more than ever*, 1990 H(8), Johns Hopkins University Population Information Program

Population Reports *Voluntary Female Sterilization*, 1990, C(10), Johns Hopkins University Population Information Program

Population Reports *Paying for Family Planning*, 1991, J(39), Johns Hopkins University Population Information Program

RICHART, R.M. and PRAGER, D.J. *Human Sterilization*, 1972, Charles C. Thomas, Springfield, Ill.

STEINHOFF, P. and DIAMOND, M. *Abortion Politics*, 1977, University Press of Hawaii, Honolulu

THOMPSON, D. 'When abortions save lives', *TIME*, 6 April 1992: 52–53

WESTOFF, C.F. 'Trends in contraceptive practice 1965–1973', *Fam. Planning Persp.*, March–April 1976, 8 (2): 54–7

WHEELER, R.G., DUNCAN, G.W. and SPEIDEL, J.J. (eds.) *Intrauterine Devices: development, evaluation, and program implementation*, 1974, Academic Press, New York

ZBELLA, E., VERMESH, M. and GLEICHER, N. 'Contraceptive practices of female physicians', *Contraception*, 1986, 33 : 423–436

Chapter 13 *Sex as work*

ASCH, R.J. and MARRS, R.P. *ART: Assisted Reproductive Technologies*, 1991, Serono Laboratories Inc., Norwell, Mass.

GARNER, C.H., MENNING, B.E. and WENTZ, A.C. *Insights into Infertility*, 1991, Serono Laboratories Inc., Norwell, Mass.

PARKER, P.J. 'Motivation of surrogate mothers: initial findings', *Am. J. Psychiatry.*, January 1983, 140 (1): 117–18

POHLMAN, E. *Psychology of Birth Planning*, 1969, Schenkman, Cambridge, Mass.

ROBERTSON, J.A. 'Surrogate mothers: not so novel after all', Hastings Center Report, October 1983: 28–34

SCHWARTZ, D. and MAJAUX, M.J. 'Female fecundity as a function of age', *New England J. Med.*, 1982, 306 : 404–406

STARK, M. 'Please, God, let it work this time...', *Boston Magazine*, January 1991: 46–49, 83–86

TOTH, A., LESSER, M.L., BROOKS, C. and LABRIOLA, D.'Subsequent pregnancies among 161 couples treated for T-mycoplasma genital-tract infection', *New England J. Med.*, 3 March 1983, 308 (9): 505–7

Chapter 14 *Watch out*

BOULOS, R., BONHOMME, M., QUINN, T. et al. 'Prevalence of HIV-1 and HTLV-1 in Gonaives, Haiti', Montreal International AIDS Conference, 1988, 980

British Medical Association, *Sexcare Digest*, 1 March 1983

DE LALLA, F., RIZARDINI, G., SANTORO, D. and GALLI, M. 'Rapid spread of HIV infection in a rural district in Central Africa', *AIDS*, 1988, 2 (4): 317–321

DELPORT, D. 'AIDS is wiping out SA workers: virus doubles every 6 months — 18–40 group most at risk', *Johannesburg Star*, 1990

DIAMOND, M., IKEGAMI, C., and THOMAS, D. AIDS: *Sex, Love, Disease*, 1988, Gendai Shokan, Tokyo

DIAMOND, M. and KARLEN, A. 'Sexually transmitted diseases', in Lief, H. (ed.) *Sexual Problems in Medical Practice*, 307–22, 1981, American Medical Association, Wisconsin

EDELSTON, K. AIDS: *Countdown to Doomsday*, 1988, Media House Publications, Johannesburg

FAZEKAS, C., DIAMOND, M., MOSE, J.R. and NEUBAUER, A. 'AIDS-related KAP among Austrian physicians', *AIDS: Education and Prevention*, 1992, 4 (3)

FELMAN, Y.M. and NIKITAS, J.A. 'Herpes genitalis', *Cutis*, October 1982, 30 (40): 442, 446–8, 452–4

GRAHAM, N., ZEGER, S., PARK, L.P., DETELS, R. and RINALDO, C.R.P. and John P. 'Early AZT

reduces risk of death', *New England J. Med.*, 16 April 1992

'Herpes: truth and consequences', *Sex. Med. Today*, June 1983: 6, 7, 12, 15

HESSOL, N.A., O'MALLEY, P. et al. 'Incidence and prevalence of HIV infection among homosexual and bizexual men 1978–1988', Montreal International AIDS Conference, 1988, 50

HIV Hotline 'Study shows one fifth of HIV-infected men don't tell their partners', *Los Angeles Times*, 6 February 1992

KENNY, J. 'Fear and humor in prevention campaigns', in Paalman, M. (ed.) *Promoting Safer Sex*, 1990, Swets & Zeitlinger, Amsterdam

LANG, N.G. 'Difficult decisions: ethics and AIDS', *J. Sex Res.*, 1991, 28 (2): 249–262

LEO, J. 'The real epidemic: fear and despair', *TIME*, 4 July 1983: 56–8

LIFF, J.M., SUNG, F.C., WONG-HO, C., GREENBERG, R.S. and FLANDERS, W.D. 'Does increased detection account for the rising incidence of breast cancer?', *Am. J. Pub. Health*, 1991, 81 (4): 462–465

LOVEDAY, C., POMEROY, L., WELLER, I.V.D., QUIRK, J., HAWKINS, A., WILLIAMS, H., SMITH, S., WILLIAMS, P., TEDDER, R.S. and ADLER, M.W. 'Human immunodeficiency viruses in patients attending a sexually transmitted disease clinic in London', *Brit. Med. J.*, 1989, 298 (6671): 419–422

MANN, J. 'AIDS and sexuality: a global perspective', in Paalman, M. (ed.) *Promoting Safer Sex*, 252, 1990, Swets & Zeitlinger, Amsterdam

MISZTAL, B.A. and MOSS, D. (eds.) *Action on AIDS: National Policies in Comparative Perspective*, 268, 1990, Greenwood Press, New York

MOORE, R.D., HIDALGO, J., SUGLAND, B.W. and CHAISSON, R.E. 'Zidovudine and the natural history of the acquired immunodeficiency syndrome', *New England J. Med.*, 1992, 324 : 1412–1416

N'GALY, B., RYDER. W., BILA, K., MWANDAGALIRWA, K., COLEBUNDERS, R.L., FRANCIS, H., MANN, J.M. and QUINN, T.C. 'Human immunodeficiency virus among employees in an African hospital', *New England J. Med.*, 1988, 319 (17): 1123–1127

NICHOLSON, T. 'The big AIDS deception', *Johannesburg Star*, 1990

PAALMAN, M. (ed.) *Promoting Safer Sex*, 1990, Swets & Zeitlinger, Amsterdam

Playboy Readers' Sex Survey, 1983, Part One (Jan): 108, 241, 242, 244, 246, 248, 250

SAMUEL, M.C., GUYDISH, J., EKSTRAND, M., COATES, T.J. and WINKELSTEIN, W.J. 'Changes in sexual practices over 5 years of follow-up among heterosexual men in San Francisco', *J. Acquired. Imm. Def. Dis.*, 1991, 4 : 896–900

SONTAG, S. *AIDS and its Metaphors*, 1988, Farrar, Strauss & Giroux, New York

TSUL, F., LAZZARIN, A., COSTIGLIOLA, P. et al. 'Human immunodeficiency virus (HIV) seropositivity in intravenous (IV) drug abusers in three cities of Italy: possible natural history of HIV infection in IV drug addicts in Italy', *J. Med. Virol*, 1987, 23 (3): 241–248

TURNER, C.F., MILLER, H.G. and MOSES, L.E. (eds.) *AIDS: sexual behavior and intravenous drug use*, 590, 1989, National Academy Press, Washington DC

World Health Organization *World Health Statistics*, 33–34, 1991, WHO, Geneva

VASQUEZ-VALLIS, E., TORRES-MENDOZA, B. and JAUREGUI-RIOS, M. 'Tendency of anti-HIV antibodies in masculine homosexuals during the last five years in Guadalajara, Jalisco', Montreal International AIDS Conference, 1988, 1013

Chapter 15 *Contemporary issues*

ALMODOVAR, N.J. 'Prostitution and the criminal justice system', in Francoeur, R.T. (ed.) *Taking Sides: clashing views on controversial issues in human sexuality*, 220–226, 1991, Dushkin Publishing Group, Guilford, Conn.

BASOW, S.A. and CAMPANILE, F. 'Attitudes toward prostitution as a function of attitudes toward feminism in college students', *Psychol. Women. Quart.*, 1990, 14 (1): 135–141

CARNES, P.J. *The Sexual Addiction*, 1983, CompCare, Minneapolis, Minn.

DIAMOND, M. 'Abortion and sexual behavior', in Shachdev, P. (ed.) *Abortion: reading and research*, 193–208, 1981, Butterworths, Toronto

DIAMOND, M. 'Selected cross-generational sexual behavior in traditional Hawaii: a sexological ethnography', op. cit. Chapter 6

DIAMOND, M. DANNEMILLIER, J.E. 'Pornography and community standards in Hawaii: comparison with other states', *Arch. Sex. Behav.*, 1989, 18 (6): 475–495

FALUDI, S. *Backlash: the undeclared war against American women*, 1991, Crown, New York

FARREL, W. *Why men are the way they are*, 1988, McGraw-Hill, New York

Federal Bureau of Investigation, Uniform Crime Report, 1977, U.S. Government Print Office, Washington DC

FOX-GENOVESE, E. *Feminism without Illusions: a critique of individualism*, 1992, University of North Carolina, Chapel Hill, NC

FRANCOEUR, R.T. (ed.) *Taking Sides: clashing views on controversial issues in human sexuality*, 1991, Dushkin Publishing Group, Guilford, Conn.

GROWTH, N.A. *Men who rape*, 1979, Plenum Press, New York

HACKER, S.S. 'The transition from the old norm to the new sexual values for the 1990s', SIECUS Report, 1990, 18 (5): 1–8

HOLBROOK, D. (ed.) *The Case Against Pornography*, 1973, Library Press, Open Court, Ill.

HOLDEN, P. HORLEMANN, J. and PFAFFLIN, G.F. *Tourism, Prostitution, Development: documentation*, 1983, Ecumenical Coalition on Third World Tourism, Bangkok

KINSEY, A.C., POMEROY, W.B. and MARTIN, C.E. *Sexual Behavior in the Human Male*, op. cit. Chapter 1

KLEIN, M. 'Why there's no such thing as sexual addiction and why it really matters', in Francoeur, R.T. (ed.) *Taking Sides: clashing views on controversial issues in human sexuality*, op. cit. above

KRONHAUSEN, E. and KRONHAUSEN P. *Pornography and the Law: the psychology of erotic realism and pornography*, 1959, Ballantine Books, New York

KUTCHINSKY, B. 'Pornography and rape: theory and practice', *Int. J. Law & Psychiatry*, 1991, 14 : 47–64

MACHLOWITZ, M. and MACHLOWITZ, D. 'Hug by the boss could lead to a slap from the judge', *New York*, 1982, 16

POGREBIN, L.C., GLEDEN, L.V. and MICOSSI, A.L. 'Can women really have it all?', *Ms*, March 1978: 47–51, 72–3

QUEEN, C.A. 'Whores fight back: lesbian, gay, and bisexual sex workers organize', *Advocate*, November 1991: 64–65

Report of the Commission on Obscenity and Pornography, 1970, Bantam Books, New York

RUSH, L.O., GARTRELL, J.W., AMEDEO, S.R. and COYNE, B.J. 'The sexual assault scale: measuring self-reported sexual assault trauma in the emergency room', *Psychol. Assessment*, 1991, 3 (3): 405 411

SANDAY, P.R. *Female Power and Male Dominance: on the origin of sexual inequality*, 1981, Cambridge University Press, Cambridge

SARREL, P. and MASTERS, W. 'Sexual molestation of men by women', *Arch. Sex. Behav.*, April 1982, *11* (2): 117–32

SAVITZ, L. and ROSEN, L. 'The sexuality of prostitutes: sexual enjoyment reported by "streetwalkers"', *J. Sex Res.*, 1988, *24* : 299–308

STEINEM, G. *Revolution from Within*, 1992, Little, Brown & Co., Boston, Mass.

STORASKA, F. *How to say no to a rapist and survive*, 1975, Warner Books, New York

WALLACH, E.J. and MARX, J.S. 'Courts draw the liability line on work place sex harassment', *Law J.*, 13 February 1989: 17–19

WINICK, C. 'Debate on legalization of prostitution', in Francoeur, R.T. (ed.) *Taking Sides: clashing views on controversial issues in human sexuality*, op. cit. above

WINICK, C. and KINSIE, P.M. *The Lively Commerce: prostitution in the United States*, 1971, Quadrangle Books, Chicago

Women's Bureau of Employment Standards Administration data, U.S. Department of Labor, 1975, Bureau of Census, U.S. Department of Commerce

Chapter 16 *Future tense*

DIAMOND, M. 'Sexuality and the handicapped', *Rehab. Literature*, February 1974, 35 (2): 34–40

DIAMOND, M. 'Bisexuality: biological aspects', in Haeberle, E.J. (ed.) *Bisexualities*, in press, Walter de Gruyter, Berlin

FRANCOEUR, R.T. (ed.) *Taking Sides: clashing views on controversial issues in human sexuality*, op. cit. Chapter 15

GOCHROS, H., GOCHROS, J. and FISCHER, J. *Helping the Sexually Oppressed*, op. cit. Chapter 9

GUTTENTAG, M. and SECOND, P.F. *Too Many Women: the sex ratio question*, op. cit. Chapter 10

LINDSEY, H. *The Late Great Planet Earth*, 1970, Zondervari, Grand Rapids, Mich.

MASLAND, R., NORLAND, R., LIU, M. and CONTRERAS, J. 'Slavery', *Newsweek*, 4 May 1992: 30–32, 37–39

SMITH, T.W. 'The Polls — A Report: The Sexual Revolution?', *Pub. Opinion Quart.*, 1990, 54 : 415–435

INDEX

Page numbers in italics refer to illustrations or information in captions

The publishers would like to express special thanks to the author, Milton DiamonD, for supplying the following photos from his own archive: 8, 10, 17, 18, 20 left, 20 right, 29, 32 left, 32 right, 35, 36, 41, 45 bottom, 48, 49, 61, 64, 65, 66, 73, 75, 77, 82 left, 82 right (photo Colin Urquhart), 83, 84, 87, 91 right, 92, 97, 101 left, 101 right, 109, 110, 112, 114, 119, 121, 124, 140, 146, 151 bottom, 155 (photo Ben F), 156, 160, 166, 170 top, 172 bottom, 181, 184, 187, 190, 193, 196, 199, 201, 202 top, 203, 204, 208, 210, 213, 216 top, 216 bottom, 218, 219, 222, 225 bottom, 228, 229 top, 229 bottom, 230 top, 230 bottom, 231, 233, 234, 235, 241, 245 bottom

Other photographs are reproduced by kind permission of: **Ancient Art and Architecture Collection** 46 • **Bridgeman Art Library** 11, 15, 38, 44, 58, 62, 100, 105, 117, 130, 133, 135, 137, 159 • **Jean-Loup Charmet** 129, 209 • **Collection/Brian Shuel** 143 • **Colorific** 60 • **C.M. Dixon** 12, 126 • **E.T. Archive** 57 • **Robert Estall** 104 bottom • **Mary Evans Picture Library** 26 top, 26 bottom, 128, 147, 168, 189 top, 194 right, 215 top • **Werner Forman Archive** 80, 115, 118 bottom, 171, 174 bottom, 175 top • **Sally & Richard Greenhill** 107 bottom, 176 • **Robert Harding Picture Library** 43, 198, back jacket • **Hutchison Library** 27, 63, 89, 91 left, 103, 104 top, 118 top, 122, 123, 179, 185, 195, 207, 212, 215 bottom, 245 top • **Multimedia Books** 25 left, 93, 96 left, 96 right, 102, 141 bottom, 148 right, 164 • **Multimedia Books – photo Kirsty McLaren** front jacket • **Panos Pictures** 88, 132 right, 173, 194 left, 238, 242, 243 • **Paul Popper** 16 • **Rex Features** 24 left, 24 right, 25 right, 30, 39, 94, 98, 107 top, 120, 125, 178, 200, 205, 214, 225 top, 227, 237, 240, 244 • **Ann Ronan Picture Library** 13, 14 • **Sceptre Books Ltd, London** *The Visual Dictionary of Sex* 45 • **Science Photo Library** 51 top, 51 bottom, 170 bottom, 174 top, 191, 202 bottom, 220, 221 • **Tony Stone Worldwide** 162 • **Young Artists (Alan Craddock "AC Spec 1")** 22 • **Z.E.F.A.** 19, 31, 40, 42, 53, 55, 68, 69 top, 69 bottom, 70, 71, 72, 78, 85, 111, 132 left, 141 top, 144, 148 left, 150, 151 top, 153, 161 left, 161 right, 172 top, 175 bottom, 182, 188 top, 189 bottom

Multimedia Books have endeavoured to observe the legal requirements with regard to the rights of suppliers of photographic material.